STRUCTURE OF THE
AUTONOMIC NERVOUS SYSTEM

D1477812

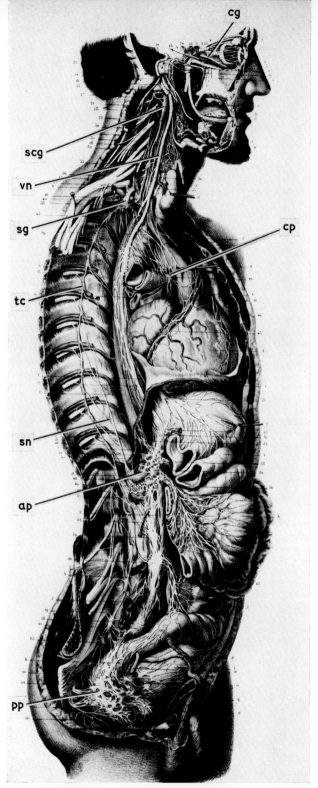

The autonomic nervous system in man, as drawn by J.-B. Leveille. (From *Nevrologie ou Description et Iconographie du Systeme Nerveux et des Organes des Sens de l'Homme*, L. Hirschfeld, Paris: Baillere 1853.) ap : abdominal plexus; cg : ciliary ganglion; cp : cardiac plexus; pp : pelvic plexus; scg : superior cervical ganglion; sg : stellate ganglion; sn : splanchnic nerve; vn : vagus nerve; tc : thoracic sympathetic chain.

STRUCTURE OF THE AUTONOMIC NERVOUS SYSTEM

Giorgio Gabella

Department of Anatomy and Embryology
University College, London

LONDON
CHAPMAN AND HALL
A Halsted Press Book
JOHN WILEY & SONS, INC., NEW YORK

LROL

First published 1976
by Chapman and Hall Ltd
11 New Fetter Lane, London EC4P 4EE
© *1976 Giorgio Gabella*
Typeset by Hope Services, Wantage, Oxon
and printed in Great Britain by
Fletcher & Son Ltd, Norwich

ISBN 0 412 13620 1

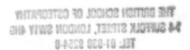

Distributed in the U.S.A. by Halsted Press,
a Division of John Wiley & Sons, Inc., New York

Library of Congress Cataloging in Publication Data

Gabella, G
    Structure of the autonomic nervous system.

    Bibliography: p.
    Includes indexes.
    1. Nervous system, Autonmic. I. Title.
QM471.G28   1976   611'.83   75-29233
    0 470-28905-8

CONTENTS

ERRATUM

Due to an error in binding, it is regretted that the Plates occur between pages 104 and 105, and their legends between pages 128 and 129.

ACKNOWLEDGEMENTS

I thank Professor G. Burnstock, Professor E.G. Gray, Dr M.R. Matthews and Dr R. Zanini, for critical comments on parts of the manuscript. I am grateful to Professor R. Amprino, Dr D.H.L. Evans, Dr J.B. Furness, Mr P.G. Gordon-Weeks, Dr M.R. Matthews, and Dr S. Nishi, for providing unpublished material for the illustrations, and to Dr T. Bennett, Dr J.H. Chamley, Dr T. Hökfelt, Professor H.W. Kosterlitz, Dr M.R. Matthews, Dr E. Mugnaini, Dr G. Pilar, and Professor J. Taxi, for allowing me to reproduce illustrations from some of their papers. Permission to reproduce copyright material was kindly granted by Cambridge University Press, Elsevier Publishing Company, Oxford University Press, The Physiological Society, The Royal Society, and Springer Verlag.

University College, London   G.G.
June, 1975

1 THE AUTONOMIC NERVOUS SYSTEM

1.1 Introduction

A conspicuous portion of the peripheral nervous system is part of the 'vegetative nervous system'; it includes all the neurons which innervate the viscera, salivary and lacrimal glands, the heart and blood vessels, all other smooth muscles of the body, notably the intrinsic muscles of the eye and the muscles of the hair. Only part of the system belongs to the peripheral nervous system: it has also its own nuclei and pathways in the central nervous system.

The distinction between visceral and somatic functions is a very old one in our culture. With the development of neurology the notion of a widespread nervous control of body functions emerged. Winslow (1732) used the term *nervi sympathici majores* for those nerves, which he thought to carry about 'sympathies' and then co-ordinate various viscera's functions. His was an anatomical breakthrough, which obscured Willis' 'intercostal nerve' and Vesalius 'cranial nerve'. The notion was developed among others by Johnstone (1764) who arrived, with the aid of some very accurate anatomical observations, at the problem of the nervous influence on motion and sensitivity of viscera. By the end of the eighteenth century, it was clear, with Bichat (1800), that what he called 'sympathetic nervous system' (and his pupil Reil, a few years later, 'vegetative nervous system') controlled visceral functions (*la vie organique*), whereas somatic functions (*la vie animale*) were under direct control from the brain and spinal cord.

However, the two systems are at tract very close (e.g. sympathetic fibres in somatic nerves; visceral, sensory neurons in spinal ganglia); interaction between the two systems, especially at supraspinal level, is an everyday experience. Moreover, the two systems share many basic structural, physiological and pharmacological properties.

La vie organique is characterized by a great autonomy from higher centres of the central nervous system, whereas *la vie animale* involves

1

on many occasions consciousness. But autonomy and consciousness provide a weak basis for classification, because they are difficult to define and, though to a different extent, are found in relation to both divisions of the nervous system. Besides, part of the 'autonomy' is due to a high degree of non-nervous control on the activity of some tissues (e.g. myogenic activity in some smooth muscles, control by hormones), which contrasts with the total submission of a skeletal muscle fibre to its motoneuron.

Interesting historical retrospects with an account of the discovery and the study of the autonomic nervous system have been published (Langley, 1916; Sheehan, 1936; Ackerknecht, 1974).

2 THE SYMPATHETIC GANGLIA

2.1   The sympathetic ganglia

The ganglia of the sympathetic nervous system can be divided into two main anatomical categories, paravertebral and prevertebral. The paravertebral ganglia are situated bilaterally along the ventro-lateral aspect of the spinal column, and with their connecting trunks they form the sympathetic chains (right and left), which extend from the base of the skull to the sacrum. The prevertebral ganglia (see Section 2.3) lie close to the median sagittal plane of the body ventral to the abdominal aorta.

In the sympathetic chain of mammals the thoracic and the lumbar regions have approximately one ganglion for each metameric segment of the body, whereas at the cervical level there is an upper ganglion (the superior cervical ganglion), a lower (the stellate ganglion, which in many species incorporates the first thoracic ganglion), and a small intermediate ganglion. In the thoracic and lumbar regions, ganglia of the sympathetic chain are numbered after the spinal nerve with which they have major connections (and not on the basis of their sequential order). In the lumbo-sacral region the right and left chains are connected by branches across the midline, and in front of the coccyx the two chains converge to form a small *ganglion impar* in the midline. There are usually about 24 sympathetic ganglia in each chain in man. Variations in number, size and distribution of the sympathetic ganglia between different species and individuals are common, and in man variations in the pattern of ganglia are particularly obvious in the neck (Becker & Grunt, 1957) (see also Mitchell, 1953, and Pick, 1970). In addition to the paravertebral and prevertebral ganglia, sympathetic neurons are found in paravisceral ganglia (Chapter 5) and in a few cases in intramural ganglia (p.130).

Other sympathetic ganglia which are neither paravertebral nor prevertebral nor part of the above mentioned group, are known as 'intermediate ganglia' and are mainly associated with the white and (more frequently) the grey rami communicantes and sometimes also with the ventral spinal roots (Wrete, 1941, 1959; Skoog, 1947; Alexander *et al.*, 1949; Boyd, 1957). Although very variable in number and size they are consistently found in the cervical and uppermost thoracic segments, whereas they are often absent in the midthoracic and sacral segments (Boyd, 1957). Ganglia of similar structure and presumably equivalent nature are present along the carotid artery and the cavernous sinus and in the orbit (Boyd, 1957).

2.2 Ganglia of the sympathetic chain

A capsule of connective tissue, which is continuous with the epineurium of the nerve trunks, invests the ganglia, and connective tissue septa divide groups of ganglion cells. The stroma (capsule and septa) is said to be particularly thick in man (Pick, 1970). The capsule of the superior cervical ganglion of the rat represents about 30 per cent of the wet weight of the ganglion (Matthieu, 1970) (Plate 2a); when the ganglion is incubated *in vitro* without opening the capsule the penetration of the medium is virtually nil even after 30 minutes (Hökfelt, 1968). In spite of the thickness of the connective tissue capsule, according to Eccles (1935) the potential changes recorded with an electrode on the surface of sympathetic ganglia are due to the action potentials of the ganglion cells themselves. For studies with intracellular electrodes many authors have preferred young, immature animals, since they have a comparatively thinner capsule (e.g. Eccles, 1955; McLachlan, 1974). Nerve endings can be seen within the capsule (see p.44).

Collagen fibrils are present around virtually each individual ganglion cell and its satellite cells. They measure (in glutaraldehyde fixed ganglia) about 50nm in diameter, as do those in the perineurium and endoneurium of peripheral nerves (Thomas, 1963), whereas collagen fibrils in the epineurium and in the connective tissues in general measure about 80nm (Schmitt, Hall & Jakus, 1942) (Plate 3b). Among the collagen fibrils there are bundles of microfilaments, less than 20nm in diameter, and amorphous or finely floccular material.

A few fibroblasts and blood vessels are present in the sympathetic ganglia. Chromaffin cells are also found (see p.23) as well as mast cells, of which there are about 24000 in the superior cervical ganglion

4

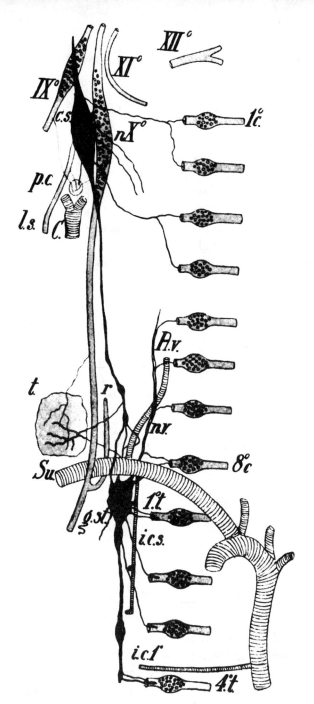

Figure 1. Schematic representation of arrangement and connections of the sympathetic trunk in the neck region in man. (From Terni, 1931.) 1°c-8°c : cervical dorsal root ganglia; 1°t-4°t : thoracic dorsal root ganglia; IX° : ganglion of the glosso-pharyngeal nerve; nX°: nodose ganglion of the vagus; XI° accessory nerve; XII° : hypoglossal nerve; A.v.: vertebral artery; C : carotid bifurcation; c.s. : superior cervical ganglion; g. st. : stellate ganglion; i.c.s. : superior intercostal artery; l.s. : superior laryngeal nerve; n.v. : vertebral nerve; p.c. : carotid paraganglion; r : recurrent laryngeal nerve; Su : subclavian artery; t : thymus; $i.c.1^{\circ}$: first intercostal artery.

of the cat (Hollinshead & Gertner, 1969) Plate 2a.

The total number of sympathetic ganglion cells has not been counted in any animal species, but neurons have been counted in individual ganglia, in particular in the superior cervical ganglion (Table 2.1). This ganglion has been preferred by most authors because it is easily identified and dissected, has clear-cut limits and neat pre- and post-ganglionic nerves (Fig. 1). In spite of individual variability in neuron number and the occurrence of accessory ganglia (see p.44), the superior cervical ganglion is a convenient ganglion for quantitative comparisons between different species.

Table 2.1

Estimated number of neurons in the superior cervical ganglion of several mammalian species. Figures are the mean ± S.E.M., number of cases in brackets.

Species	Number of neurons	Number of cases	References
cat	123 000	[1]	Billingsley and Ranson, 1918
cat	66 000; 96 000	[2]	Wolf, 1941
cat	114 000	[1]	Levi-Montalcini and Booker, 1960b
mouse	14 900 ± 616	[6]	Levi-Montalcini and Booker, 1960b
rabbit	67 000 ± 577	[3]	Levi-Montalcini and Booker, 1960b
man	911 000 ± 48 100	[6]	Ebbeson, 1968
chimpanzee	753 000 ± 59 800	[3]	Ebbeson, 1968
baboon	324 000; 471 000	[2]	Ebbeson, 1968
stumptail monkey	206 000; 258 000	[2]	Ebbeson, 1968
macaca	220 000; 265 000	[2]	Ebbeson, 1968
squirrel monkey	63 000	[1]	Ebbeson, 1968
rat	32 000	[1]	Levi-Montacini and Booker, 1960b
rat	39 000 ± 500	[4]	Klingman, 1972
rat ♀	44 000 ± 1100	[3]	Gabella and Miller, 1975
rat ♂	53 000 ± 500	[3]	Gabella and Miller, 1975

The table shows that larger species have a greater number of neurons. However, in species with large body size not only the number of neurons but also the average size of cells increases (Table 2.2). Studies on spinal ganglia and the central nervous system have shown that the size of neurons whose processes project to the periphery is to some extent correlated with the size of the innervation territory (Levi, 1925). A similar correlation seems to exist in sympathetic ganglia.

6

Table 2.2

Packing densities and sizes of ganglion cells in the superior cervical ganglion in different species, correlated to the body weight. (From Lapique, 1946)

species	body weight kg	number of neurons*	number of glial cells	diameter of neurons
rat	0.2	24	120	15·5
cat	3	17	112	20
dog	5	13	116	24
dog	18	11	109	26
dog	25	10	106	28
ox	300	9	133	35

*number of neurons in a square of 220 μm side, corrected for the section thickness.

Increase in the size of ganglion cells is accompanied by an increase (in number, length and diameter) of their dendrites; both factors will decrease the number of ganglion cells per unit volume (i.e. increase the 'mean cell territory', which is defined as the reciprocal of cell density (Bok, 1936)). As indicated in Table 2.2, with a 1500-fold increase in body weight the number of glial cells hardly changes at all, but the ganglion cells are more than twice as large in average diameter (and the volume of the cell body alone increases from 1950μm^3 in the rat to 22450μm^3 in the ox) and their packing density is reduced to nearly one third (Lapique, 1946). In the primate species studied by Ebbeson (1968) a clear correlation exists between body size, number of ganglion cells and packing density (Table 2.3).

Sympathetic ganglion cells are invested by glial cells (satellite cells, amphicytes), which form a complete sheath around each of them, sometimes referred to as the capsule of the ganglion cell (e.g. Hillarp, 1946) (Plate 2c). In some regions it is only a slender lamella intervening between the perikaryal surface and the surrounding connective tissue. It is thicker in the nuclear region of a satellite cell, and can also be formed by several overlapped cytoplasmic lamellae (Fig. 9). The glial sheath extends from the perikaryon to cover the entire surface of the cell processes (Plate 4a, d), with the exception of a few localized areas (see p.13) (Plate 4c). The outer surface of the satellite sheath is covered by a basal lamina (Plate 4a, b). The parikaryal surface, therefore, does not come in direct contact with the connective tissue or the extracellular space proper, but only with the

7

Table 2.3

Quantitative studies of the superior cervical ganglion in a variety of primates including man (from Ebbeson, 1968a, b)

species	body weight kg	volume of ganglion mm³	number of neurons 10³	mean cell density cell mm⁻³ × 10³	number of preganglionic × 10³	% myelinated	ratio/neurons preganglionic axons
squirrel monkey	0·6	1·9	63·6	32·5	2·3	47	28:1
macaca	4·5	8·6	219·8	25·6	5·4	49	41:1
macaca	3·5	—	265·3	—	4·5	51	59:1
stumptail monkey	6·0	9·7	258·3	26·5	4·9	75	52:1
stumptail monkey	5·0	12·6	206·5	16·4	3·6	52	57:1
baboon	15·0	13·5	323·9	24·0	6·8	44	47:1
baboon	12·0	40·8	471·0	11·5	6·1	63	77:1
chimpanzee	50·0	101·9	828·2	8·1	8·8	50	95:1
chimpanzee	25·0	77·6	634·8	8·1	5·2	66	123:1
chimpanzee	25·0	54·3	795·5	14·7	9·2	33	87:1
man	—	—	1003·4	—	11·8	20	85:1
man	—	—	760·4	—	12·0	23	63:1
man	—	—	942·0	—	8·0	20	117:1
man	—	—	1041·7	—	5·3	95	196:1
man	53·0	133·3	947·3	7·1	7·0	44	134:1
man	53·0	173·5	773·1	4·5	5·6	61	138:1

inner surface of the satellite cells. Between the membranes of the two cells an electron-lucent space 15–20nm wide is visible in the electron micrographs (Elfvin, 1963a; Cravioto & Merker, 1963) (Plate 3a). A connection between ganglion cells or dendrites and extra-cellular space proper is provided by thin 'channels', i.e. the spaces between adjacent processes of the satellite cells. The satellite cell sheath of ganglion cell bodies and dendrites is continuous with the Schwann cell sheath of the post-ganglionic axons. No structural dif-ference between Schwann cells of the unmyelinated axons and the satellite cells has been found (Matthews & Nelson, 1975), but the two types of cell have a distinct behaviour in tissue culture (Chamley et al., 1972b).

The relation between perikaryal volume and the volume of satellite cells and sheath has not yet been investigated in sympathetic ganglia, nor has the role and significance of these cells attracted much interest. It has been reported that after prolonged electrical stimulation of the preganglionic fibres, the satellite cells of the superior cervical ganglion of cats and dogs increase in number (Schwyn & Hall, 1965) by amitotic division (Kuntz & Sulkin, 1947). These observations need confirmation under more controlled con-ditions.

Mammalian sympathetic ganglion cells are multipolar neurons (De Castro, 1932), showing great variability in the appearance of their cell processes (Plate 1). In silver-impregnated ganglia the dendrites are usually numerous (Plate 1a, b, d), relatively thick and profusely branched; with the Golgi impregnation method many dendrites show short expansions similar to the 'spines' described in neurons of the central nervous system (De Castro, 1932). The dendrites can run a great distance from the cell body (Plate 1d, f), or can branch locally into an intricate net (Plate 1c); they can abut on neighbouring neurons and seem to form pericellular nests around them, and some-times several dendrites converge upon a single neuron ('pericellular dendritic nests', Cajal, 1911). Occasionally, dendrites from two or more ganglion cells converge into a 'dendritic glomerulus', to which preganglionic fibres also contribute (De Castro, 1932) (Plate 1b). Such glomeruli are common in man (Cajal, 1911; Ranson & Billingsley, 1918; Gairns & Garven, 1953) less frequent in cattle and horses (Delorenzi, 1931), and are rare or absent in small mammals (Delorenzi, 1931; McLachlan, 1964). They are already present in em-bryonic ganglia, but their number and complexity increase with age

9

(De Castro, 1932). The neurons contributing to one glomerulus appear to be enclosed within a common satellite cell sheath (De Castro, 1932).

The variety and complexity of ramification of dendrites, particularly in man, is difficult to describe and cannot be reduced to a few basic patterns (Plate 1a–f). Hardly anything is known of the significance of this astonishing structural complexity. Even in small-sized animals the dendritic tree may be more complicated than shown by silver impregnation. By injecting a fluorescent dye intracellularly into neurons of the superior cervical ganglion of the guinea-pig McLachlan (1974) has found 13 dendrites per cell on average and calculated the ratio of dendrites to some surface area to be about 2.16:1.

Other ganglion cell processes, the accessory or secondary dendrites or intracapsular processes, are short and thin, and contained entirely within the satellite cell sheath. These short processes are very common in man and monkey (De Castro, 1932), but are rarely found in the dog and cat. Their numbers in man increase conspicuously with age (Amprino, 1938). The authors who have worked with silver impregnation methods, have observed in sympathetic ganglia, particularly in large-sized species, other cytoplasmic expansions of ganglion cells, described as looped processes, fenestrated processes, etc.; such processes have been widely described (but again only by silver methods) in the spinal ganglia of many vertebrates. Cajal (1911) illustrates a protoplasmic process in the human superior cervical ganglion emerging from the perikaryon and extending out of the satellite cell sheath, giving rise to long dendrites and an axon. Besides forming dendritic glomeruli and pericellular nests the long dendrites and their branches can end with an enlarged knob or can form a simple but clear-cut contact with another dendrite ('receptor plates') (De Castro, 1932).

It is said that in silver preparations it is difficult to recognize the axon (post-ganglionic fibre) from the long dendrites (De Castro, 1932); in most of the cases the axon is seen to emerge from a dendrite, together with secondary dendritic branches. Investigations using electron microscopy and electrophysiology may show whether this is really the case. In silver preparations the axon appears darker, smoother and straighter than a long dendrite (De Castro, 1932). Usually axons show no collaterals (Cajal, 1911; De Castro, 1923,

10

1932); the few collaterals which have been described, e.g. by Dogiel (1899), are interpreted by the Spanish authors as collateral dendritic branches. Obviously experiments with other techniques are necessary to answer this important question.

Several attempts to distinguish on a structural basis different classes of neurons in sympathetic ganglia have been carried out — and have met with severe criticism. One well-known classification was developed by Dogiel (1896), based upon observations on the cardiac and intestinal ganglia of the cat, but subsequently considered to have a more general validity (see p.122). Carpenter and Conel (1914) have argued that in the sympathetic ganglia the cell types of Dogiel are variations of a single, multipolar, motor neuron type. (Note 2.1) In the classification proposed by Cajal (1911) for man there are three types of ganglion cell: (a) cells with many short ('intracapsular') dendrites, and few long dendrites; (b) cells with long dendrites only, which are numerous and long; (c) cells similar to the previous ones but with short dendrites as well. For species other than man a classification in four groups, based on length and course of dendrites, was proposed. However, Amprino (1938) has subsequently shown that dramatic changes in the pattern of cell processes occur during the life span of the individual, especially in the superior cervical ganglion. In the newborn and the young, for example, all the ganglion neurons have long processes only, the short intracapsular processes developing later in life.

De Castro and Herreros (1945) classified the neurons of the superior cervical ganglion of the cat and man on the basis of cell body size, and their suggestion that large neurons ($33-50\mu$m in diameter) provide the intrinsic innervation of the eye, whereas medium-sized neurons ($25-32\,\mu$m) provide vaso- and pilomotor fibres, is indirectly supported by electrophysiological evidence (Bishop & Heinbecker, 1932; Eccles, 1935). (Note 2.2). No function was suggested for the small neurons; these measure $15-24\mu$m in diameter, are oval or pear-shaped, contain argentophilic granules, and have only a few dendrites which, although of the long type, are shorter than those of the other ganglion neurons. Some of these dendrites end in the glomeruli, but no mention was made of their axons. These small neurons persist throughout life, and they were interpreted by De Castro and Herreros (1945) to be elements retarded in their development; some of them, however, probably cor-

11

respond to the small intensely fluorescent cells which have been described more recently (see below). However, the number of small neurons observed by De Castro and Herreros (22 per cent of all the ganglion cells in the superior cervical ganglion; 10—17 per cent in the thoracic and lumbar ganglia) is higher than that reported for the small fluorescent cells, and it is possible that some of them do indeed represent immature elements which persist throughout life. In other ganglia of man and cat and in the sympathetic ganglia of many other mammals the range of cell sizes is narrower, and a classification based on cell size is less feasible. Moreover, even for the ganglia studied by De Castro and Herreros, it is not yet clear whether the cells of the three groups are clear-cut cell populations or part of a continuum of cell sizes. An increase in cell sizes throughout life has been shown for the superior cervical ganglion of the rat (Gabella & Miller, 1975).

Age-related changes are far more striking in man than in other mammals, and more so in the superior cervical ganglion than in other sympathetic ganglia. Amprino (1938) described the formation during post-natal life of an increasing number of short dendrites and branching and increasing complexity of the long dendrites. This process varies between individuals and does not affect all the neurons at the same time; neurons 'young' in appearance (small size, few dendrites, little pigment) are present at all ages; in old age the number of ganglion cells decreases. Other age-related changes include the accumulation of pigment, which can be very extensive in the superior cervical ganglion of man (Delorenzi, 1931, De Castro, 1932, Amprino, 1938), and the horse (Delorenzi, 1931), but is virtually non-existent in cattle (Delorenzi, 1931). It is unfortunate that these early attempts to analyse age-related changes in ganglion morphology with silver impregnation methods (Terni, 1922; De Castro, 1932; Amprino, 1938; Vandervael, 1943) have not been followed up using electrophysiological and electron microscopical techniques.

In the electron microscope the sympathetic ganglion cells show many of the usual features of nerve cells (see Pick, 1970) (Plate 2c). The nucleus is poor in chromatin. Nuclear inclusions of various types have been consistently found in the sympathetic neurons of the stellate and superior cervical ganglia of the cat (Elfvin, 1963a; Seite, 1970). They are formed by microtubules and neurofilaments arranged in very regular patterns (Seite, Escaig & Couineau, 1971). Nissl bodies are clumped in most of the cytoplasm, and are more abundant in the deeper part of the cell; between them there are often micro-tubules and bundles of neurofilaments. There are numerous mito-chondria, Golgi profiles and dense bodies (Elfvin, 1963a, 1963b; Matthews & Raisman, 1972), and free ribosomes are present singly or in clusters. In the superficial part of the cells clusters of small granu-lar vesicles (i.e. of the adrenergic type) are observed (Hökfelt, 1969) and these sometimes occupy a mushroom-shaped process evaginated from the cell surface (Van Orden, Burke, Greyer & Lodgen, 1970a). The granules of these vesicles are difficult to preserve and are not seen in most preparations of sympathetic ganglia fixed with glutar-aldehyde or osmium – not even after administration of 6-hydroxy-dopamine (Tranzer et al., 1971); only after permanganate fixation (as recommended by Richardson, 1966) are they consistently ob-served. In other preparations these mushroom-shaped processes seem to contain a reticular system of membranes. Other granular vesicles, usually larger, are scattered in the cytoplasm, particularly near the Golgi apparatus (Taxi, 1965; Grillo, 1966).

Long cylindrical processes originate from the ganglion cells. Struc-tural features have not been found that permit the origin of the axon to be distinguished from that of dendrites and the axon may origin-ate from a dendrite. Even at some distance from the cell body it is frequently difficult to tell an axon from a dendrite. Axons contain mainly microtubules and neurofilaments, while dendrites show in-clusions of a kind usually found in the cytoplasm of the cell soma, such as ribosomes and rough endoplasmic reticulum; some dendrites also have spines (Plate 4d). Axons tend to be of regular and rather uniform diameter and to run in budles, while dendrites often have irregular contours (Matthews, 1973). Clusters of small vesicles (30–50 nm in diameter), granulated or more frequently non-granulated (in glutaraldehyde fixed tissues), similar in appearance to those near the surface of the cell body, are observed in dendrites (Plate 4a). They probably represent the catecholamine stores which give the dendrites their beaded and fluorescent appearance in fluorescence microscopy. The significance of these vesicles is not clear, nor indeed is the function of apparently large amounts of neurotransmitter in the dendrites clear. Autoradiographic studies show that these vesicles have the same properties of uptake and storage of noradrenaline, as those in the axon terminals (Taxi, 1974). Cell processes are wrapped by glial cells; only rarely does the surface of a dendrite lie directly

13

beneath the basal lamina, and underneath these areas clusters of vesicles are common and the membrane shows some dense projections (Taxi, Gautron & L'Hermite, 1969) (Plate 4c). In the superior cervical ganglion of the cat there are some dendrites that are packed with mitochondria (Williams, Jew & Palay, 1973).

Elfvin (1963b) studying serial sections in electron microscopy observed numerous areas of intimate contact between dendrites in the superior cervical ganglion of the cat. Some were juxtapositions of two dendrites with a gap of about 7 nm; in other contacts, with a similar intercellular gap, there were accumulations of dense material on the cytoplasmic side of both membranes (Plate 4b).

Preganglionic fibres provide the ganglion neurons with a large number of synapses (Plates 3a, 4a, d). The fibres run parallel or wind around the dendrites, each forming several axo-dendritic synapses *en passage* (Elfvin, 1963b). All authors agree that in mammalian sympathetic ganglia synapses on the soma are far less numerous than on dendrites (Elfvin, 1963b; Forssmann, 1964: Taxi, 1965; Pick, 1970). The same was observed in human sympathetic ganglia (Pick, De Lemos & Gerdin, 1964). In the superior cervical ganglion of the rat only 14 per cent of the synapses are axo-somatic; 71 per cent are on dendrites less than $0.5\,\mu$m in diameter (Tamarind & Quilliam, 1971). In this ganglion the synapses on dendritic spines (processes which lack microtubules and neurofilaments, and have a finely filamentous matrix) (Plate 3a) are 2·4 times more numerous than those on dendritic shafts (processes characterized by longitudinally-orientated microtubles and neurofilaments, ribosomes and endoplasmic reticulum) (Plate 4a); 2 per cent of the synapses are on spine-like projections from the cell body (Matthews and Nelson, 1975). Preganglionic nerve endings are about $0.3-1.5\,\mu$m in diameter and $1.0-2.7\,\mu$m in length (Elfvin, 1963b; Birks, 1974). A few boutons, however, have a diameter up to $5\,\mu$m and presumably correspond to the boutons terminaux described by Gibson (1940) (Birks, 1974). Preganglionic endings contain round, agranular synaptic vesicles, 30—50 nm in diameter, some of which lie clustered on the preganglionic membrane and its dense material (Plate 3a). A few large granular vesicles, mitochondria, and smooth endoplasmic reticulum are also present. When the superior cervical ganglion of the cat is fixed by perfusion with glutaraldehyde containing 110 mM Mg^{2+} the vesicles appear closely packed, occupying 66 per cent of the cross-sectional

14

area and 80 per cent of the length of the endings, i.e. about 53 per cent of the ending's volume (Birks, 1974). With this fixation procedure the calculated total number of vesicles per ending is about 6000. In electrically-stimulated ganglia the number of vesicles is reduced by up to 75 per cent; since similar procedures do not deplete the acetylcholine stores of the ganglia, the author suggests that whereas at rest the acetylcholine is stored in vesicles, during maintained activity more than half of the acetylcholine is free in the cytoplasm (Birks, 1974).

In the superior cervical ganglion of the rat and cat a small proportion (6 per cent and 2 per cent respectively) of endings contain small granular vesicles of the adrenergic type; in the rabbit this type of ending amounts to about 25 per cent of the total (Tamarind & Quilliam, 1971). These endings were interpreted as being recurrent axon collaterals of post-ganglionic fibres. These interesting observations need to be confirmed, particular attention being given to the fact that dendrites also contain small granular vesicles and store noradrenaline and have membrane contact specializations. As will be discussed later, few, if any, unequivocal synaptic junctions remain in sympathetic ganglia following preganglionic denervation. A few synapses in sympathetic ganglia of various mammalian species exhibit a subsynaptic formation in the shape of a row of electron-dense dots (Taxi, 1965; Taxi & Babmindra, 1972) (Plates 3a, 4a). This is similar to the subsynaptic apparatus found in sympathetic ganglia of the frog (Taxi, 1961) and in various regions of the central nervous system (Gray, 1963; Milhaud & Pappas, 1966).

2.2.1 *Catecholamines*

The majority of neurons in sympathetic ganglia display a formaldehyde-induced fluorescence when processed with the Falck-Hillarp method (Note 2.3), revealing the presence of catecholamines (adrenergic neurons) (Plate 5a). The main amine stored in mammalian sympathetic ganglia is noradrenaline, with traces of dopamine and adrenaline (Muscholl & Vogt, 1958) (see the extensive review by Holzbauer & Sharman, 1972). Noradrenaline can be detected in the perfusate from isolated superior cervical ganglia of cats: since its amount is unchanged in preganglionically denervated ganglia, the origin of this noradrenaline is therefore chiefly the ganglion neurons (Reinert, 1963). Comparisons between different ganglia and animal species are difficult, because of the different biochemical methods used by various authors. From the table compiled by Holzbauer & Sharman (1972), however, one gets the impression that the concentration of noradrenaline is lower in the thoracic sympathetic chain than in the cervical sympathetic ganglia, and it is highest in the prevertebral ganglia. The dopamine content of the stellate ganglion, in the rabbit, cat, dog, goat and sheep, seems to be higher than in any other ganglion. Adrenaline is abundant in the prevertebral ganglia of the dog, where it is accounted for by the presence of chromaffin tissue (Muscholl & Vogt, 1958).

By fluorescence microscopy it has been confirmed that the main amine stored in the majority of the sympathetic ganglion cells is noradrenaline. The fluorescence which is intense in about 5–10 per cent of ganglion cells, and moderate in the majority of the remainder, appears as fluorescent 'granules' at the periphery of cell bodies, but it is superimposed on an even fluorescence through the nerve cell cytoplasm (Eränkö, 1972). The 'granular' fluorescence, originally considered to be an artifact (Norberg & Hamberger, 1964), corresponds in fact to the clusters of small granulated vesicles near the cell surface. On the other hand, the presence of an even fluorescence in the cytoplasm led O. Eränkö (1972) to conclude that in sympathetic nerve cells a large part of the noradrenaline is stored outside the vesicles in a 'diffuse' pool. Autoradiography after injection of tritiated noradrenaline shows labelling of the granulated vesicles of perikaryon and dendrites; only in the presence of inhibitors of monoaminoxidase is the rest of the cytoplasm labelled (Taxi & Droz, 1969). Many dendrites also show a weak specific fluorescence and appear either smooth or varicose (varicosities reflect the shape of the dendrite or are due to the distribution of fluorescent 'granules' along it), impinging on neighbouring fluorescent and non-fluorescent neurons (Jacobowitz & Woodward, 1968).

With the resolution provided by the fluorescence method it is not possible to ascertain how close is the relation between two structures. This method, therefore, cannot provide direct evidence that adrenergic fibres synapse on ganglion neurons. Furthermore, it is even more difficult than with other histological methods to identify the axons from the dendrites, and the possibility of diffusion of the fluorophores (especially in frozen sections) may lead to incorrect interpretation.

Varicose fluorescent fibres (axons) have been described in the superior cervical ganglion of the cat, and were interpreted as axon collaterals (Csillik, Kâlmàn & Knyihar, 1967; Jacobowitz & Woodward, 1968). It is, however, difficult to exclude the possibility that such structures are dendrites, as Jacobowitz recently (1970) seemed more inclined to think; this is also in better agreement with the observation that in this ganglion all synapses degenerate after preganglionic nerve section (see p.72). The situation may be different in the superior cervical ganglion of other species (e.g. rabbit: brightly fluorescent nerve terminals in close contact with ganglion cell perikarya are illustrated by Norberg, 1967 and it is certainly different in prevertebral ganglia and in some para-visceral ganglia (see p.100).

It is not yet known whether the obvious variations in the fluorescence intensity (reflecting differences in the noradrenaline contents) indicate the presence of different cell populations or the occurence of (cyclic?) changes within individual neurons. The intensity of flourescence is not correlated with the nerve cell size (Notes 2.4, 2.5). The intensity of fluoresence of cell bodies is much less than that of their terminals in the peripheral organs. It has been estimated that each ganglion neuron of the superior cervical ganglion of the cat contains on average about 0·4 picograms of noradrenaline, while about 300 times more noradrenaline is contained in the nerve terminals (varicosities) of the same neuron (Dahlström & Häggendal, 1966a).

Neurons devoid of specific fluoresence are present in the sympathetic ganglia of many species (Norberg, 1967), and are considered to be non-adrenergic. Injection of Nialamide produces a slight general increase in fluorescence of the cell bodies, but not an increase in the number of fluorescent cells (Hamberger & Norberg, 1963). It is very likely that non-fluorescent sympathetic ganglion cells are cholinergic neurons, providing sudimotor and vasodilator fibres to the limbs (see p.42). By treating adjacent cryostat sections of cat lumbar sympathetic ganglia for visualization of noradrenaline and of acetylcholinesterase activity, Hamberger, Norberg and Sjöqvist (1965) showed that all the ganglion cells devoid of specific fluorescence had intense acetylcholinesterase activity and *vice versa*. On the other hand, Eränkö (1966), by performing both histochemical reactions on the same histological section of the rat superior cervical ganglion, found that intense acetylcholinesterase activity could be associated with a weak, moderate, or strong fluorescence, and *vice versa*. Yamauchi and Lever (1971) confirmed the conclusion of Hamberger *et al.*

(1965) in the superior cervical ganglion of the rat, sheep and pig, but it is difficult to assess the specificity of their histochemical methods.

2.2.2 *Cholinesterase*
The histochemical reaction for acetylcholinesterase is negative or of moderate intensity in the majority of the sympathetic ganglion cells (Plate 6a). However, a minority of neurons display an intense reaction — rat superior cervical ganglion: 10 per cent of the ganglion cells (Giacobini, 1956); cat superior cervical ganglion: 0·5 per cent (Holmstedt & Sjöqvist, 1957); cat stellate ganglion: 7 per cent (Holmstedt & Sjöqvist, 1957); rat, sheep and pig superior cervical ganglion: 4, 5 and 6 per cent respectively (Yamauchi & Lever, 1971). In the cat stellate ganglion the intensely positive cells are mainly located at the caudal end of the ganglion (Holmstedt & Sjöqvist, 1957, 1959). In the prevertebral ganglia of the cat less than 1 per cent of the ganglion cells show an intense acetylcholinesterase activity (Holmstedt & Sjöqvist, 1957; Taxi, 1965), the remainder of the population giving a negative reaction. Only in the hedgehog do all the nerve cells of sympathetic ganglia appear of similar size and of equally intense acetylcholinesterase activity (Cauna, Naik, Leaming & Alberti, 1961). Other authors have found that no sharp distinction can be drawn between adrenergic and cholinergic cells in sympathetic ganglia of man and rat (Härkönen, 1964; Härkönen & Penttilä, 1971). This result is not surprising since the acetylcholinesterase activity is no longer regarded as the best indicator of cholinergic neurons. Biochemical studies of enzymic activities (acetylcholinesterase, cholinacetylase, monoaminoxidase) on isolated neurons of the 7th lumbar ganglion of the cat have shown two cell populations: a cholinergic population, about 10—15 per cent of all the ganglion cells, characterized by the presence of cholinacetylase, high intensity of acetylcholinesterase and absence of monoaminoxidase activity and of catecholamine fluorescence, and an adrenergic population, 73—88 per cent of the ganglion cells, which exhibits fluorescence for noradrenaline and monoaminoxidase activity, contains low or moderate acetylcholinesterase and no measurable cholinacetylase activity (Buckley, Consolo, Giacobini & Sjöqvist, 1967; Consolo, Giacobini & Karjalainen, 1968). It is likely that ganglion cells with high cholinacetylase activity (and probably those with an intense acetylcholinesterase activity as well) are

18

cholinergic neurons, and correspond to the sympathetic cholinergic post-ganglionic neurons that provide vasodilator fibres to the limbs and the sudimotor fibres to the skin.

In addition to the acetylcholinesterase of perikarya there is activity in nerve fibres and endings. The overall content of acetylcholinesterase of sympathetic ganglia (Feldberg & Gaddum, 1934) falls to about 20 per cent after degeneration of preganglionic fibres (Koelle, Davis & Koelle, 1974). The acetylcholinesterase of neurons has been separated in an internal or 'reserve' portion (localized in the cytoplasm with an identical distribution with the Nissl bodies) and an external or 'functional' portion, involved in the mechanism of cholinergic transmission (see McIsaac & Koelle, 1959). In the stellate and superior cervical ganglia of cat all the 'functional' acetylcholinesterase is found to be presynaptic (Koelle & Koelle, 1959). At the ultrastructural level it has been reported that in the superior cervical ganglion of the rat enzymic activity is present on the synaptic surfaces of axo-dendritic but not of axo-somatic synapses (Kasa & Csernovszki, 1967).

At synapses the acetylcholinesterase limits the duration of action of acetylcholine (see Bornstein, 1974); in addition it provides choline which is taken up by the nerve endings and re-used to synthesize the transmitter (Perry, 1953; Collier & MacIntosh, 1969).

2.3   Prevertebral ganglia

Usually the prevertebral ganglia are not bilaterally symmetrical; they are often ill-defined and form a plexus, ventral to the abdominal aorta and around its main branches, the abdominal plexus, which is the most intricate in the body. The main constituents of the abdominal plexus are the coeliac, superior mesenteric and inferior mesenteric ganglia. The coeliac and superior mesenteric ganglia are formed by irregular ganglionic masses which constitute a crescent-shaped structure (ganglion semilunare) on both sides of the coeliac artery and between the coeliac artery and superior mesenteric arteries; it is also called the solar plexus since it gives rise to (or receives) a number of nerve trunks in all directions, including the hepatic, gastric, aortico-renal plexuses, the splanchnic nerves and the intermesenteric nerves. The latter are 6 to 12 interconnected nerve trunks lying on the ventral and ventro-lateral aspects of the aorta.

19

The medial ones lead into the inferior mesenteric ganglion (or plexus), the lateral ones extend directly into the hypogastric nerves. All the above-mentioned plexuses and nerves may contain small additional ganglia. Even when there are two bilaterally symmetrical ganglia (e.g. the inferior mesenteric ganglia of the cat (Lloyd, 1937), and in the hypogastric plexus of most species) they both receive preganglionic fibres from both sides of the spinal cord (Langley & Anderson, 1894). Prevertebral ganglia receive the spinal cord output through preganglionic fibres which pass through the sympathetic trunk and from there emerge forming the splanchnic nerves.

From each thoracic sympathetic trunk three splanchnic nerves emerge, the greater, the lesser and the least splanchnic nerve. In man the greater splanchnic nerve arises from the fifth or sixth to the ninth or tenth thoracic ganglia by three or four large roots and a variable number of smaller ones (Kuntz, 1956). The nerve pierces the homo-lateral crus of the diaphragm and terminates in the abdominal ganglion. The lesser splanchnic nerve usually arises by one to three rootlets from the ninth and tenth or the tenth and eleventh thoracic ganglia, whereas the least splanchnic nerve arises from the last thoracic ganglion (Kuntz, 1956). A systematic study of the variability of these nerves in one hundred human subjects has been published by Edwards and Baker (1940). In the cat the greater splanchnic nerve arises from the twelfth or twelfth and thirteenth thoracic ganglia, but in this animal the fibres arise at more cranial levels and travel for several segments within the sympathetic trunk (Kuntz, 1956).

From the lumbar sympathetic chain usually four or more lumbar splanchnic nerves pass to the prevertebral ganglia. In man the second and third lumbar splanchnic nerves are the more conspicuous; they arise by several rootlets and end in the intermesenteric ganglion (Kuntz, 1956).

In the greater, lesser and least splanchnic nerves of man (one case) Kuntz, Hoffman and Schaeffer (1957) counted about 10 000, 1400 and 720 fibres respectively (percentage of unmyelinated fibres 39, 20 and 65 respectively), and in the first, second, third and fourth lumbar splanchnic nerves there are 300—400 fibres (Kuntz et al., 1957). In the cat great splanchnic nerve there are about 10 500 fibres (one case) (Kuntz et al., 1957) or 13 800 on average (5 cases) (Foley, 1948), of which about 25 per cent are myelinated (both authors).

The splanchnic nerves have a complex composition: pre- and post-

20

ganglionic sympathetic fibres, ganglion cells and afferent fibres contribute to them. On the basis of experimental nerve sections, Foley (1948) calculated that in the cat great splanchnic nerve about 43 per cent of the fibres are preganglionic sympathetic axons (the majority of the remainder being probably sensory fibres). Physiological evidence for the occurrence of sensory fibres is provided by the work of McSwiney and collaborators (see p.43). Foley (1948) has calculated that several thousand fibres in the cat great splanchnic nerve are sensory. As regards the post-ganglionic fibres they are adrenergic fibres issuing from ganglion cells of the sympathetic chain and from small ganglia scattered along the splanchnic nerves (see below). These fibres can be visualized in fluorescence microscopy, by exploiting the fact that after crushing of the nerve there is accumulation of catecholamines in the proximal stump (Dahlström & Fuxe, 1964). The site of termination of these post-ganglionic fibres is not known. A macroscopic ganglion is consistently present in the human greater splanchnic nerve approximately at the level of the eleventh thoracic vertebra. Smaller aggregates of ganglion cells, visible only in histologic sections are scattered along the three thoracic splanchnic and the lumbar splanchnic nerves. In one two-year-old human subject, Kuntz (1956) made serial sections of the thoracic splanchnic nerves and counted about 44 000 ganglion cells distributed in about 25 small ganglia. Of the preganglionic fibres which enter the inferior mesenteric ganglion of the cat (about 4000 on average) a quarter do not stop there but pass to more peripherally located ganglia (see pelvic plexus, p.95) (Harris, 1943).

Few neuron counts have been performed on prevertebral ganglia. In the mouse the coeliac and superior mesenteric ganglia contain about 25 000 ganglion cells each (Klingman & Klingman, 1967). In the prevertebral ganglia of cat and man the ganglion cells show a remarkable uniformity of size (De Castro, 1932) (see also Lloyd, 1937) and are said to be, on average, larger than in paravertebral ganglia and to display accumulations of lipofuscin granules more frequently (Fredricsson & Sjöqvist, 1962). In the coeliac and inferior mesenteric ganglia of man and the cat most of the ganglion cells are multipolar neurons with long dendrites which radiate in all directions and branch relatively infrequently (Kuntz, 1938 and 1940). In man, dendrites of one ganglion cell often form a nest around an adjacent neuron (De Castro, 1932; Kuntz, 1938 and 1940). Dendritic glomeruli (see p.9) are also found (though less frequently than in thoracic sympathetic ganglia) and dendritic fasciculi, where numerous dendrites lie parallel and closely packed. In electron microscopy Elfvin (1971c) observed a considerable number of specialized contacts between large dendrites in the inferior mesenteric ganglion of the cat. Such specializations consist of symmetrical membrane thickenings, about 80—200 nm long, separated by a gap 6—8 nm wide, containing lightly stained material; usually axo-dendritic synapses are present on both dendrites within 1—3 μm from the dendro-dendritic junction. Elfvin (1971c) suggests that such junctions are part of an inhibitory system by which one ganglion cell can modulate the activity of a neighbouring cell. In addition to the long dendrites there are short, accessory, 'intracapsular' dendrites (De Castro, 1932). They are 1—3 μm long, usually connected to the cell body by a stalk often only about 0·1 μm in diameter; they display large numbers of vesicles, 20—50 nm in diameter, with an electron dense core (Elfvin, 1971a). On the majority of the short processes there is a synaptic ending. Numerous synapses are found on the long dendrites and on most of the short dendrites. The number of axo-somatic synapses varies between cells (one neuron followed in serial sections had 27 axo-somatic synapses, another had none) but on average they are very few (Elfvin, 1971a). On the other hand, in the coeliac ganglion of the rabbit axo-somatic synapses are not uncommon, although the axo-dendritic ones predominate (Taxi, 1965). Symmetrical membrane thickenings (with accumulations of vesicles) between adjacent axons are common and led Elfvin (1971b) to suggest the possible existence of axo-axonic synapses. On the basis of his morphological evidence Elfvin (1971a) concluded that there is only one type of nerve ending, i.e. from the cholinergic preganglionic fibres.

Strong evidence against the view that there is only one type of input to the prevertebral ganglia, i.e. from the preganglionic fibres issuing from the spinal cord (as seems to be the case for paravertebral ganglia, is provided by physiolgical and experimental histological studies. Experimental studies by Kuntz and collaborators have shown that following bilateral section of the splanchnic and vagus nerves and extirpation of the upper lumbar segments of the sympathetic chain in the cat, not all the fibres reaching the coeliac ganglion degenerate (Kuntz, 1938). Following division of the nerves to the stomach and small intestine, degenerating endings are seen in the coeliac ganglion, presumably originating from afferent neurons in the gastro-intestinal wall. This hypothesis is supported by studies on intestinal reflexes, and by electrophysiological studies of the prevertebral ganglia (see p.43 afferent fibres). In studies of ganglion cells of the inferior mesenteric ganglion of the guinea-pig by intracellular recording it was found that most of these neurons have an input from the spinal cord (preganglionic fibres), from other ganglia of the abdominal plexus, and from the wall of the colon (Crowcroft & Szurszewski, 1971; Crowcroft, Holman & Szurszewski, 1971). Morphological studies should elucidate the structure and the distribution of the three orders of input.

Studies with fluorescence microscopy for detection of catecholamines, the neurons of the prevertebral ganglia display varying degrees of fluorescence intensity. In the coeliac ganglion of rabbit a number of ganglion cells appear enclosed by prominent pericellular nests of adrenergic fibres (Norberg, 1967). These pericellular systems of terminals are the most well-developed of all the sympathetic ganglia (Hamberger, Norberg & Ungerstedt, 1965).

The acetylcholinesterase reaction is consistently very low in all ganglion cells of the prevertebral ganglia. Ganglion cells with intense reaction are found only occasionally within the capsule of the ganglia or embedded in nerve bundles separated from the mass of the ganglion cells (Fredricsson & Sjövist, 1962).

2.4   Chromaffin cells

Many sympathetic ganglia also contain *chromaffin cells*, i.e. cells which have an affinity for, and stain with, bichromate salts, although less intensely and less consistently than adrenal medullary cells. Chromaffin cells are small in size, have few, short processes, and are clustered in groups; Smirnow (1890) and Stöhr (1939) using a silver impregnation method reported that, in the prevertebral ganglia, they are innervated by preganglionic fibres. Chromaffin-positive cells in the superior cervical ganglion of the cat were observed by Bülbring (1944), but they were not found in the same ganglion in other species, e.g. the rat. In fluorescence microscopy, with the far more sensitive and specific method of Falck—Hillarp, it has been shown that cells of similar description are present in most sympathetic ganglia among ordinary ganglion cells and have a high content of catecholamines (so high as to produce in some cases positivity to the chromaffin reac-

23

tion); they go under the name of small intensely fluorescent (S.I.F.) cells (Norberg & Hamberger, 1964; Eränkö & Härkönen, 1965). Other similar fluorescent cells were found along nerve trunks and in parasympathetic ganglia (see p. 106). In the abdomen there are small organs which are entirely composed of cells of similar appearance (paraganglia) (see Coupland, 1965; Eränkö & Härkönen, 1965).

Small intensely fluorescent cells correspond, therefore, to chromaffin cells. They in turn correspond to cells identifiable in electron microscopy (see p.25) and described as *granular* or granule-containing *cells*. Although some of the granular cells are negative to the chromaffin reaction (a fact which is easily explained by the lower sensitivity of this technique), the term chromaffin cells is used here as a general label for this category of cells; the terms small intensely fluorescent cells and granular cells refer to the same cells, of which they point out the most prominent feature in fluorescence and electron microscopy respectively, and are therefore considered synonymous with chromaffin cells. The possibility that different populations of cells within this group occur, as discussed on p.29, should not be obscured by the present use of a single term. The introduction of a better nomenclature can perhaps wait until more is known about different types of the cell indicated by the general term of chromaffin cell (Note 2.6).

The chromaffin cells are characterized by an intense formaldehyde-induced fluorescence, indicating the presence of biogenic amines in high concentration. From the cell body, measuring $10-15\,\mu$m in diameter, emerge a few short varicose processes also intensely fluorescent – up to $40\,\mu$m long in the superior cervical ganglion of the rat (Norberg, Ritzén & Ungerstedt, 1966) and hundreds of microns in the rabbit (Libet & Owman, 1974). These cells are clustered in small groups particularly around blood vessels. There is still some uncertainty as to the type of amine stored by these cells; it is probably not the same in the chromaffin cells of different ganglia and species (Eränkö & Eränkö, 1971). It has been shown biochemically that the chromaffin cells of the dog inferior mesenteric ganglion (Muscholl & Vogt, 1964) and those of the pelvic ganglia of dog, cat and rabbit (Owman & Sjöstrand, 1965) contain adrenaline. By microspectrofluorimetry Björklund, Cegrell, Falck, Ritzén & Rosengren, found dopamine in the chromaffin cells of sympathetic ganglia of the pig, cat and rat, whereas Eränkö & Eränkö (1971) showed

24

by a similar method that those of the rat superior cervical ganglion contain noradrenaline. Liber and Owman (1974) reported that in the superior cervical ganglion of the rabbit these cells contain dopamine; moreover, when experimentally depleted of the catecholamine, they are able to take up exogenous dopamine and restore their fluorescence. In the superior cervical ganglion of the rat the chromaffin cells lack any histochemically-demonstrable dopamine-β-hydroxylase, the enzyme which catalyses the synthesis of noradrenaline from dopamine (Fuxe, Goldstein, Hökfelt & Joh, 1971).

Comparing fluorimetric assays with fluorescence observations and electron microscopy, van Orden, Schaeffer, Burke & Lodoen, (1970b) estimated that of the total amount of amines in the rat superior cervical ganglion 70 per cent was associated with adrenergic ganglion neurons and 30 per cent with chromaffin cells. In the superior cervical ganglion of the rat there are 400 to 1000 chromaffin cells, with little numerical change from birth to maturity (Eränkö & Eränkö, 1971). Prevertebral ganglia have a greater number of chromaffin cells than the superior cervical ganglion. In the paracervical ganglion (see Chapter 5) of several mammals the number of chromaffin cells varies between 0·9 (*Macacus rhesus*) and 1·6 (rat) per cent of the number of ganglion cells (1·2 per cent in the rabbit, 1·3 per cent in the cat, 1·4 per cent in the dog); in the mouse the percentage is higher (3·2 per cent) but it falls below 1 per cent after castration (Blotevogel, 1927, 1928).

The chromaffin cells of the sympathetic ganglia are readily identifiable in the electron microscope (granule-containing cells) (Grillo, 1966; Siegrist, *et al.*, 1966 and 1968; Hökfelt, 1968; Matthews & Raisman, 1969; Taxi *et al.*, 1969; Williams & Palay, 1969; Matthews & Nash, 1970; van Orden *et al.*, 1970b; Tamarind & Quilliam, 1971; Yokota, 1973; all working on the superior cervical ganglion of the rat; Elfvin, 1968, inferior mesenteric ganglion of the rabbit; and others) (Plate 7a). They measure 6–12 μm in diameter, are round or polyhedral in shape, and have a central nucleus often without a nucleolus and rich in chromatin (Matthews & Raisman, 1969). They are sheathed by satellite cells morphologically similar to those around the ordinary ganglion cells, but when they are clustered together the cells are often directly apposed and interdigitate without intervening satellite cells and with a gap of 15–20 nm (Siegrist *et al.*, 1968; Matthews & Raisman, 1969; Williams & Palay, 1969; Yokota, 1973).

25

In four chromaffin cells, which were serially sectioned, 17—38 per cent of the cell surface was directly contacting another similar cell, and about 2 per cent was occupied by attachment plaques with other cell bodies (Yokota, 1973). Only between 0·1 per cent and 2·3 per cent of the cell surface lay in direct contact with the basal lamina and the extracellular space (Yokota, 1973), a fenestrated capillary often being close to the exposed surface of the cells (Siegrist *et al.*, 1968; Matthews & Raisman, 1969). The cytoplasm of the chromaffin cell has a few cisternae of rough endoplasmic reticulum, and an abundance of ribosomes (Matthews & Raisman, 1969) and mitochondria which are larger than those of the ganglion cells (Siegrist *et al.*, 1968). Vesicles containing electron-dense granules are prominent; they appear more densely packed in the superficial parts of the cell body. In the chromaffin cells of the superior cervical ganglion of rat, vesicles measure 60—120 nm (of which 30—75 nm are taken up by the granule) (Hökfelt, 1969; Matthews & Raisman, 1969; Taxi *et al.*, 1969; Williams & Palay, 1969). The granules have a similar electron density but a smaller size than those found in the chromaffin cells of the adrenal medulla, where they are 50—350 nm in diameter and are even more densely packed (Coupland, 1965; Elfvin, 1965). In other ganglia the granulated vesicles are reported to be larger: 90—170 nm, inferior mesenteric ganglion of rabbit (Elfvin, 1968); 150—250 nm, inferior mesenteric ganglion of rat (van Orden *et al.*, 1970); 100—250 nm, hypogastric ganglion of guinea-pig (Watanabe, 1971); 80—300 nm, paracervical ganglion of rat (Kanerva & Teräväinen, 1972); however, detailed stereological studies on these vesicles have not been published. According to Eränkö & Eränkö (1974) the size of granular vesicles is a crucial factor for the outcome of the chromaffin reaction. Siegrist *et al.*, (1968) described small and large granules. The large granules, surrounded by an electron-lucent halo, lie in contact with the membrane of vesicles (up to 300 nm in diameter) the population of granules is mixed in all the cells, but only one type of granule predominates in any one cell, so that two types of cells are identifiable. To what extent these large granules and vesicles are affected by the preparative procedure is not known, although they are not visible in preparations of the same ganglion by other authors (Matthews & Raisman, 1969; Williams & Palay, 1969). Variability in the electron densities of the granules has been noted by most of the authors, and Williams and Palay (1969) observed that

26

some of the granules had a substructure consisting of units of about 10 nm, more or less tightly packed.

The cell processes are crowded with granules similar to those found in the cell body. The processes also contain mitochondria, microtubules or microfilaments (Matthews & Raisman, 1969), and a few ribosomes (Williams & Palay, 1969). The nature and significance of these processes remain to be clarified, and none of them has the structural features of an axon.

Nerve endings containing numerous agranular synaptic vesicles, 30–40 nm in diameter, synapse on the cell body, and to a lesser extent on the processes (Yokota, 1973), of the chromaffin cells of the superior cervical ganglion of the rat (Grillo, 1966; Siegrist et al., 1968; Matthews & Raisman, 1969; Williams & Palay, 1969; Yokota, 1973). These nerve endings originate from the spinal cord as do other preganglionic fibres (Taxi et al., 1969; Matthews, 1971; Quilliam & Tamarind, 1972; Matthews and Ostberg, 1973) and are probably cholinergic (Plate 7a). In addition to afferent synapses some chromaffin cells of this ganglion display specialized contacts with thickenings of the membranes and a localized clustering of granular vesicles, these configurations are interpreted as efferent synapses (Siegrist et al., 1968; Matthews & Raisman, 1969; Williams & Palay, 1969; Yokota, 1973) (Plate 7b). The majority of them seem to arise from the cell body (Matthews & Raisman, 1969). Only in a few cases has the post-junctional element been identified as a sympathetic adrenergic ganglion cell, by the presence of small granulated vesicles (Taxi et al., 1969; Yokota, 1973). However, Taxi et al. (1969) have been cautious in their identification of efferent contacts from the small granular cells and argue that there is not yet sufficient evidence to consider such junctions to be synapses, and prefer the term 'zone synaptoid'. Moreover, several authors have reported that after section of the superior cervical sympathetic trunk all synapses disappear from the superior cervical ganglion (Ceccarelli, Clementi & Mantegazza, 1971, the cat); Hamori, Land & Simon, 1968, in the cat; Taxi et al., 1969, in the rat; Bamindra & Diatchkova, 1970, in the dog; Lakos, 1970, in the cat. However, Grillo (1966) and Lakos (1970) reported that some rare synapses were present several days after preganglionic denervation in the rat only, and it may be that they originated from chromaffin cells. Recently Raisman, Field, Ostberg, Iversen & Zigmond (1974) in a quantitative study of the synapses in normal and preganglionically denervated superior cervical ganglia of rats observed only a few synapses present after denervation and none of them showed the morphological characteristics of small cell processes. Therefore it seems that there is not yet enough evidence to conclude that chromaffin cells in the sympathetic ganglia function as interneurons. It is unfortunate that the only ganglion of the sympathetic chain where the fine structure of the chromaffin cells has been thoroughly investigated is the rat superior cervical ganglion. For this ganglion it seems likely that some chromaffin cells hold the position of interneurons; but Yokota (1973) reports that of four chromaffin cells followed in serial sections only two had 'efferent synapses', whereas van Orden et al. (1970) failed to observe any junction of this type. Further studies are needed to ascertain how frequently these cells appear as interneurons in other species and in other sympathetic ganglia. While by definition interneurons are neurons with afferent and efferent synapses, the absence of efferent synapses from chromaffin cells would not rule out their function as 'modulators' of ganglionic transmission. It has been suggested that these cells act as endocrine cells, releasing catecholamines which would reach the ganglion neurons either by diffusion or through the capillaires (Grillo, 1966; Siegrist et al., 1968; Matthews & Raisman, 1969). Such a role is supported by recent experimental studies according to which, (a) the fibre network of chromaffin cells in the rabbit superior cervical ganglion is in close contact with virtually every ganglion cell body, and (b) the slow inhibitory post-synaptic potentials are due to the release of dopamine from chromaffin cells, activated via cholinergic (muscarinic) receptors (Libet & Owman, 1974). Eränkö and Eränkö (1971) and Tamarind and Quilliam, (1971) also suggest that the chromaffin cells of sympathetic ganglia may act as chemoreceptors.

The great interest during the past ten years on the chromaffin cells in sympathetic ganglia is related to the observations that catecholamines affect ganglionic transmission, as originally observed by Marrazzi (1939) and Bülbring (1944) (see reviews in Volle, 1966; Kosterlitz & Lees, 1972). Bülbring (1944) found that the perfusate of the cat superior cervical ganglion during preganglionic stimulation contained an adrenaline-like substance, which she suggested was released by the chromaffin tissue of the ganglion. A variety of findings suggest that catecholamines have a physiological inhibitory role in sympathetic ganglia (De Groat & Saum, 1971). The action of dopamine and other catecholamines is primarily due to an inhibition of the acetylcholine output from the preganglionic nerve endings, and to a minor extent to a direct effect on ganglion neurons (Christ & Nishi, 1971; Dun & Nishi, 1974). The catecholamines present in the sympathetic ganglia can originate from several sources: the chromaffin cells, recurrent adrenergic axons, the circulating boood, the perikarya and, in particular, the dendrites of ganglion cells. The relative importance of these various sources remains to be seen.

Many morphological data on the chromaffin cells in sympathetic ganglia, particularly as regards the appearance of their large granular vesicles and the presence of synapses, suggest the existence of different types of these cells (see Matthews, 1971). Recently, Williams and collaborators (1975) have described two types of small cells in the superior cervical ganglion: a type I, with long process running in close apposition to ganglion cells, and a type II, located in the interstitial or subcapsular portion of the ganglion, with short processes which end in close relation to blood vessels. Of about 6500 cells counted in the superior cervical ganglion of a cow, 24 per cent were of type I and 76 per cent of type II; in the cat only about 100 cells were found, 98 per cent of which were of type II. It is possible that cells of the same origin and of rather similar structure can attain different final specializations, ranging from an endocrine function (e.g. in some paraganglia) to an interneuron function (e.g. in some cells of the sympathetic ganglia). If a variety of roles exists it should be interesting to know under which conditions these cells assume one or another of them, and what degree of plasticity they retain after differentiation.

2.5   Sympathetic ganglia in amphibians

The organization of sympathetic ganglia in Amphibia is reviewed by Pick (1970). In the frog the preganglionic outflow is restricted to the 2nd to 7th spinal nerves (Langley & Orbeli, 1911). Pick (1957, 1970) accepts the notion, put forward by several authors (e.g. Lucas & Miksicek, 1936; Bishop & O'Leary, 1938), that the dorsal root ganglia contain sympathetic neurons which receive preganglionic fibres through the dorsal and ventral roots. However, histological evidence of the occurrence of such cells has not emerged from recent

29

studies of dorsal root ganglion cells in Amphibia (e.g. Kohno & Nakayama, 1973).

In the frog the ganglion cells are unipolar, the single large process forming the post-ganglionic fibre (Smirnov, 1890). Each preganglionic fibre may branch in the vicinity of the ganglion cell to provide terminals to several of them, having spiralled around the initial tract of the axon and the neighbouring part of the cell body to form a pericellular nest. Such terminals appear to be present on almost every ganglion neuron (Johnson, 1918). The images obtained using silver or methylene blue staining methods suggest that each pericellular nest is derived from a single preganglionic fibre, but in some situations there is evidence of convergence of several preganglionic fibres upon single ganglion cells (see p.31). Synapses are found on the cell body, and to a lesser extent over the remainder of the neuronal surface (Taxi, 1965). The cell body appears smooth in silver preparations, but in electron micrographs shows short processes (Pick, 1963, in *Rana pipiens*), which remain beneath the satellite cells ensheathing the neuron. Such short processes were only rarely seen by Taxi (1965) over the cell body in *Rana esculenta*, but he observed similar short processes originating from the initial region of the axon.

The nuclei of the sympathetic ganglion neurons are eccentrically located (Plate 8a). In the superficial region of one pole of the cytoplasm a large crescent-shaped accumulation of glycogen granules has been observed (Pick, 1963; Yamamoto, 1963). Seasonal variations in glycogen content in ganglion cells and axons have not been investigated, however, an important omission since it is known that the glycogen content of the liver in the frog *Rana pipiens* is five times as large in November as it is in May (Mizell, 1965). These neurons have been divided into two classes: large neurons in the cortex of the ganglion, with poorly developed Nissl bodies, and small neurons, more deeply situated with abundant Nissl bodies (Fujimoto, 1967); in light microscopy these two types are recognizable as clear and dark neurons. Similar dark and clear neurons have been described in the cranial and spinal ganglia of Amphibia (Dawson, Hossack & Wyburn, 1956; Rosenbluth, 1962). Numerous pigment cells are present in the capsule of the ganglion and among ganglion cells (Plate 8a).

Each ganglion cell is invested by a sheath of satellite cells which is continuous with the Schwann cell sheath around the process. At the level of the mergence of the process from the cell body, the satellite

30

cell sheath splits into two layers, one lying in contact with the neuron, the other at some distance from it, forming a labyrinthine system of extracellular space cavities, in which are situated the spires of the terminal part of the preganglionic axon (Taxi, 1967) (Plate 8b). Satellite cells are characterized by large numbers of gliofilaments (Plate 8b).

Many years ago, Bishop and Heinebecker (1930) observed both 'B' and 'C' electrical waves in the post-ganglionic sympathetic nerves of Amphibia, and attributed these to the presence of myelinated and non-myelinated fibres respectively. Numerous post-ganglionic fibres are in fact myelinated, to such an extent that certain 'grey' (post-ganglionic) rami communicates to the somatic nerves consist chiefly of myelinated fibres (Bishop & O'Leary, 1938). The post-ganglionic fibres are said to outnumber the preganglionic fibres by about 7 to 1 (Huber, 1899). In the lumbar sympathetic ganglia of toad two types of post-ganglionic fibre, i.e. 'B' and 'C' fibres, with average conduction velocities of $2 \cdot 4 \, \text{ms}^{-1}$ and $0 \cdot 2 \, \text{ms}^{-1}$ respectively, have been identified; the 'B' fibres have electrical properties of myelinated axons (Nishi, Soeda & Koketsu, 1965). The corresponding cell bodies, termed 'B' and 'C' neurons, are also clearly distinguishable by their electrical properties. 'C' neurons are smaller (about $18 \, \mu\text{m}$ in diameter) than 'B' neurons (about $35 \, \mu\text{m}$ in diameter) and receive synaptic input from two and sometimes three spinal roots, i.e. from more than one level of the spinal cord. On the other hand, most of the 'B' neurons receive synaptic inputs from one spinal level only (monosegmental innervation). Preganglionic fibres with different conduction velocities ($0 \cdot 19 - 0 \cdot 32 \, \text{ms}^{-1}$ and $5 \cdot 0 \, \text{ms}^{-1}$) are connected to the two types of ganglion neurons: in the 'B' neuron system, the conduction velocity of the preganglionic axon is faster than that of the post-ganglionic fibre, whereas the relationship is reversed in the 'C' neuron system. Honma (1970b) has confirmed the bimodal distribution of ganglion cell sizes in the 10th lumbar sympathetic ganglion of the toad, and has provided evidence to support the hypothesis that the 'B' neuron system innervates the toxic glands of the skin and the 'C' system the vascular system of the lower limbs. These findings are in agreement with previous electrophysiological evidence (Hutter & Loewenstein, 1955). Each 'B' neuron is innervated by a single preganglionic fibre, or possibly by a few fibres having the same threshold and conduction velocity (Nishi et al., 1965). On the other hand 'C' neurons not only receive multisegmental innervation, but probably receive a multiple innervation from each ventral roots.

The fine structure of nerve terminals in amphibian sympathetic ganglia has been reported by several authors since the first description by De Robertis and Bennett (1954, 1955). Numerous synapses are found on the axon (Uchizono, 1964; Taxi, 1965; Hunt & Nelson, 1965; Nishi, Soeda & Koketsu, 1967). Other terminals much larger than those found on the axon, synapse on the perikaryon (Plate 9), or on short stout processes which stem from it. Nishi, Soeda and Koketsu (1967) calculate that in the toad lumbar sympathetic ganglion approximately 10 per cent of the neuron cell surface is covered by nerve terminals, approximately 55 nerve terminals being found on a 'B' neuron and 15 on a 'C' neuron. Some nerve endings deeply invaginate the neuronal surface (Hunt & Nelson, 1965). The nerve terminals contain electron-lucent vesicles with a diameter of approximately 50 nm (Uchizono, 1964), together with a few large granular vesicles. Many of the terminals contain a large number of glycogen granules, and these can be so abundant that some terminals appear completely filled with them (Pick, 1963; Fujimoto, 1967). In the sympathetic neurons of the frog (*Rana esculenta*) and axolotl there is frequently a subsynaptic apparatus (Taxi, 1961, 1965), formed by a band of electron-dense material approximately 25 nm thick lying a few tens of nanometres beneath the post-synaptic membrane. This apparatus was less common in Fujimoto's preparations (*Bufo vulgaris jap.*) and was absent from Pick's (1970) material (*Rana pipiens*). From the appearance of their content of vesicles it seems probable that there is only one type of nerve terminal (Nishi, Soeda & Koketsu, 1967), despite Uchizono's (1964) description of three types. The transmitter involved is acetylcholine (Blackman, Ginsborg & Ray, 1963).

A high activity of acetylcholinesterase is detectable histochemically in the preganglionic fibres of the frog (Giacobini, 1956). This cholinesterase activity is intense in about 10 per cent of the neurons, and moderate or absent in the others, a pattern not dissimilar to that seen in the cat and the rat. The intracellular distribution of acetylcholinesterase has been studied by Brzin, Tennyson and Duffy (1966), who found the reaction end product to be concentrated mainly in the sacs of the rough endoplasmic reticulum.

32

All the amphibian sympathetic ganglion cells show specific fluorescence for catecholamines (Norberg & McIsaac, 1967; Honma, 1970a; Woods, 1970a). The intensity of this reaction varies between cells but it is not related to cell size; non-fluorescent ganglion cells are not observed. Since the work of von Euler (1946) it has been generally accepted that the catecholamine involved is adrenaline, as demonstrated by Loewi (1921). This finding has been confirmed in several species of frog and toad (Azuma, Binia & Visscher, 1965; Angelakos, Glassman, Millar & King, 1965), but newts possess only noradrenaline (Angelakos et al., 1965). Although the post-ganglionic fibres store and release upon stimulation mainly adrenaline (Azuma et al., 1965), the sympathetic ganglia of the frog contain larger amounts of noradrenaline than of adrenaline (in the ratio of approximately 5:1, Azuma et al., 1965), the content of noradrenaline probably being accounted for by the granular cells (see below). Seasonal changes in catecholamine content occur in nerves of Amphibia, with values significantly higher in summer than in winter, but there is no change in the velocity of the distally directed transport of catecholamines along the axons (Rodriguez-Echandia, Donoso & Pedroza, 1972).

In addition to the ganglion cells (some of which show many large dense core vesicles in their cytoplasm) the sympathetic ganglia contain chromaffin cells (granule-containing cells) grouped in clumps or short cords and frequently in close proximity to blood vessels (Fujimoto, 1967), their cytoplasm being filled with granular vesicles 20–60 nm in diameter. These vesicles are round and dense in osmium-fixed ganglia and oval or rod-shaped and less dense in glutaraldehyde-fixed ganglia; furthermore a distinct clear halo surrounds the granule after osmium fixation but this is barely visible following glutaraldehyde (Fujimoto, 1967). Such granular cells are closely associated with nerve fibres, and although synapses have not been seen on them, Fujimoto (1967) suggests that their secretion is under direct nervous control. The granular cells correspond to the cells with intense formaldehyde-induced fluorescence (chromaffin cells), containing high concentrations of catecholamines (Norberg & McIsaac, 1967; Honma, 1970a; Jacobowitz, 1970). The histochemical properties of these cells indicate that they contain noradrenaline rather than adrenaline (Woods, 1970a). Ganglion cells in amphibian sympathetic ganglia have adrenergic receptors, and the possibility exists that catecholamines modulate transmission through the ganglion (Nakamura & Koketsu, 1972), as has been suggested for mammalian ganglia (see p.28).

2.6 Sympathetic ganglia in reptiles

The arrangement of sympathetic ganglia in reptiles is described and illustrated by Hirt (1921). In *Lacerta* rami communicantes containing both pre- and post-ganglionic fibres are found in the paravertebral ganglia corresponding to spinal nerves 9 to 24; most of the preganglionic fibres arise from the 9th and 10th spinal nerves (Adams, 1942). In the turtle (*Emys orbicularis*) preganglionic fibres are myelinated and lose their myelin sheath very close to the terminals (Szentágothai, 1964).

In the reptilian sympathetic ganglia some neurons are multipolar, although unipolar neurons predominate, and bipolar neurons are absent (Huber, 1899; Colborn & Adamo, 1969). In the lizard ganglion neurons measure $20-30\mu m$ in diameter, are invested by a myelin sheath, and have nuclei eccentrically situated (Colborn & Adamo, 1969); some neurons have at one pole a large crescentic area of glycogen granules (Smith, 1959). Some neurons have masses of closely packed ribosomes without membrane attachments ('areticular Nissl substance', Smith, 1959; Colborn & Adamo, 1969). In the turtle there are loosely arranged myelin lamellae around the cell bodies; the preganglionic fibres, containing lucent vesicles $30-50\,nm$ in diameter, synapse mainly on dendrites, rarely on cell bodies (Szentágothai, 1964). In the lizard Taxi (1965) observed axo-dendritic synapses, while Colborn and Adamo (1969) also found great numbers of axo-somatic synapses particularly at the base of the emerging nerve processes. In the turtle the predominant catecholamine of sympathetic neurons is noradrenaline (Azuma *et al.*, 1965); the same conclusion is indicated by the characteristics of the sympathetic fibres of lizard in fluorescence microscopy (Read & Burnstock, 1968).

2.7 Sympathetic ganglia in birds

The gross anatomy of the sympathetic chain in birds is reviewed and illustrated by Pick (1970) and Terni (1931) has a detailed description of its cervical component. In the cervical and most of the thoracic

34

levels sympathetic ganglia are fused with spinal nerves and no rami communicantes are apparent. Unlike the mammals, birds have a sympathetic ganglion on each cervical spinal nerve (Langley, 1904; Terni, 1931).

The ganglion cells have extremely long dendrites which extend well outside the ganglion of origin (Cajal, 1911). The cells measure $15-60 \mu$m in diameter and the majority of them show low to moderately intense fluorescence for catecholamines in their cell bodies and larger dendrites (Plate 10a—c), but a minority of the ganglion cells show no specific fluorescence (Plate 10a) (Bennett & Malmfors, 1970). The intensity of the fluorescence varies from cell to cell (Plate 10a—c), and small cells tend to be more intensely fluorescent than large cells. Nerve fibres of differing fluorescent intensities pass through the sympathetic ganglia, but only few varicose fibres were found in association with either the fluorescent or the non-fluorescent nerve cell bodies (Bennett & Malmfors, 1970). In the fowl the intensity of the fluorescence of the smooth non-terminal tract of the adrenergic axons is higher than that seen in mammals, so that in the sciatic nerve, for example, a number of fluorescent fibres are detectable in normal conditions (Bennett & Malmfors, 1970). Also a large number of small cells with bright, yellow fluorescence (chromafffin cells) are found in avian sympathetic ganglia (Plate 10a). The very great majority of nerve fibres given off by the sympathetic ganglia are myelinated (Langley, 1904). Axons acquire a myelin sheath a short distance from the ganglion cell bodies. Post-ganglionic fibres as recognized in fluorescence microscopy are seen passing from the sympathetic ganglia to the spinal nerves, but only a few are visible in the interganglionic connectives, suggesting that most of the ganglion neurons innervate structures within the field of distribution of the spinal nerves (Bennett, 1971), as had already been noted by Langley (1904).

The histochemical properties of the adrenergic post-ganglionic fibres indicate that the neurotransmitter is noradrenaline (Baumgarten & Holstein, 1968; Enemar, Falck & Håkanson, 1965; Bennett, 1970); however, many organs innervated by the sympathetic fibres also contain adrenaline and dopamine. In the heart (Ignarro & Shideman, 1968) and the spleen (Manukhin, 1969) of the chick the adrenaline content is greater than that of noradrenaline, and this may be accounted for by the occurrence of chromaffin (small intensely

35

fluorescent) cells, but in the vas deferens of the chick (Sjöstrand, 1965) and in the pigeon heart (Anton & Sayre, 1964) noradrenaline is by far the most predominant catecholamine present. The relative concentrations of the two catecholamines within the sympathetic ganglia themselves have not been determined.

Characteristic of the autonomic nervous system is the ganglionated nerve of Remak, a nerve trunk running parallel to the intestine within the mesentery and the mesorectum. It extends from the level of the duodeno-jejunal junction, where it is connected to the coeliac plexus, to the level of the cloaca, where it is connected to the pelvic plexus (Nolf, 1934). There are a great number of thin nerve connections between the nerve of Remak and the intestine. The trunk contains numerous ganglia, which are larger at the level of the rectum and decrease in size towards the duodenum. At the level of the duodenum the ganglia are composed entirely of adrenergic neurons, showing specific fluorescence for catecholamines; no fluorescent nerve endings are visible in the ganglia. Moving towards the caudal end, non-fluorescent neurons appear in increasing numbers among the fluorescent ones, and nests of varicose fluorescent fibres occur around them (Bennett, 1970). Efferent fibres from Remak's ganglia reach the myenteric plexus neurons (and in the rectum may also reach the musculature). The synaptic connections of Remak's ganglia are not fully understood. It is known that there are interganglionic connections, that there are fibres arising or coming from the myenteric plexus and connections with prevertebral and paravertebral ganglia. Although it is thought to be an ascending pathway, originating from the hypogastric plexus (Romanoff, 1960) or from the sacral parasympathetic system (Yntema & Hammond, 1955), cranially it is connected to the coeliac plexus which supplies fibres descending along the nerve (Bennett, 1970) and possibly also to the vagus nerve (Pera, 1971).

2.8 Preganglionic fibres

The preganglionic fibres to the sympathetic ganglia originate from neurons in the thoracic and lumbar levels of the spinal cord (see Chapter 11). They reach the paravertebral ganglia through the ventral roots and the white rami communicantes, ending in the ganglia of the corresponding level, or ascending or descending along the sympathetic chain to more cranial or more caudal ganglia. Preganglionic fibres branch and can provide terminal branches to different ganglia. The details of this arrangement are not well known but there is physiological evidence of preganglionic fibres supplying branches which synapse on ganglion cells of the 5th lumbar sympathetic ganglion of the cat and passing to more distally located ganglia (Obrador & Odoriz, 1936). Langley (1899) found that pilo-motor preganglionic fibres descend along the lumbar sympathetic chain of the cat and synapse on neurons in three successive ganglia. More recently Blackman and Purves (1969) have shown electrophysiologically that preganglionic fibres in the thoracic sympathetic chain of the guinea-pig may either ascend or descend several segments making synapses in more than one ganglion.

Preganglionic fibres represent a heterogeneous population of fibres in term of size, presence of myelin sheath, and conduction velocity. These features vary also along the length of individual fibres; furthermore, preganglionic fibres are often mixed with some post-ganglionic fibres. Foley & DuBois (1940) calculated that in the white rami communicantes contributing fibres to the superior cervical trunk of the cat 5 to 60 per cent (on average 23 per cent) of the preganglionic fibres are unmyelinated. Myelinated fibres are very few in the sympathetic chain and in the rami communicantes of the rat (De Lemos & Pick, 1966).

Table 2.4 reports some quantitative studies on the cervical sympathetic trunk, a nerve which contains the preganglionic fibres to the superior cervical ganglion.

Several rami communicantes contribute fibres to the cervical sympathetic trunk. By selective destruction of thoracic roots of the cat, Foley and Schnitzlein (1957) calculated the number of preganglionic axons contributed by each root from T1 to T8: the 2nd, 3rd, 4th and 5th thoracic root contribute approximately equal numbers of fibres, whereas the contribution below the level of T5 is minimal. By electrical stimulation of single thoracic roots Langley (1892) obtained characteristic effects on either the pupil and the nictitating membrane or the submandibular glands or the blood vessels or the hair of the face and neck of the cat.

De Castro (1951) classified the preganglionic fibres in the superior cervical trunk of the cat in three groups on the basis of their diameters; Eccles (1935) found four groups of fibres identifiable by their excitability and conduction velocities. Folkow, Johansson and Oberg (1958) differentiated three groups of preganglionic sympa-

37

Table 2.4

Number of axons in the cervical sympathetic trunk. All counts made on silver-impregnated or osmic acid preparations, except by Bray and Aguayo who used the electron microscope. Figures are means ± S.E.M., number of cases in brackets.

Species	Number of neurons	Number of cases	Reference
cat	7400 ± 450 (40–68 per cent unmyelinated)	(8)	Foley and DuBois, 1940
dog	9950 ±1050 (42–64 per cent unmyelinated)	(8)	Foley and DuBois, 1940
rat	2950 ± 150 (98–99 per cent unmyelinated)	(8)	Foley and DuBois, 1940
cat	5988	(1)	Wolf, 1941
cat	7400 ± 400	(18)	Foley, 1943
rabbit	2100 ± 270 (myelinated 820 ± 100)	(7) (14))	Butson, 1950
cat	7600 ± 480	(10)[a]	Foley and Schnitzlein, 1957
rat	4880 ± 360 (95·8—99·6 per cent unmyelinated)	(14)[b]	Bray and Aguayo, 1974

[a] Plus approx 400 post-ganglionic fibres.

[b] Left and right trunks from 7 rats; no significant difference between the two sides.

thetic fibres; they are, in order of increase in stimulation threshold (i.e. of decrease in diameter): (1) fibres to the neurons innervating the pupil, the nictitating membrane and the arterio-venous anastomoses of the skin; (2) fibres to neurons involved in the vasoconstriction of the skin and skeletal muscles; (3) fibres to the neurons which supply vasodilator fibres to striated muscles.

Three types of myelinated fibres were found by Williams *et al.* (1973) in the cat cervical sympathetic trunk, characterized by different diameters and myelin thicknesses, intermingled with unmyelinated fibres constituting about 50 per cent of the axons. Most unmyelinated preganglionic axons have a thin individual sheath of Schwann cell cytoplasm, whereas up to 20 post-ganglionic axons are invested by each Schwann cell (Williams *et al.*, 1973). A wide range in sizes and conduction velocities has also been found in the cervical sympathetic trunk of rat (Dunant, 1967), where 96–99 per cent of the axons are unmyelinated (Foley & DuBois, 1940; Forssman, 1964; Bray & Aguayo, 1974).

Preganglionic fibres are many times less numerous than ganglion neurons. The ratio was found to vary between 1:11 and 1:17 in the superior cervical ganglion of the cat (Wolff, 1941), which corresponds to the ratio 1:32 calculated for the myelinated fibres only (Billingsley & Ranson, 1918), these being about 50 per cent of the total. The ratio between preganglionic fibres and ganglion neurons for the superior cervical ganglion ranges in various species of primates from 1:28 to 1:196, with wide variations even in individuals of the same species (e.g. in man from 1:63 to 1:196) (Ebbeson, 1963 and 1968a). Ebbeson (1968) found that in primates the numbers of preganglionic fibres serving specific functions are of the same order of magnitude in species of different body size, but they are distributed to a different number of ganglion cells, the latter being to some extent related to the body size (see p.8). This interesting conclusion should be confirmed by more accurate (i.e. using electron microscopy) counts of the preganglionic fibres, of which 6 to 80 per cent were unmyelinated in Ebbeson's material (Note 2.7).

Since all the counts show that the number of preganglionic fibres is in excess of that of ganglion cells, there is a clear indication of a divergence of impulses along the efferent pathway which is substantially greater than that found in parasympathetic ganglia (see below). The divergence is greater than suggested by the ratio between pre-

and post-ganglionic units, since most ganglion neurons receive synapses from many preganglionic fibres. It is, however, not known how extensively the preganglionic fibres branch before reaching the ganglia, i.e. how many preganglionic fibres entering one ganglion are issued by one spinal preganglionic neuron. The evidence for a divergence of each preganglionic fibres onto several ganglion cells is borne by electrophysiological experiments on the superior cervical ganglion of rabbit (Erulkar & Woodward, 1968; Libet & Tosaka, 1969) and guinea-pig and rat (Perri *et al.*, 1970). Libet and Tosaka (1969) found that as many as seven preganglionic neurons can converge on one ganglion cell. A neuronal model with divergence (spread to several ganglion cells) and convergence (of several fibres onto one ganglion cell) of preganglionic fibres is discussed by Brimble *et al.* (1972).

Furthermore, the counts give an *average* ratio between pre- and post-ganglionic fibres, *as if* all the preganglionic fibres spread evenly to the same number of ganglion cells, which may well not be the case. In addition, it is rare to find a purely preganglionic nerve; the presence of small ganglia along nerve trunks has been discussed on p.4; in the cervical sympathetic trunk besides the preganglionic fibres, there are a few ascending and descending post-ganglionic fibres (in the cat they form a readily identifiable bundle [Jacobowitz & Woodward, 1968]) and some vagal fibres: a fasicle containing between 400 and 1700 descending fibres from the vagus nerve was found in 4–10 per cent of the cases in the cervical sympathetic trunk of the cat (Foley, 1945).

2.9   Post-ganglionic fibres

The axons of ganglion neurons leave the sympathetic ganglia directed to the periphery, and reach the effector structures. These include all smooth muscle of blood vessels and viscera, heart musculature, iris muscles and hair muscles. Vegetative fibres reach also some of the fat tissue, most of the sensory organs, and various glandular tissues. The occurrence of recurrent branches has been discussed above (p.7). The post-ganglionic fibres from the thoraco-lumbar sympathetic ganglia form the *grey rami communicantes* which reach the spinal nerves and through them they run to the periphery. Those from the superior cervical ganglion are in addition grouped in the carotid and other small perivascular nerves. Those from the prevertebral ganglia reach the peripheral organ in small nerves satellite to arteries.

In mammals post-ganglionic fibres are usually unmyelinated axons. However, in the cat the grey rami communicantes and the post-ganglionic nerves emanating from the superior cervical ganglion contain a variable but often considerable number of small myelinated fibres (Langley, 1896); in the grey ramus of the 7th lumbar ganglion this author counted up to 300 myelinated axons, most of them issuing from the corresponding sympathetic ganglion as shown with selective lesions and degeneration experiments. These results were confirmed by Kuntz, Hoffman and Jacobs (1956), who also suggested that the same situation occurs in man. Ekholm and Skoglund (1966), having found a reduction in the number of small (less than $3\,\mu$m) myelinated fibres to the hind limb of the cat after sympathetic ganglionectomy and periarterial sympathectomy, concluded that some fibres of this class are sympathetic. The significance of these myelinated post-ganglionic fibres is unknown. Their occurrence varies between different species and ganglia. Langley (1896) using the same experimental approach found no myelinated post-ganglionic axons in the rabbit. According to Bishop and Heinebecker (1932) one in 10 of the fibres arising from the superior cervical ganglion of the rabbit is myelinated (in the cat 1 in 3). The post-ganglionic fibres of the prevertebral ganglia are all unmyelinated: the mesenteric nerves of the rabbit contain almost exclusively unmyelinated fibres (Simpson & Young, 1945). Myelinated fibres are present in the renal nerves, but they are afferent fibres connected to mechanoreceptors (Niijima, 1975). In birds the very great majority, if not all, of the fibres given off by the sympathetic vertebral ganglia are myelinated (Langley, 1904).

More conclusive evidence on adrenergic myelinated axons is provided by the experiments by Kosterlitz, Thompson and Wallis (1964). The nerve supplying the medial muscle of the nictitating membrane of the cat contains mainly myelinated fibres of various diameters (Thompson, 1961) and conduction velocities (Fig. 2). After superior cervical ganglionectomy the fine myelinated fibres, with conduction velocity of $1\cdot7-3\cdot8\,\mathrm{ms}^{-1}$ disappear together with the corresponding action potential. Therefore the motor fibres for this muscle (see p.152) originate in the superior cervical ganglion and are thinly myelinated (Kosterlitz et al., 1964); they are all adrenergic and probably cor-

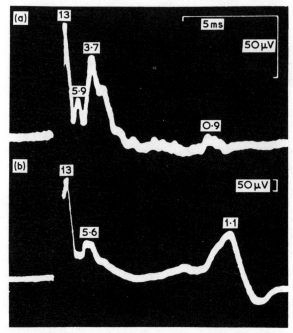

Figure 2. Compound action potential recorded from a nerve branch to the nictitating membrane of a cat 17 days after excision of the superior cervical ganglion. (Reproduced by courtesy of Professor H.W. Kosterlitz, from Kosterlitz, Thompson & Wallis, 1964.) (a) Control unoperated side: the three deflections correspond to three groups of axons conducting at the velocities indicated. (b) After excision of the superior cervical ganglion the deflection due to fibres conducting at $1 \cdot 7$-$3 \cdot 8 \, \text{ms}^{-1}$ (very fine myelinated fibres) is abolished.

respond to the (thinly myelinated) post-ganglionic fibres conducting at 5-$8 \, \text{ms}^{-1}$ observed by Eccles (1935) in the cervical sympathetic trunk.

Most of the somatic motor nerves contain a large proportion of unmyelinated fibres, but only some of them are sympathetic. For example, after degeneration of the sympathetic fibres the ratio of myelinated to unmyelinated fibres in the nerve to the vastus medialis (motor) of the cat is $1 : 0 \cdot 4$ and in the saphenous is $1 : 3 \cdot 8$ (Ranson & Davenport, 1931; Sheehan 1933). After bilateral extirpation of the abdominal sympathetic chain 75 per cent of the surviving (non-sympathetic) fibres of the saphenous nerve are unmyelinated (Sheehan, 1933).

The great majority of the post-ganglionic fibres originating from sympathetic ganglia are adrenergic. Their structure is examined in the next chapter. A minority of fibres are cholinergic, originating from non-adrenergic sympathetic ganglion cells (p.48). These sympathetic cholinergic fibres are secretory fibres to the sweat glands (Dale & Feldberg, 1934) and vasodilator fibres to skeletal muscles (Bülbring & Burn, 1935) and to the muscles of the tongue (Erici, Folkow & Uvnäs, 1952) (see review in Uvnäs, 1954).

2.10   Afferent fibres

Few anatomical data are available on the sensory innervation of viscera and cardio-vascular system. The exact localization of sensory cell bodies, the structure of sensory nerve endings and the types of neuro-transmitter involved, are often still a matter of speculation. On the other hand there is no doubt of the importance of afferent fibres in the activity of the autonomic nervous system. Although the autonomic nervous system has often been considered to be constituted exclusively of efferent pathways, notably by Langley (1921), it is here preferred to include the afferent elements as part of it, in spite of the meagre information on their structure.

Vagal fibres (see p.142) are largely sensory fibres, whose cell bodies are part of the nodose and jugular ganglia, and carry afferent impulses from heart, larynx, pharynx, oesophagus, stomach and ileum. Other afferent fibres from the stomach, small intestine and mesentery are present in the splanchnic nerves. In a series of experiments on the cat where the dilatation of the pupil and reflex changes of blood pressure were used as indexes of afferent impulses, McSwiney and co-workers (Irving, McSwiney & Suffolk, 1937; McSwiney & Suffolk, 1938) demonstrated that the stomach, pylorus and duodenum receive sensory fibres from the two vagus nerves and the splanchnic nerves; jejunum and ileum are less sensitive to distension that the stomach and duodenum and are mainly innervated by the splanchnic nerves. It was, and still is, thought that afferent fibres pass through the sympathetic ganglia without interruption and have their cell bodies in the dorsal root ganglia, although there is no direct evidence for this. The levels of entry into the spinal cord of afferent fibres travelling in the splanchnic nerves span T3 to L2. Ranson and Billingsley (1918) found that the large myelinated fibres (considered to be afferent) were most numerous in the seventh to tenth thoracic white rami of the cat.

Large myelinated fibres in the white rami are sensory fibres originating from dorsal root ganglia, but sensory fibres are present also in the groups of small myelinated fibres and unmyelinated fibres. It should be mentioned here that Gaskell (1886) thought the dorsal root ganglia also contained autonomic ganglion cells giving rise to post-ganglionic sympathetic fibres, a view which has not been supported by experimental evidence. The thoracic and upper lumbar dorsal root ganglia have no structural features which distinguish them from dorsal root ganglia of other spinal levels. (Note 2.8)

Petras and Cummings (1972) by performing unilateral thoracic or lumbar sympathectomy followed by section of some dorsal roots, found no degenerating fibres in proximity of chromatolytic neurons, i.e. afferent fibres are not directly connected with the preganglionic neurons. Since at least one interneuron occurs between sensory primary afferent and motor neurons, this visceral reflex pathway involves a four neuron chain: a dorsal root ganglion cell, an interneuron (which may be in the nucleus intermedialis or in the nucleus proprius cornu dorsalis), a preganglionic neuron and a ganglion neuron with its post-ganglionic fibre. Some intestino-intestinal reflexes are abolished by cutting dorsal roots (Chang & Hsu, 1942) or by spinal anaesthesia (Johansson & Langston, 1964).

The afferent systems described above involve sensory neurons located in cerebro-spinal ganglia (Note 2.9). Are there sensory neurons in the sympathetic ganglia? The classification of Dogiel, where type II neurons are supposed to be sensory, has been reported on p.122. As regards the superior cervical ganglion, according to Carpenter and Conel (1914) (who worked on the cat with the silver nitrate method) the types of Dogiel 'are to be regarded as extremes of the variation which occurs among the multipolar sympathetic cells. If their structural similarity is an indication of similarity in function, then all must be motor, since it is the presence of intrinsic sensory neurons only that is open to question.' Since then there has been no physiological or anatomical evidence disproving this view.

In silver preparations of the stellate ganglion of the cat neurons can be seen which send a thick long process into the connective tissue of the ganglion capsule, where they form complex terminal arborizations; these structures have all the features of sensory endings within the capsule (Abraham, 1952). It is not known whether such endings occur in other sympathetic ganglia. It may be reported in this context that Bernard (1858) noted no sign of pain during extirpation of the superior cervical ganglion of the rabbit, whereas pain was very evident when operating on the stellate ganglion. (Note 2.10)

There is abundant physiological evidence that some visceral reflexes are unaffected by decentralization of the prevertebral ganglia (Kuntz, 1938, 1940; Crowcroft & Szurszewski, 1971). Decentralization of the coeliac and inferior mesenteric ganglia in the cat does not result in degeneration of all the fibres ending in these ganglia (Kuntz, 1938) and in the superior mesenteric nerves of the rabbit as many as 30 per cent of the axons remain intact distal to a surgical division of the nerves (Ross, 1958). Degenerating nerve endings may be present in the coeliac ganglion of the cat after resection of part of the small intestine (Ungvàry & Léránth, 1970). All the above results indicate that in the intramural plexuses there are afferent neurons which project onto prevertebral ganglion cells. Intramural afferent neurons are also involved in the intrinsic reflex activity of the intestine (see p.123). Electrophysiological experiments indicate that sensory neurons may be present in the pelvic ganglion of the rat (Puriton, Fletcher & Bradley, 1971).

In summary, afferent neurons are an integral part of the autonomic nervous system, but their structure is poorly known. Autonomic afferent neurons are present in dorsal root ganglia, and project onto the spinal preganglionic neurons probably through an interneuron. There is no evidence for the presence of sensory neurons in the sympathetic trunk ganglia (except possibly for a few neurons innervating the capsule of the cat stellate ganglion). As regards the prevertebral ganglia they appear not to contain afferent neurons but they receive afferent fibres from the intestine which synapse on ganglion cells.

Note 2.1
In 7 out of 90 human superior cervical ganglia, stained with silver impregnation, Terni (1925) observed a conspicuous number (up to a few hundreds) of neurons identical to those of the nodose ganglion: they were pseudo-unipolar and one of the two processes reached the nodose ganglion via a small nerve trunk connecting the two ganglia.

Note 2.2
Few attempts have been made to localize within sympathetic ganglia groups of neurons with specific projections. Jacobowitz and Woodward (1968) observed that the neurons of the upper third of the cat superior cervical ganglion contributed to the internal carotid nerve, those in the middle third and part of the lower third contribute to the external carotid, while the axons of the most caudal ganglion cells descend in the cervical sympathetic trunk.

Note 2.3

The method of Falck and Hillarp (Falck, 1962) is based on the property of formaldehyde gas (developed from paraformaldehyde heated at 80°C) to form a fluorescent compound with certain biogenic amines, in the presence of proteins. The chemical reactions which lead to the formation of the fluorophore have been investigated (Corrodi & Jonsson, 1967; Björklund, Falck, Lindrall & Svensson, 1973). For the detection of catecholamine or 5-hydroxytryptamine the tissues are freeze-dried, exposed to the formaldehyde, embedded and sectioned, and examined in the fluorescence microscope. The method can be adjusted so as to distinguish different biogenic amines. Thin organs (such as the iris of small albino animals, or the mesentery) or organs which can be dissected in thin laminae (such as the intestinal wall) can be dried in the air and directly processed with formaldehyde (Falck & Owman, 1965).

A similar technique which employs glyoxylic acid (into which the tissues are immersed) instead of formaldehyde has been developed (Axelson *et al.*, 1973): compared with the Falck and Hillarp method, this technique is more sensitive and detects a larger number of compounds. Grillo, Jacobs and Comroe (1974) succeeded in obtaining the specific fluorescence for catecholamines in ganglia fixed by perfusion with aldehydes. The sections, after being studied in the fluorescence microscope, were post-fixed in osmium and processed for electron microscopy. The results are very promising, although the method seems to show only the structures which are intensely fluorescent (chromaffin cells of sympathetic ganglia, of the adrenal medulla, of the carotid body).

Recently immunohistochemical techniques have been developed which make it possible to study the localization on tissue sections of at least three enzymes involved in the catecholamine synthesis (dopamine-β-hydroxylase, aromatic L-amino acid decarboxylase, phenylethanolamine N-methyltransferase) (Hökfelt *et al.*, 1973).

Note 2.4

Wurtman and Axelrod (1966) have found that the total noradrenaline content of the rat pineal and submandibular glands (which is due to a rich supply of adrenergic fibres originating from the superior cervical ganglion [Ariens Kappers, 1960]) varies with a 24-hour rhythm; it is greatest at the end of the night and falls during the day.

For diurnal and seasonal changes in the content of noradrenaline of tissues see Axelrod (1971).

Note 2.5
Only Krinke *et al.* (1974) observed a consistent trend of more intense fluorescence in the small ganglion neurons than in the large ones and they suggest that the catecholamine content is the same in all adrenergic ganglion cells irrespective of their sizes.

Note 2.6
For the cells of this group which function as interneurons the term *granular cells* (i.e. granule-containing cells) could be changed to *granule cells* (i.e. very small neurons).

Note 2.7
Electron microscopy provides a more reliable method of counting the axons, allowing the investigator to count and measure each and all of them individually. It should, however, be noted that in many cases counts carried out in the electron microscope were not much different from those done on silver impregnated nerves. For example Foley and DuBois (1940) found about 50 per cent of unmyelinated fibres in the cervical sympathetic trunk of the cat, and 98 per cent in the rat, i.e. about the same figures which have been obtained by electron microscopy (Williams *et al.*, 1973; Bray and Aguayo, 1974).

Note 2.8
Owman and Santini (1966), however, observed a moderate number of fluorescent adrenergic fibres (some encircling the perikarya, usually those of larger size) in the thoracic dorsal root ganglia and very few in the other spinal sensory ganglia.

Note 2.9
For the level of distribution of the afferent fibres of the autonomic nervous system see Fig. 6 on page 147.

Note 2.10
This observation may be explained either by the presence of sensory fibres passing through the ganglion, or on the basis of a sensory innervation of the ganglion.

3 THE ADRENERGIC FIBRES

The structure of adrenergic fibres and the mechanism of adrenergic transmission have been in the last few years the subject of a number of reviews. A monograph appears in the present series (Burnstock & Costa, 1975) and the reader is referred to it for an up-to-date account of this field, of which only the outlines will be given here.

3.1 The adrenergic fibres

The axons leave the sympathetic ganglia as post-ganglionic sympathetic fibres, usually unmyelinated (though the occurrence of myelinated adrenergic fibres is well ascertained, see p.41). The axons issuing from the superior cervical ganglion of the rat have a diameter which ranges between 0·1 and 0·8 μm (mean 0·73 μm) (Matthews, 1973), and up to a dozen of them are sheathed by every individual Schwann cell.

The length of the fibres depends on the distance of the innervated organ from the sympathetic ganglion. It ranges from a fraction of a millimetre to a metre or more. On the basis of the length of the axon Sjöstrand (1965) describes 'long' and 'short' adrenergic neurons, the former being the neurons of the para- and prevertebral ganglia, the latter those annexed to the uro-genital organs (see p.95). In terms of volume the axon represents the largest part of the neuron. The volume of the cell body can be less than one per cent of the total volume of the cell; as in most neurons, however, the axon and its terminals depend on their cell body for a steady supply of organelles and of substances, in particular proteins, that cannot be synthesized locally (see Banks & Mayor, 1973).

Within the peripheral organs, the adrenergic fibres branch extensively and acquire a characteristic beaded appearance with thin and thick tracts; the latter are the *varicosities* or nerve endings, although they are not the anatomical end of the fibre, and the part of the axon bearing varicosities is its terminal portion (the pre-terminal portion is an ill-defined part of the non-varicose length of the fibre). There are 20—30 varicosities per 100 μm of terminal axon (Norberg & Hamberger, 1964; Malmfors, 1965; Dahlström & Haggendal, 1966a; Dahlström, Häggendal & Hökfelt, 1966), but the range is wide; while in some tissues the varicosities are evenly sized and distanced, giving the fibre a very regular beaded appearance, other fibres show a more irregular pattern. The last two or three varicosities of a fibre are usually more intensely fluorescent than the rest (Plate 5c).

It has been calculated that in the rat iris one neuron has a total axonal arborization of about 10 cm and it is therefore provided with about 26 000 varicosities; the terminal arborization of the adrenergic fibres in the rat and cat sciatic nerve is 10 and 26 cm long respectively (Dahlström & Häggendal, 1966a and b; Dahlström et al., 1966). The rat iris would therefore contain more than 10^6 nerve terminals and 1 cm of vas deferens over 50×10^6 (Dahlström et al., 1966). These calculations are approximate and should be treated with caution, but there is little doubt that the number of varicose endings amounts to several thousands for each adrenergic neuron, compared with less than two hundred even in a big motor neuron for the skeletal musculature. The significance of the varicose shape of the terminal part of adrenergic axons is not known. A similar appearance is observed also in autonomic cholinergic axons, parasympathetic or intramural, whereas it is not known to occur in the somatic peripheral nervous system, where motor fibres branch repeatedly but terminate in discrete endings at the motor end-plates. The arrangement of a number of varicosities or endings spread over a length of the axons allows an economy in the number of axonal branches, whereas the occurrence of discrete endings at the end of each axonal branch probably allows a high conduction velocity to be maintained to within a very short distance of the ending. The conduction velocity of impulses in the varicose part of an adrenergic axon is unknown, but the anatomical characteristics suggest that it is slower than in the non-varicose portion of the fibre.

Between varicosities the axon has a diameter ranging from about 1 μm to less than 0·2 μm. It contains microtubules, sometimes neurofilaments, and rarely a synaptic vesicle. Although microtubules are seen to enter the varicosity, a continuity of microtubules of successive inter-varicose lengths is not apparent, nor is it known whether the number of microtubules remains constant.

3.2   Location of adrenergic endings

Adrenergic nerve endings are found either synapsing on ganglion neurons or close to an effector, usually a smooth muscle cell.

Synapses of adrenergic fibres have been found on neurons of the pelvic ganglia (Watanabe, 1971), on neurons of the intestinal intramural plexuses (Gabella, 1972; Wong, Helme & Smith, 1974). They are probably also numerous on the neurons of some prevertebral ganglia (see p.19). However, as has been discussed on p.16, the observation in fluorescence microscopy of varicosities around a cell body is not sufficient evidence of the presence of adrenergic synapses: these must be identified in electron microscopy. The adrenergic synapses can be located on cell bodies or on short processes protruding from them, or on dendrites; more rarely the synapses are axo-axonic.

The other group of adrenergic endings are mainly in relation to smooth muscle cells. The varicose fibres run parallel to the smooth muscle cells and each axon can make several contacts with the same cell, and each axon contacts several muscle cells. The arborization of intramusclular nerve bundles can be very extensive, and they decrease progressively in diameter. In some smooth muscles (e.g. vas deferens) the axon bundles divide until single axons are left (Plate 11b); these lose all Schwann cell investement and can be very close to the smooth muscle cells, usually invaginating their surface. In other smooth muscles (e.g. ileum, uterus) there are no single axons, or they are very rare; the whole terminal portion of the axons is within a small axon bundle and all the varicosities retain part of their Schwann cell investement. In the bundles the adrenergic axons are accompanied by axons of different nature (e.g. cholinergic axons). Between these two types of innervation there are intermediate ones, where both single axons and small axon bundles are present (e.g. cat nictitating membrane). For a discussion of the functional implications of these patterns of innervation see Bennett (1972).

Intramuscular nerve bundles are made of axons of different origin and nature (e.g. cholinergic and adrenergic), wrapped together by the same Schwann cell (Plate 12b). Characteristically large parts of the axonal surfaces are directly apposed to each other, with a visible gap of 15–20 nm (Plate 18b). At this areas of close apposition membrane specializations can be present (e.g. Ehinger *et al.*, 1970). On this mor-

50

phological evidence and on the basis of pharmacological experiments it has been suggested that there is an interaction between cholinergic and adrenergic nerve terminals (for a review see Kosterlitz and Lees, 1972). An earlier version of this notion was put forward by Burn and Rand (1959) and Koelle (1961) who thought that acetylcholine was stored in adrenergic endings and when released triggered the release of noradrenaline; the Burn and Rand hypothesis in its original form has received little experimental support, but an interaction between cholinergic and adrenergic endings may well occur in physiologic conditions.

The distance between varicosities and smooth muscle cells (i.e. the minimal distance between the two plasma membranes) varies characteristically in different smooth muscles. In the vas deferens of the guinea-pig there is a large number of single axons, usually deeply embedded in the muscle cells, and in many of them the neuro-muscular distance is only about 20 nm (Taxi, 1965; Furness & Iwayama, 1972); at these areas of intimate contacts no basal lamina intervenes between varicosity and muscle cell. On the other hand, in blood vessels the apposition between varicosities and muscle cells is never closer than 100 nm (Simpson & Devine, 1966; Verity & Bevan, 1968). Again, there are numerous other arrangements intermediate between these two extreme ones.

The width of the neuromuscular gaps is obviously important in characterizing neuro-muscular transmission. There are, however, only few accurate quantitative studies of this problem (e.g. Taxi, 1965; Merrillees, 1968; Furness & Iwayama, 1972) and more are needed if better structure-function correlations are to be established. A description of the pattern of sympathetic innervation of a tissue or of the distribution of adrenergic endings should take into account the minimal as well as the average neuro-muscular distance, and other quantitative parameters. An important morphological problem is that of the effect of the mechanical activity of an effector on the intramuscular fibres. Some smooth muscles (taenia coli, sphincter pupillae) are capable of shortening, during contraction, to a quarter of their length when relaxed. It is likely that the enormous mechanical deformation involved affects the intramuscular varicose fibres, which are very thin, are sometimes devoid of a Schwann cell or are provided with only a partial investment, and run long distances parallel to the muscle cells. For the skeletal muscle, it is known that in the frog a

51

stretch enhances neuromuscular transmission, by raising both the frequency of miniature end-plate potentials and the mean quantum content (Fatt & Katz, 1952; Hutter & Trauttwein, 1956; Turkanis, 1973). Recently, it has been shown that in blood vessels (rabbit ear) the distance between nerve endings and muscle cells decreases with distension of the vessel's wall; presumably, therefore, the efficiency of transmission is maximal when the vessel is distended (relaxed) (Govyrin, 1975).

In addition to the ending close to smooth muscle cells or synapsing on ganglion neurons, there are adrenergic endings closely associated with secretory cells of exocrine glands (e.g. lacrimal and salivary glands) (see Chapter 10). Other adrenergic endings are found in relation to sensory organs: mechanoreceptors (Loewenstein & Altamirano-Ortego, 1956; Fuxe & Nilsson, 1965; Santini, 1969; Nilsson, 1972), muscle spindles (Hines & Tower, 1928; Paintal, 1973), taste receptors (Gabella, 1969), acoustic receptors (Spoendlin & Liechtensteiger, 1966), chemoreceptors (Duncan & Yates, 1967; Milss, 1968; Sampson, 1972), baroceptors (Aars, 1971; Belmonte, Simon, Gallego & Baron, 1972). Although Bernard (1851) had suggested that sympathetic nerves may modulate the sensory input, the functional significance of the adrenergic fibres associated with sensory receptors remains obscure. A rich innervation by adrenergic fibres, originating from the superior cervical ganglion (Ariens Kappers, 1960), is present in the pineal gland (De Iraldi & Zieher, 1966) (Plate 12a).

Adrenergic endings lying several microns from an effector cell are occasionally observed in many tissues, but no experimental evidence has been obtained on their role.

3.3 Structure of adrenergic endings

Adrenergic nerve endings synapsing on ganglion neurons are expansions along the length of the terminal part of the axon (for example in the myenteric plexus of the guinea-pig ileum). They are up to 3μm in diameter, and contain mitochondria and granular synaptic vesicles; the latter provide the only criterium so far available for identifying these endings from other types of ending in electron microscopy. A majority of the vesicles measure 40–60 nm in diameter and contain a highly electron-dense core (small granular vesicles). The core or granule can occupy a large part of the vesicle but an electron-lucent halo is always present around it; sometimes the granule appears eccentrically placed. The trilaminar membrane of some vesicles appears extremely electron-dense; some vesicles have only a very dense membrane and no granule. In addition to the above described granular vesicles, adrenergic endings contain electron-lucent vesicles indistinguishable from those of cholinergic endings. The ratio between small granular vesicles and electron-lucent vesicles varies between nerve endings and even more so between different preparations. In view of the difficulty of preserving the cores of the small granular vesicles in the preparations for electron microscopy (in case of failure all the vesicles appear electron-lucent) it is not yet possible to discuss the significance of these lucent vesicles (whether for example they are 'small granular vesicles' whose cores have not been stained, or vesicles which have discharged their cores, etc.). There is not yet sound ground for discussing these differences in appearance in terms of structural or functional differences between vesicles, rather than as effects of the histological procedure. A small number of vesicles 80—100 nm in diameter with a granule of medium electron density are also present in adrenergic synapses. Part of the area of contact between adrenergic nerve ending and ganglion cell show typical synaptic specialization, with a synaptic gap of 20—25 nm. The presynaptic membrane shows an accumulation of dense material on its cytoplasmic side.

Nerve endings which are interpreted as adrenergic in the myenteric ganglia of the large intestine of the guinea-pig, monkey and man contain vesicles 50—90 nm in diameter with an electron-dense granule surrounded by a clear-cut halo (Baumgarten, Holstein & Owman, 1970). No membrance specializations were observed at the contact points of these endings and the intramural neurons, but, since serial sections were not made, this may not yet indicate that adrenergic synapses are absent in this part of the gut.

Adrenergic nerve endings (varicosities) which are related to effectors (muscular, glandular) measure about $1\,\mu$m in diameter and $1—3\,\mu$m in length, and are distributed along the length of the fibres. They contain 'synaptic' vesicles and mitochondria; microtubules, which occupy the intervaricose portions of the axons, are seen at the poles of a varicosity, but can rarely be followed through it.

The characteristic vesicles of adrenergic varicosities are 30—60 nm in diameter and contain an electron-dense granule (small granular vesicles). They were first described by De Robertis and De Iraldi (1961) and a wealth of correlative studies with biochemical, pharmacological, and electron-microscopical methods have confirmed that these vesicles are characteristic of adrenergic endings (see a review in Geffen and Livett, 1971).

The visualization of the dense cores of the small granular vesicles in tissues fixed in glutaraldehyde is difficult and somewhat erratic (Plate 12b); in tissues fixed in osmium only, it occasionally succeeds. On the other hand by using an appropriate fixation procedure, e.g. with permanganate (Richardson, 1966) (Plate 11a) or dichromate (Tranzer & Thoenen, 1971) (Plate 11b), the great majority of the small vesicles of adrenergic endings contain an electron-dense granule. After exposing the tissue to a 'false' transmitter, i.e. a non naturally occurring, electron-dense catecholamine (like 5-hydroxydopamine), the cores are particularly prominent and present in almost all the vesicles, while other endings, presumably cholinergic, show no granular vesicles (Plate 11c).

In addition to small granular vesicles, adrenergic endings contain large granular vesicles, about 85 nm in diameter, with a core about 50 nm in diameter of medium to high electron density. In the adrenergic endings (isolated as 'synaptosomes' by fractionation and centrifugation) of the cat spleen capsule 24 per cent of the vesicles are of the larger type, the rest being small granular vesicles; in the vas deferens of the rat the percentage of large granular vesicles is only 4 per cent (Bisby & Fillenz, 1971). In histological sections of the bovine spleen capsule the adrenergic endings contain 40 per cent large granular vesicles, 55 per cent small granular vesicles and 5 per cent small agranular vesicles (Tranzer, 1973). Large granular vesicles in adrenergic endings of the rat vas deferens are about 10 per cent (Tranzer, 1973) or 4 per cent of vesicles (Farrell, 1968); they are 2 per cent in the rat iris dilator muscle (Hökfelt, 1969). During postnatal development in the adrenergic fibres of the vas deferens there is a decrease in the percentage of the large granular vesicles (from 10 per cent at birth to 3 per cent at 6 months) and an increase in the percentage of small vesicles showing a dense core (from 37 to 85 per cent) (Yamauchi & Burnstock, 1969). After cell fractionation of the spleen capsule, part of the noradrenaline was found in the low density fraction containing the small granular vesicles, and part in the high density fraction containing large granular vesicles (Bisby & Fillenz, 1971). This and other biochemical evidence has led to the conclusion that both small and large granular vesicles in adrenergic endings store noradrenaline (see review in Smith, 1972), as had already been suggested on morphological and histochemical grounds (Hökfelt, 1968; Tranzer & Thoenen, 1968).

Large granular vesicles are also found in non-adrenergic endings, where it is most unlikely that they contain a catecholamine. Whereas the nerve endings contain both large and small granular vesicles, it is said that the non-terminal part of the axon contains mainly, in some cases only, large granular vesicles, similar to those seen in the terminals (Kapeller & Mayor, 1969; Smith, 1972). However, Tranzer (1973), in a systematic study of adrenergic nerves, by means of a fixation technique which gives an adequate preservation of the small granular vesicles, has found the same ratio between large and small granular vesicles in the axons as in the nerve endings, while the packing density of vesicles is much greater (140 times in the rat vas deferens) in the endings.

The large granular vesicles isolated from the bovine spleen nerve contain in addition to noradrenaline, ATP, a protein (chromogranin A) and dopamine-β-hydroxylase (Hortägle et al., 1969); the latter enzyme is present also in small granular vesicles (Bisby, Fillenz & Smith, 1973).

In addition it has been shown biochemically that some noradrenaline is not stored in synaptic vesicles; this amount is small and varies with the tissues studied (Iversen, 1967; von Euler, 1971). This extra-vescicular storage compartment may, in part at least, correspond to the tubular endoplasmic reticulum described by Tranzer (1972) in adrenergic endings; by using an improved technique for the localization of biogenic amines in electron microscopy this author found that adrenergic axons, and especially their terminals, contained tubular reticulum with a specific electron-dense precipitate indicative of a catecholamine store.

The origin of large and small granular vesicles in adrenergic endings is still not clear. It has been suggested that large granular vesicles are formed in the perikaryon and are transported to the nerve endings, where they are transformed into small granular vesicles, after the release of their content, including the neurotransmitter (Geffen & Ostberg, 1969; Smith, 1971). Morphological evidence of transformation of large vesicles into small ones has not been provided.

3.4 Release, uptake, synthesis and inactivation of the transmitter

A review of the processes of release, uptake, synthesis, and inactivation of the transmitter is beyond the scope of this work, and only a cursory account of them will be given. According to a widely held notion, the transmitter of adrenergic nerves is released by a mechanism of exocytosis, i.e. the vesicles partly fuse with the axolemma of the nerve ending, and open at the surface of the nerve ending discharging their 'content' into the synaptic cleft. The concept is borrowed from the studies on the secretory mechanism in glandular cells, and the adrenal medulla is the organ which has given the clue to the link between secretory processes and release of neurotransmitters (Blaschko & Welch, 1953). There is strong biochemical evidence that in the adrenal medullary cells the vesicles release catecholamines (as hormones) be exocytosis: ATP and chromogranins are released with the catecholamines, and the ratio between these substances is the same as in the vesicles (Douglas, 1966; Kirshner, Sage, Smith & Kirschner, 1966); on the other hand, constituents of the vesicle membrane, like cholesterol and phospholipids, are not released (Schneider, Smith & Winkler, 1967). Few authors have observed by electron microscopy images of vesicles just opened into the extracellular space or extruded granules (Diner, 1967; Grynszpan-Winograd, 1971): if exocytosis does occur, it appears that it is difficult to detect by conventional transmission electron microscopy.

The occurrence of exocytosis in adrenergic endings (and in nerve endings in general) has been debated for some years and it is considered the most likely mechanism for the release of catecholamines from the nerve endings (see Geffen & Livett, 1971; Blaschko & Smith, 1971). This hypothesis is now being actively tackled by biochemical and histochemical (particularly by immunofluorescence) methods, by transmission electron microscopy (with procedures which allow a better preservation of granular vesicles), by freeze-fracturing (which allows to see the cell surface *in extenso*).

The membrane of the vesicle is not extruded with the release of

56

neurotransmitter; it is possible that it is re-used more than once. Whether, and by which mechanism, this occurs is not known. It is possible that the vesicle merges with the cell membrane and opens to the outside for a short time, then closes up again, or it may be that the vesicle membrane flattens completely and becomes part of the nerve ending membrane re-forming a vesicle only when, after having slid to the periphery of the synaptic area, it is 'pinched in' into the nerve ending again.

By studying the amount of noradrenaline accumulating proximal to a ligature, it has been calculated that the cell body pumps into the axon the equivalent of about 1 per cent of the total content of noradrenaline of its nerve endings (Geffen & Rush, 1968). Although the study of nerve crush is not the ideal method of studying the physiological axonal flow, there is sound evidence that only a small amount of neurotransmitter is shipped from the cell body to the nerve endings; since in the latter the turnover of noradrenaline occurs in only about 10 h (Iversen, 1967) mechanisms in the nerve endings themselves must be able to provide most of the neurotransmitter.

One such mechanism is the re-uptake by the nerve ending of the released neurotransmitter. The importance of this mechanism (neuronal uptake) varies in different tissues. The uptake mechanism is also effective (together with enzymatic inactivation by mono-aminoxidase and catechol-o-methyltransferase) in terminating the action of the transmitter at the junction. Adrenergic endings can take up noradrenaline originating from a different part of the organism and also exogenous noradrenaline. The amount of tritiated noradrenaline taken up after injection by the adrenergic endings of an organ can readily be measured, and an accurate localization can be obtained by autoradiography (Plate 12a) (Note 3.1). Different amines than the one released can be taken up by an adrenergic ending. Substances which do not naturally occur in the organism, and are, when injected, taken up and released by the nerve endings are known as 'false transmitters'. 'False transmitters' such as 5-hydroxydopamine and 6-hydroxydopamine which are particularly electron-dense have been used to load the small granular vesicles, making them highly electron-dense and thus labelling the adrenergic endings: these experiments also confirm that exogenous catecholamines are taken up and stored in the vesicles of adrenergic endings.

On the basis of the presence of the relevant enzymes it is thought that synthesis of noradrenaline from tyrosine can take place in the adrenergic endings. Tyrosine is taken up from the extracellular space (hence from the blood stream), whereas the enzymes arrive from the neuron cell body by axonal flow.

A mechanism of regulation is provided by the presence of adreno-ceptors on the adrenergic endings themselves, through which the released noradrenaline may inhibit further release of transmitter (negative feedback) (Starke, 1971; Langer, 1973).

3.5   Degeneration of adrenergic endings

Section of the post-ganglionic fibres (axotomy) is followed by de-generation of the distal parts of the axons (see also Section 4.5.1). The noradrenaline content of the innervated organs falls to undetect-able or very low levels and the varicose fluorescent fibres disappear (see review in Thoenen, 1972). The time course of degeneration varies in different organs, and probably in different species, and there are of course different criteria for ascertaining the degeneration (paralytic symptoms, failure of transmission, reduction and dis-appearance of the neurotransmitter, presence of structurally altered fibres, disappearance of fibres, absence of uptake). In the submandib-ular gland of the rat the noradrenaline content is down to 60 per cent the control values 12 h after extirpation of the superior cervical ganglion, and to nonmeasurable values after 24 h (Benmiloud & Euler, 1963). In the nictitating membrane of the cat noradrenaline values are still normal after 24 h and fall rapidly during the second day (Kirpekar, Cervoni & Furschgott, 1962; Smith, Trendelenburg, Langer & Tsai, 1966). In the interscapular brown adipose body of the rat the noradrenaline content falls to less than 1 per cent in 24 h (Sidman, Perkins & Weiner, 1962).

The network of adrenergic fibres in the iris of rat appears un-changed in fluorescence microscopy 8 h after excision of the superior cervical ganglion, but no fluorescence is detectable after 28 h (Malm-fors & Sachs, 1965a); in this organ the disappearance of neurotrans-mitter (as visualized by the absence of fluorescence) is not gradual — it occurs suddenly, with a different time of onset for different fibres, and uniformly affects the entire system of branches and terminals belonging to one neuron.

By electron microscopy all adrenergic fibres are found to have disappeared from the rat iris within 48 h (Roth & Richardson, 1969) and from the cerebral vessels within 38 h (Iwayama, 1970) after excision of the superior cervical ganglion. The onset of degenerative changes is not simultaneous in all nerve endings, so that during the second post-operative day endings normal in appearance are found close to endings with gross degenerative changes (van Orden *et al.*, 1967). The first fine structural change in degenerating nerve endings of the cat nictitating membrane is a decrease in the proportion of granular vesicles, and in the total number of vesicles per varicosity (van Orden *et al.*, 1967). An increase in the electron density of the endings ensues, with a further loss of vesicles so that many endings appear 'empty'. Eventually there is lysis of the axon and the debris are taken up by Schwann cells and macrophages (Knoche & Terwort, 1973). Similar changes and time course were observed in degenerating adrenergic endings of the rat cerebral arteries (Iwayama, 1970) (Note 3.2).

Degeneration of adrenergic nerve by pharmacological and toxicological means has been discussed in Chapter 4.

The adrenergic fibres have a high ability to regenerate and to re-establish functional neuro-muscular junctions (De Castro, 1932; Butson, 1950; Guth, 1956). Regeneration of the axons of adrenergic neurons also occurs in ganglia grown in vitro (Silberstein *et al.*, 1971) or transplanted, e.g. in the sciatic nerve (Olson, 1969) or in the anterior eye chamber (Olson & Malmfors, 1970), that is in the absence of preganglionic fibres. Adrenergic fibres regenerating in the sciatic nerve of adult rats grow at a rate of 1·4 mm per day during the first week and 2·9 mm per day during the second week (Olson, 1969).

In the transplant experiments when iris and superior cervical ganglion of one side were transplanted into the contralateral anterior eye chamber (and the eye was also sympathetically denervated) both irises were re-innervated by the transplanted ganglion. Fibres from a transplanted ganglion, however, did not grow into tissues which were already innervated. Re-innervation could also be demonstrated after transplants from one species to another (mouse ganglion into rat eye) and after transplant of other sympathetic ganglia (coeliac, lumbar sympathetic, pelvic ganglia) (Olson & Malmfors, 1970).

Note 3.1
On the other hand, a good uptake of tritiated noradrenaline by

sympathetic perikarya is obtained only in the presence of an inhibitor of the monoamine-oxidase; in these conditions the silver grains appear located randomly in the cytoplasm, suggesting that they are not bound to an organelle. In the absence of the inhibitor the labelling of the perikaryon is poor and limited to the clusters of vesicles (p.13) (Sotelo & Taxi, 1973; Taxi, 1974).

Note 3.2
Iwayama (1970) observed that about 18 h after the operation, and only for a few hours, a greater number of vesicles with dense cores were present in the degenerating fibres than in control fibres; the latter, in fact, as is common experience with rat tissues, show only a few dense-core vesicles (see p.54).

4   THE SYMPATHETIC GANGLIA IN DEVELOPMENT AND EXPERIMENTAL CONDITIONS

4.1   Development

A comprehensive review of the less recent papers on the development of the autonomic nervous system is found in Kuntz (1946). For an up-to-date review of the development of the peripheral adrenergic neurons the reader is referred to the book by Burnstock and Costa (1975).

The ganglia of the sympathetic chain originate from cells migrated from the neural crest (Yntema, 1947; Andres & Kautsky, 1955), as demonstrated by depletion experiments (Muller & Ingvar, 1923; Yntema & Hammond, 1945; Hammond & Yntema, 1947) and tritium marking (Weston, 1963). The developmental stages of the sympathetic ganglia are remarkably similar in all classes of vertebrates (Kuntz, 1910a, b, 1946). In man the first visible primordia of the sympathetic trunk appear near the aorta in the thoracic and lower cervical regions; later the trunk extends along the neck and reaches the base of the skull (Lutz, 1968). In the mouse the first visible primordia of the sympathetic chain appear in the thoracic region in embryos of 11 days gestation (Fernholm, 1971). At 12 days the trunk reaches from the base of the skull to the sacral region. At 16 days there is a well developed trunk with the superior cervical and the stellate ganglia, and segmentally arranged ganglia in the thoraco-lumbar region. Migration of sympathicoblasts ventral to the sympathetic chain to form the abdominal plexus begins at 13 days gestation and lasts for at least 5 days (Fernholm, 1971). In chick embryos sympathicoblasts can already be observed by silver impregnation methods during the 3rd day *in ovo* (Tello, 1925) (Note 4.1) and the first synapses of preganglionic fibres are seen by electron microscopy at the 9th day (Wechsler & Schmekel, 1967).

The earliest appearance of adrenergic neurons in mammalian ganglia has not yet been studied; in the chick embryo as early as at the 84th incubation hour ganglia with neurons displaying a weak specific fluorescence for catecholamines are observed (Enemar *et al.*, 1965; Cohen, 1972). Fluorescence for catecholamines is first detected in sympathicoblasts assembling to form primary sympathetic ganglia dorsal to the aorta and ventral to the notocord (Cohen, 1972). Induction of catecholamine synthesis in cells (sympathicoblasts) migrating from the neural crest is effected by the somatic mesoderm: segments of neural tubes containing neural crest, grown on the chorioallantoic membrane give origin to catecholamine-containing sympathicoblasts only when somites are present (Cohen, 1972). In 13—15 day old rat fetuses the sympathicoblasts of the sympathetic trunk show an intense specific fluorescence for catecholamines (Champlain, Malmfors, Olson & Sacks, 1970; Owman, Sjoberg & Swedin, 1971). Bundles of fluorescent sympathetic nerves are visible at the periphery of various organs (sub-mandibular gland, heart, kidney, small intestine, male genital tract) at about 20 days of gestation. However, a terminal innervation of these organs, suggestive of a functional transmitter mechanism, is not apparent until immediately after birth, When the growing adrenergic fibres penetrate into the effector organ, they form thin branches with weakly fluorescent varicosities. The fluorescence intensity of the varicosities increases rapidly to adult levels, while that of the preterminal part of the fibres decreases (Champlain *et al.*, 1970; Owman *et al.*, 1971).

On the basis of the great variability in the catecholamine content of various organs in newborn rats, Iversen *et al.* (1967) concluded that there are considerable differences in the rate of development of the adrenergic innervation of various tissues. The density of adrenergic innervation of the intestine, for example, seems considerably greater than that of the heart, an observation confirmed by fluorescence microscopy by Champlain *et al.* (1970). In the rabbit an adrenergic innervation of the cardio-vascular system is already present at birth (Schwieler, Douglas & Bouhuys, 1970; Friedman, Pool, Jacobowitz, Seagren & Braunwald, 1968). In this species fluorescent cells are already present in thoracic sympathetic ganglia at 14 days of gestation (Papka, 1972). Papka (1972) has identified in electron microscopy an 'indifferent cell' which is the common precursor of sympathetic neurons and chromaffin cells. There is in fact some difficulty in identifying in fluorescence microscopy the two types of cell in embryonic tissues (e.g. Champlain *et al.*, 1970). In the earliest cases studied (14 day old rabbit embryos) the supporting cells (satellite and Schwann cells) already constitute a separate cell type and are wrapped around cell bodies and axons (Papka, 1972).

After birth there is a large increase in ganglion cell size, and the cell density per unit volume decreases. In the stellate ganglion of the cat the nerve cell density per unit volume decreases from the 2nd week after birth, due to a rapid growth in size of the neurons, to an increase in number of glia cells (by mitosis they double their number during the first two postal-natal weeks), and to an increase in the amount of connective tissue (Thurn, 1972). A connective tissue capsule is usually absent in embryonic ganglia (e.g. Papka, 1972). Mitotic activity in the neurons of the rat superior cervical ganglion comes to an end between the 7th and 9th day after birth (Levi-Montalcini & Booker, 1960a). In this ganglion glial cells are poorly represented at birth and in the electron microscope many developing ganglion neurons (sympathicoblasts) are in direct contact with each other (L. Eränkö, 1972). After birth there is also a progressive increase in the fluorescence intensity of the ganglion cells. In the early post-natal stages the ganglion cells (early sympathicoblasts) display a diffuse fluorescence; later the neurons show also a granular fluorescence, with an appearance similar to that of adult ganglia, and clusters of small granular vesicles become apparent in the cytoplasm (L. Eränkö, 1972). Synapses, presumably of the cholinergic type, are already present at birth (L. Eränkö, 1972). It has been estimated that in the superior cervical ganglion of the newborn mouse there are about 8000 synapses, as against 3 millions in the adult animal (Black, Hendry & Iversen, 1971). In the rat the total number of preganglionic axons per transverse section of the cervical sympathetic trunk decreases from approximately 16 000 two days before birth to about 5500 six days after birth (Aguayo, Terry & Bray, 1973). On the other hand Schwann cells increase in number, and both factors contribute to a several-fold reduction of the ratio axons/Schwann cell (Aguayo *et al.*, 1973).

The adrenergic nerve endings of the vas deferens of the mouse are structurally mature, in terms of intensity of fluorescence and synaptic vesicle population, at about 12 days after birth (Yamauchi & Burnstock, 1969a), about 6 days before the first excitatory junction potentials could be recorded in smooth muscle cells. These results seem to indicate a delay between the appearance of morphologically mature axons and neuromuscular junctions and the onset of neuro-muscular transmission (Furness *et al.*, 1970). The density of inner-vation, in terms of number of axons per 100 muscle cells and number of close neuro-muscular junctions, continues to increase up to at least 6 months (Yamauchi & Burnstock, 1969b). On the other hand in the vas deferens of the rat the first responses to transmural nerve stimulation are obtained in preparations from 3 day old animals (Swedin, 1972) i.e. at about the time when a network of adrenergic fibres becomes visible throughout the smooth muscle layers (Champ-lain *et al.*, 1970; Owman *et al.*, 1971).

4.2   Effects of nerve growth factor

Mammalian sympathetic ganglia, including human ganglia, are sensi-tive to nerve growth factor (NGF), both *in viva* and *in vitro* (Levi-Montalcini, 1966). Injection of NGF in the *adult* mouse produces neuronal hypertrophy in sympathetic ganglia but no increase in neuron number (Levi-Montalcini & Booker, 1960a); the latter effect is obtained only if NGF is injected before the age at which mitotic activity comes to an end or during the period when in normal condi-tions there is a reduction in neuron number. The hypertrophic neurons in the adult animals show an increase in basophilia and in the number of nucleoli (from 3–4 on the average to 5) (Levi-Montalcini & Booker, 1960b). These results have been confirmed by Banks, Charlwood, Edwards, Vernon & Walter (1975), who also observed that both the increase in neuron number and size are reversible and that they are maintained only as long as injection of NGF is continued. No changes were seen in satellite and glial cells using light microscopy. No effect was found in adult mice on any other type of nerve cell, including the spinal ganglia, which are highly sensitive to NGF during embryonic life. It has also been observed that the outgrowth of new processes from rat superior cervical gang-lia cultured *in vitro* is greatly enhanced by NGF. When the iris is cul-tured in proximity to the ganglia, NGF enhances the rate and extent of the reinnervation (Silberstein, Johnson, Jacobowitz & Kopin, 1971). Recent experiments have also shown that NGF stimulates the regeneration of axotomized adrenergic neurons in the central nervous system, if a target organ like a transplanted iris, is provided (Björklund & Stenevi, 1972). In adult mice regeneration of adrenergic terminals destroyed by treatment with 6-hydroxydopamine is enhanced by systemic administration of nerve growth factor (Bjerre, Björklund & Mobley, 1973).

4.3 Sympathectomy

Sympathectomy is the destruction of sympathetic nerves by surgical and other means (see a review in Thoenen, 1972). Although the assumption that the functions missing from a sympathectomized organ will closely correspond to the physiological role of sympathetic fibres is not entirely tenable — in view of the functional plasticity of organs, their multiple innervation, denervation changes, etc. — sympathectomy has proved a valuable tool in the study of adrenergic nerves.

The term 'sympathectomy' will here be used to indicate excision or destruction of sympathetic ganglia. Since nerve cells do not regenerate, this is followed by a permanent or long-term sympathetic denervation of the corresponding organ. 'Sympathetic denervation' is used to indicate the disappearance, temporary or permanent, of post-ganglionic sympathetic fibres from their innervation territory (see 4.5).

Partial sympathectomy is obtained by excision of selected sympathetic ganglia. Total sympathectomy has been obtained in adult cats by gradual removal of the entire sympathetic chain on both sides and of the prevertebral ganglia with several operations over a period of 6 months (Cannon, Newton, Bright, Menkin & Moore, 1929; Cannon & Rosenblueth, 1937). Not only did these animals survive, but they were apparently in healthy condition. In the females reproduction, fecundation, pregnancy and lactation occurred as in control animals. The main difference with control animals was their inability to regulate body temperature and blood pressure and to raise the hair. Bacq (1932) obtained similar results by sub-total sympathectomy in the rat. The oestrus cycle, fecundation and gestation were not affected by abdominal sympathectomy; however, male rats became impotent because of the absence of ejaculation (Bacq, 1932). These experiments have never been repeated. Wrete (1941) at the conclusion of his study of 'intermediate' or accessory ganglia in laboratory mammals argues that the presence of such ganglia may vitiate the interpretation of the results of sympathectomies. Sub-total sympathectomy is a more accurate description of Cannon's experiments. Similar experiments of sub-total sympathectomy in the dog failed since the extirpation of the prevertebral ganglia was followed by uncontrollable increase in intestinal motility to which the animals finally succumbed (Verney & Vogt, 1938).

An extensive sympathectomy is obtained in adult rats by prolonged administration of guanethidine ($25-30$ mg kg^{-1} d^{-1} for 6 weeks) (Burnstock, Evans, Gannon, Heath & James, 1971). More than 98 per cent of the ganglion cells of the superior cervical ganglion are destroyed; the effects are less obvious in other ganglia (e.g. hypogastric ganglion), but are also present in the neurons innervating the male genital system. Guanethidine has a similar effect when injected in newborn rats or mice (20 mg per kg every second day for 2 weeks): two months later only $3-5$ per cent of the control number of neurons is observed in the superior cervical ganglion (Angeletti, Levi-Montalcini & Caramia, 1972).

In fact sympathectomy (and sympathetic denervation, see Section 4.5) can more easily be obtained by immunological and chemical means applied to immature animals.

Injection of an antiserum to nerve growth factor in newborn mice (daily, for several days) effects the permanent destruction of up to $90-95$ per cent of the ganglion cells, in the superior cervical ganglion, the stellate and thoracic paravertebral ganglia (Levi-Montalcini & Booker, 1960b). No regeneration or replacement of the lost cells occurs. There is a corresponding reduction in the volume of the ganglion. A similar effect was obtained in rats, in a few cats (decrease of 92 per cent in the number of cells in the superior cervical ganglion) and rabbits (decrease of about 85 per cent) (Levi-Montalcini & Booker, 1960b); on the other hand in the newborn guinea-pig the effects are considerably less severe (Levi-Montalcini, 1972). The earlier structural changes after NGF antiserum injection in immature animals are visible in the nucleolus which appears denser and internally disorganized. Later the nuclear envelope breaks and other signs of cytolysis appear (Sabatini, Pellegrino De Iraldi & De Robertis, 1965; Angeletti, Levi-Montalcini & Caramia, 1971b; Schucker, 1972).

The effect of antiserum as nerve growth factor in adult sympathetic ganglia is less severe and to some extent reversible. Daily injections of NGF antiserum for $2-3$ weeks result in a volume decrease of sympathetic ganglia to $50-70$ per cent that of controls (Levi-Montalcini & Cohen, 1960; Levi-Montalcini & Booker, 1960b; Angeletti, Levi-Montalcini & Caramia, 1971a); in the only rat in which the number of neurons in the superior cervical ganglion was counted, this was reduced to 30 per cent of controls (Levi-Montalcini & Booker, 1961b). The surviving neurons (after a 5-day treatment) are smaller, less basophilic and poorer in neurofibrillar material than control ganglia; however, three months after discontinuation of the antiserum treatment the ganglia are only slightly smaller than controls, the neurons are comparable in aspect, and the noradrenaline content and uptake are very close to those of controls (Angeletti, Levi-Montalcini & Caramia, 1971a).

The 'antiserum-to-nerve-growth-factor' has similar, though less intense, effects on prevertebral ganglia. Destruction of up to 95 per cent of the neurons in the coeliac ganglion of the mouse and rat has been obtained by Levi-Montalcini (1972) but usually the effect is less severe than in paravertebral ganglia (Levi-Montalcini & Angeletti, 1966). In fact adrenergic fibres persist in the intestine and the adrenal medulla (Hamberger, Levi-Montalcini, Norberg & Sjöqvist, 1965). When antisera of low titer were used a higher percentage of neurons survived in the prevertebral than in the paravertebral ganglia (Levi-Montalcini, 1972). Differences in the titers of antisera could explain the lack of effect reported by Vogt (1964) and Zaimis, Berk and Callingham (1965). It seems that among prevertebral ganglia, the superior mesenteric is more sensitive to antiserum than the coeliac (Zaimis et al., 1965; Klingman, 1970).

The neurons which are closely associated with the male genital organs (see Section 5.2) show no detrimental effect by NGF antiserum (Hamberger et al., 1965); nor indeed do they show any volume increase in mice treated with nerve growth factor (Levi-Montalcini & Angeletti, 1968). Also the adrenergic innervation of female genital organs is unchanged in rats treated with nerve growth factor antiserum (Hamberger et al., 1965). Derry, Schönbaum and Steiner (1969) have reported that the brown adipose tissue of the rat has two types of adrenergic fibres (see Section 10); the perivascular fibres issuing from the sympathetic chain are destroyed by immuno-sympathectomy, whereas the fibres close to the adipocytes (possibly arising from 'local' ganglia) remain.

The different sensitivity of the three groups of sympathetic ganglia (paravertebral, prevertebral and paravisceral) to the nerve growth factor antiserum is confirmed by studies on the uptake of exogenous noradrenaline. The uptake is down to 40 per cent of controls in the heart and to less than 2 per cent in the submandibular gland; in the small and large intestine it is down to 33 and 47 per cent respectively; whereas in the vas deferens uptake is even greater than in controls (Sjöqvist, Taylor & Titus, 1967). It is not known whether the minority of cholinergic neurons in sympathetic ganglia are affected by the antiserum. However, Klingman (1970) found among the neurons of the superior cervical ganglion of the rat, which survive immunosympathectomy, cells with intense, moderate or weak acetyl-cholinesterase activity, approximately in the same proportions as in control ganglia. Assuming that no change in acetylcholinesterase activity takes place in the ganglion cells which survive the treatment with antiserum, the result indicates no relationship between acetyl-cholinesterase activity and sensitivity to the antiserum. The adminis-tration of the false transmitter 6-hydroxydopamine (6-OHDA) (see p.57) to newborn rats and mice at doses which do not result in any detrimental effect on the growth of the animals, causes a very exten-sive and permanent destruction of para- and prevertebral sympathetic ganglia (Angeletti & Levi-Montalcini, 1970). Signs of nuclear pyknosis and cytolysis are already apparent a few hours after the first injection of the drug. Sympathetic neurons of the genital organs are also affected, but to a smaller extent (the content of noradrenaline of the vas deferens is about 20 per cent of controls (Angeletti, 1972)). The only other significant histological change observed in the mice treated with 6-OHDA is a hypertrophy (unspecified) of the adrenal medulla (Angeletti, 1972). In adult rats which had been treated with 6-OHDA in the first postnatal days, levels of noradrenaline were as low as 28 per cent (spleen, salivary glands) or 5 per cent (heart), but the peri-vascular adrenergic innervation (in the mesentery) appeared intact and the vasoconstrictor response to periarterial nerve stimulation was not impaired (Finch, Haësler & Thoenen, 1973). This effect is inter-preted by the authors as due to prompt regeneration of perivascular neurons, whereas neurons with fibres for non-vascular tissues are des-troyed by early administration of 6-OHDA and do not regenerate.

Comment
By surgical, immunological or chemical means it is possible to obtain an extensive destruction of the sympathetic ganglion neurons. None

of the methods produce a total sympathectomy, but in some experiments only a small percentage of ganglion cells remains. It seems that the differences in the extent of sympathectomy can be explained on the basis of different titers of antisera, injection schedules of drugs, etc. The differences in sensitivity of various ganglia to these procedures are still unexplained. The adrenergic neurons of the genital system appear unaffected by antiserum to nerve growth factor, whereas they are destroyed in great numbers (though less than, say, the superior cervical ganglion) by 6-OHDA. In the latter case, however, little is known of the effects on the ganglion cells themselves and the conclusions are inferred from the effects on the nerve endings.

In laboratory conditions only small changes are present in sympathectomized animals compared with controls. The experiments show that at least in the mouse, rat and cat the main sympathetic ganglia are not essential for survival. This does not, in my opinion, allow one to conclude that the sympathetic system plays only a minor role in the regulation of vital functions. On the contrary; so vital are the functions controlled by the sympathetic system, that additional mechanisms are provided and can take over in case of failure of the sympathetic system. At least three points are worth mentioning in this context: (a) there is a rich source of catecholamines in the adrenal medulla; (b) prompt changes in sensitivity of denervated organs (or ganglion cells) tend to compensate the lack of nerve activity; (c) compensatory adjustments in the antagonistic nerve or muscular system may partly correct the effects of sympathectomy.

4.4 Preganglionic denervation

4.4.1 *Preganglionic denervation*

Section of preganglionic fibres is followed by degeneration and disappearance of the distal part of the fibres (disconnected from the cell bodies), and failure of conduction and of transmission through the ganglion; synaptic transmission fails before the preganglionic fibres cease to conduct (Coppée & Bacq, 1938). Most of the experimental work has been carried out on the superior cervical ganglion. In the rat failure of transmission was observed from the 28th–33rd hour after section of the cervical sympathetic trunk (which in this species is made almost entirely of unmyelinated fibres – see p.00) (Hillarp, 1946). In the cat (whose cervical sympathetic trunk con-

69

tains about 50 per cent of myelinated fibres — see p.39) conduction of nerve impulses remains practically normal during the first 2 or 3 days after the operation (Gibson, 1940). When the distal stump of the sectioned cervical sympathetic trunk is short, failure of synaptic transmission appears earlier than when a greater length of nerve is left to degenerate (Davidovich & Luco, 1956). At 24—36 hours after de-centralization the response of the sympathetic ganglia of the frog to stimulation may still appear normal, but repetitive stimulation produces gradual and irreversible failure (Hunt & Nelson, 1965). The ganglia which would normally receive the preganglionic fibres which have been severed are said to be 'denervated', 'de-afferented' or 'de-centralized'.

4.4.2 Fate of preganglionic fibres

From about 24 h after preganglionic nerve section, and lasting for 3—4 days, degenerating synaptic endings are apparent in the lumbar sympathetic ganglia of the frog (Hunt & Nelson, 1965) and in the superior cervical ganglion of the rat examined in the electron microscope (Quilliam & Tamarind, 1967). In the latter ganglion, degenerating endings appear either electron-lucent and swollen, or shrunken and filled with electron-dense material in which altered mitochondria or synaptic vesicles clumped together can be recognized. These two distinct aspects of degenerating axons were also found in frog ganglia one week after preganglionic nerve section (Taxi, 1965; Sotelo, 1968); in these ganglia the earliest degenerative changes, seen in some fibres as early as 24 h after the operation, were a swelling of mitochondria and the disappearance of synaptic vesicles from the regions immediately adjacent to the synaptic membrane (Hunt & Nelson, 1965). In the de-centralized superior cervical ganglion of the cat, aggregation of synaptic vesicles at some distance from the site of contact are visible as early as 12 h after the operation. Such aggregates are soon surrounded by a membrane and develop into inclusions similar to cytolysosomes, which appear in the cytoplasm of Schwann cell processes (Hamori et al., 1968). In the same tissue studied by silver impregnation methods, degenerative changes are already visible 17 h after the operation (De Castro, 1951; Berselli & Mattioli, 1955): e.g. swelling of nerve endings, fragmentation of terminal rings, granular appearance of preterminal fibres. In the following 24 h these changes become more apparent. Processes of glial cells 'break' the synaptic

70

complex, separating the post-synaptic membrane (on perikarya in the frog lumbar ganglia, on dendrites in the rat superior cervical ganglion) from the degenerating nerve ending. The latter usually becomes completely engulfed in the glial cell, before disappearing.

The morphological study of degenerating axons is hindered by the difficulty in identifying such fibres even with the electron microscope. The time course of degeneration is not the same for all the fibres of a given nerve trunk, and the sequence of structural changes occurring during degeneration is probably not the same in all endings. Regeneration occurs rather rapidly and may complicate the analysis of observations. In addition sensory fibres and post-ganglionic fibres are often present in preganglionic nerve trunks. This further difficulty is probably minimal when experimenting with the superior cervical ganglion (in fact the post-ganglionic descending fibres are usually gathered in a separate bundle, and there is no evidence of the occurrence of afferent fibres) but may be more important in other ganglia. Moreover, dense profiles similar to those regarded as representing degenerating nerve endings are sometimes found in unoperated ganglia (Raisman et al., 1974). It remains to be seen whether they represent a spontaneous degeneration (and regeneration) or if they simply indicate the inaccuracy of our criteria for identifying degenerating nerve endings.

As one would expect, the great majority of synapses in the superior cervical ganglion degenerate and disappear after section of the cervical trunk (Taxi et al., 1969; Quilliam & Tamarind, 1972; Raisman et al., 1974). However, a very small number of synapses may survive the decentralization (Quilliam & Tamarind, 1972; Raisman et al., 1974). Quilliam and Tamarind (1972) considered some of the surviving synapses to be collaterals of post-ganglionic fibres, since they showed small granulated vesicles: the total number of this type of terminal seemed to be greater than in control ganglia and the authors suggest that they may have increased from the third day after the decentralization. The preservation of dense cores for electron microscopy in the superior cervical ganglion of the rat is, in the experience of several authors, rather difficult, and these surviving nerve endings cannot be interpreted beyond doubt as adrenergic. Raisman et al. (1974) in their accurate quantitative study of the decentralized ganglia found that about a tenth of the synapses survived the operation, but could not decide whether they were preganglionic fibres

71

following a different route than the cervical sympathetic trunk, or regenerated preganglionic fibres or post-ganglionic collaterals. None of the surviving synapses showed the characteristics of the chromaffin cell processes. Similar observations had been reported by Lakos (1970) who thought the surviving synapses represented endings of interneurons (but it seems that they could also be recurrent collaterals, particularly since some of the synaptic vesicles show dense cores). No surviving synapses were observed after a similar operation in the cat (Lakos, 1970).

The choline-acetylase activity in the decentralized ganglia is reduced to 1–2 per cent of the control values (Buckley *et al.*, 1967; Raisman *et al.*, 1974) (in agreement with previous observation on the reduced power of a decentralized ganglion to synthesize acetylcholine (Feldberg, 1943; Bannister & Scrase, 1950)), which indicates that no significant numbers of cholinergic synapses survive the operation. The total acetylcholinesterase activity of the cat superior cervical ganglion falls to about 20 per cent of controls (Sawyer & Hollinshead, 1945; Koelle, *et al.*, 1974). Histochemically there is a nearly complete loss of AChE staining of the neurites throughout the ganglia (Fredricsson & Sjöqvist, 1962; Taxi, 1965; Koelle *et al.*, 1974).

4.4.3 *Changes in the ganglion cells*

The post-synaptic membrane specializations show little or no change following preganglionic section (Sotelo, 1968; Hamori *et al.*, 1968; Quilliam & Tamarind, 1972; Raisman *et al.*, 1974), even when the pre-synaptic ending is engulfed by glial cells and eventually disappears. In the lumbar sympathetic ganglia of the frog, preganglionic nerve section leaves both post-synaptic membrane and sub-synaptic apparatus unchanged for at least twelve days (the longest period investigated), by which time almost all the axon terminals have disappeared (Sotelo, 1968). In the superior cervical ganglion of the rat post-synaptic membrane specializations (considered, the axon terminals being absent, as 'vacated synaptic thickenings') were still present six months after decentralization without regeneration (Raisman *et al.*, 1974). Starting about 2½ months after the operation, however, the number of vacated synaptic thickenings is less than the total number of synapses in the same area of controls, and possibly with longer times of survival they become less numerous (Raisman *et al.*, 1974). At these long survival times it was observed that the vacated synaptic thickenings (and the actual synapses in the re-innervated ganglia) tend to be located slightly more frequently on dendritic shafts than normal and occasionally are directly located on the soma, suggesting that spines may shrink upon prolonged de-afferentation (Raisman et al., 1974).

A slight decrease in the average ganglion cell size was observed in the superior cervical ganglion of the rabbit two to five months after de-afferentation (Hamlyn, 1954). Reduction of Nissl bodies in de-centralized ganglia does not occur (Eve, 1896) or only to a very limited extent (Hamlyn, 1954). The dendritic tree of ganglion cells, as seen with intracellular injection of a fluorescent dye, was similar in decentralized and in control superior cervical ganglia of the guinea-pig (McLachlan, 1974).

The content of noradrenaline of the superior cervical ganglion of the cat is either unaffected by preganglionic denervation (Muscholl & Vogt, 1958) or is slightly increased (Kirpekar et al., 1962; a similar result has been obtained by Fischer and Snyder (1965) in the rat). By a microanalysis on about 500 ganglion cells Giacobini, Karjalainen, Kerpel-Fronius and Ritzén (1970) found a small but significant increase in the content of noradrenaline in lumbar sympathetic ganglia of the cat upon decentralization. On the other hand the intensity of formaldehyde induced fluorescence in the neurons of the superior cervical ganglion of the cat is unaffected by decentralization. Only when the surgical section is close to the ganglion (about 1 mm) does a small group of ganglion cells, which send a descending post-ganglionic fibre in the cervical trunk, show an increase in fluorescence intensity (see Section 4.5).

No significant changes in the electrical parameters (resting membrane potential, threshold for firing action potential, cell input resistance) were observed in the ganglion cells of the superior cervical ganglion of the guinea-pig 3—6 weeks after decentralization (McLachlan, 1974). Denervation of amphibian autonomic ganglion cells produces increase in membrane resistance, without significant change in membrane potential (Hunt & Nelson, 1965; Kuffler, Dennis & Harris, 1971).

4.4.4 *Other changes in denervated ganglia*
De-centralized superior cervical ganglia of the cat show no change in weight (about 13 mg) (Hollinshead & Gertner, 1969). The dis-

appearance of the preganglionic fibres is accompanied by an increase in the connective tissue (Hamlyn, 1954) and by a proliferation of Schwann cells (Taxi, 1961; Hunt & Nelson, 1965). There is also an increase by 27 per cent of the mast cells in the superior cervical ganglion of the cat 20 days after preganglionic nerve section (Hollinshead & Gertner, 1969), a change which corresponds to the increase in number of mast cells in sectioned nerves (Gamble & Goldby, 1961; Enerbäck, Olsson & Sourander, 1965).

4.4.5 *Long term effects of preganglionic nerve section*

Clark (1933) studied the structure of cat sympathetic ganglia, which had been decentralized more than two years before and had not been re-innervated. In sections stained by a silver impregnation method or with toluidine blue 'the cells were remarkably normal in appearance'. His conclusion was that sympathetic ganglion cells survive in good conditions for years in the absence of the input from the central nervous system. On the other hand, De Castro (1932) states that 'contrary to what happens in grafted cerebrospinal ganglia the cells of autotransplanted sympathetic ganglia survive only a few days'; even when the vascular supply had been left intact, the cells of the superior cervical ganglion did not survive long. Several authors have subsequently found that decentralized ganglia of adult animals can survive for long periods of time with only minor structural changes, results which are well in line with Clark's conclusion. Ward (1936) found ganglion cells of normal appearance in lumbar sympathetic ganglia of the cat which had been transplanted in an intercostal muscle nine months before. He suggested that neurons of transplanted ganglia might survive indefinitely under suitable conditions. The results reported in Section 4.4.3 indicate that the appearance of decentralized ganglion cells is very similar to that of control ganglion cells. Even with the electron microscope only minor changes have so far been observed. This points to a remarkable difference between sympathetic (and other autonomic) ganglion cells and the neurons of the central nervous system, *i.e.*, that most neurons of the central nervous system show dramatic changes upon interruption of their synaptic input (trans-neuronal degeneration), whereas the neurons of sympathetic ganglia remain in healthy conditions after decentralization, even if this involves the interruption of all, or nearly all, the synaptic inputs. This seems to point to a further reason for maintaining the term 'autonomic nervous system' — autonomic in the sense that it is less dependent upon the trophic influence of higher nerve centres. The well known statement of Marinesco (1907) that a nerve centre separated from those neurons which send excitations to it, is bound to atrophy, is not fully valid for the autonomic ganglia of adult animals, at least those which have so far been investigated.

4.4.6 *Regeneration of preganglionic fibres*
The great power of regeneration of the sympathetic nervous system has long been known (see Lee, 1930). When the preganglionic nerve after being severed is sutured, or when instead of being cut it is crushed or frozen, a successful regeneration consistently occurs. When there is a gap between the two stumps, a regeneration may or may not succeed. In the cat the regenerating fibres seem able to bridge large gaps (successful regeneration with a gap of 10 mm, but fail with a gap of 16 mm in the cervical sympathetic trunk [Butson, 1950]; Lee (1930) reports a case of regeneration across a gap of 25 mm), whereas this is not the case in the rabbit (Butson, 1950). Functional recovery can be ascertained by the remission of the para-lytic signs, which in the case of the cervical sympathetic trunk are: ptosis (Note 4.5), miosis, enophthalmus, protrusion of the nictitat-ing membrane, vasodilation (warmer skin), drooping of the whisker hairs. In the cat the ear temperature first returns to normal, to be followed later by return to normal of the pupil size and recovery from ptosis (Butson, 1950); upon recovery the skin on the operated side becomes sometimes cooler than on the control side (Lee, 1930; Butson, 1950; see also Machida, 1928). The time of recovery greatly varies with the surgical procedure employed (e.g. crush vs. section). Moreover it seems to vary between species. Following a nerve injury immediately below the superior cervical ganglion the mean time for functional recovery was 12 days in 5 cats and 33 days in 5 rabbits (Butson, 1950). The closer the lesion is to the ganglion the quicker is the recovery. When the cervical trunk of the rabbit was crushed close to the superior cervical ganglion on one side and 50 mm below on the other side, function recovered on the latter side 20–25 days later than on the other side, which gives a mean rate of 'advance of func-tional recovery' of about 2 mm d^{-1}; a mean rate of 2·7 mm d^{-1} was calculated in similar experiments in the cat (Butson, 1950).

75

The recovery of function, of course, requires not only re-growth of the axons, but also formation of new synapses and then functional maturation. From about 25 days after the crush synapses begin to reappear in the superior cervical ganglion of the rat and the number of vacated synaptic endings (see Section 4.4.3) begins to fall. The number of synapses in the reinnervated ganglion reaches the control value by the middle of the third post-operative month; but at no time after the operation (even after six months) does the number of regenerated synapses exceed the number of synapses in control ganglia (Raisman et al., 1974). A similar picture and a similar time-course had been worked out by Hillarp (1946), who studied the superior cervical ganglion of rats by methylene blue and silver impregnation methods.

In the re-innervated superior cervical ganglion of the guinea-pig the ratio of axo-somatic to axo-dendritic synapses is the same as in control ganglia, 1:3 (McLachlan, 1974). There is a parallel recovery of the total choline-acetylase activity, which, however, reaches only about 50 per cent of the value for control ganglia (Raisman et al., 1974). Further section of the regenerated preganglionic nerve is, as expected, followed by disappearance of the regenerated nerve endings. However, the degeneration process appears slower, at least with silver impregnation methods, than in control (simply denervated) ganglia (Berselli & Mattioli, 1955), a condition which the authors interpreted as due to the increased number of satellite cells in re-innervated ganglia.

Regenerating axons branch repeatedly, so that a newly regenerated preganglionic trunk shows a much greater number of axons than intact nerves. In the cervical sympathetic trunk of the rat there is, within two weeks, a fourfold increase in the number of axons distal to a crush (Bray, Aguayo & Martin, 1973). With accurate estimation in the electron microscope of the total number of nerve fibres in the rat cervical sympathetic trunk one month after a crush Bray and Aguayo (1974) found the following proportions (calculated by the present author; each figure is the mean of two experiments):

contralateral trunk	100
proximal to the crush	136
at the level of the crush	223
distal to the crush	392

After three months the proportions are: 100, 118, 100, 229, and after six months they are within the normal range. The ratio of axons to Schwann cells, which is about 3–4 to 1 in control trunks, also increases and can be more than 20 to 1 distal to a crush after one month; it decreases afterwards and is within the normal range by six months (Bray & Aguayo, 1974). The regenerated fibres are much smaller than the control ones (median 0.35μm as against 0.7μm) one month after crushing; they increase in size in the following months but after six months they are still significantly smaller than the controls (Bray & Augayo, 1974). In similar experiments in the rabbit and the cat it was found that at the time of recovery of function the number of myelinated fibres in the cervical sympathetic trunk was less than 5 per cent than in controls, and in some cases there were no myelinated fibres at all (Butson, 1950). This author found no change or a large decrease in the total number of axons in the regenerated trunk, but it is possible that the silver impregnation method employed detected only a proportion of the small unmyelinated axons.

Experiments of partial denervation have shown that the surviving axons produce, by a process called collateral sprouting, new axonal branches which take the place of the degenerated fibres. A similar process of collateral sprouting has long been known to occur in somatic sensory and motor nerves (see Edds, 1953). At the end of the process each motor or sensory or preganglionic fibre will innervate a larger motor lunit or area of skin or number of ganglion cells. As a consequence, in the latter case, some ganglion cells will receive preganglionic fibres from rami other than the normal contribution.

Experimental evidence supporting the occurrence of collateral sprouting in the autonomic nervous system has been obtained by Geohegan and Aidar (1942) and Murray and Thompson (1957). Geohegan and Aidar (1942) cut the ventral roots T_3 or T_4 to T_{11}, which, in the cat, contain the preganglionic fibres corresponding to the forepad. After 2–6 months, stimulation of T_1 or T_2 produces the skin resistance changes in the forepad which on the unoperated side or in control animals is obtained only by stimulation of $T_4 - T_{10}$. Stimulation of T_3 which has only moderate effect in normal conditions, produces large responses in operated cats. Since following the interruption of preganglionic pathways to the forepad, preganglionic pathways develop from roots which do not normally contribute

77

to the forepad, the authors conclude that functional re-organization takes place, probably by growth of axon collaterals.

In a more refined experiment Murray and Thompson (1957) partially denervated the superior cervical ganglion of cats by cutting the rami communicates $T_1 - T_3$, the other rami and the sympathetic chain being left intact. A few weeks after the operation (before regeneration had occurred) the number of axons in the cervical sympathetic trunk was about 15–20 per cent that in controls, the majority of axons, which are contributed by $T_1 - T_3$ (Langley, 1900; De Castro, 1951), having degenerated. Stimulation of the surviving fibres initially produces a very small contraction of the nictitating membrane (whose innervation is usually provided by $T_1 - T_3$), but after a few weeks the response to stimulation equals that on stimulation of the whole cervical trunk on the normal side. Histologically, in the partially denervated ganglion the remaining preganglionic fibres show collateral sprouts coming into close apposition with the majority of cells denervated by the previous operation. The number of terminal twigs increases in the days immediately after operation, until it is significantly larger than in control ganglia. Subsequently these endings undergo a process of growth and maturation which is complete by 4–8 weeks (Murray & Thompson, 1957). Some collateral sprouts have been seen to originate in the preganglionic trunk at some distance from the ganglion (Murray & Thompson, 1957), but most of the collateral sprouts probably arise in the terminal, intra-ganglionic part of the fibres.

The experiments of Foley and Schnitzlein (1957) showed that the contribution of each ramus communicans to the cervical sympathetic trunk can be estimated (a) by cutting one ramus only, or (b) by cutting all the pertinent rami minus one, and counting the number of axons left in the cervical trunk. The sum of the estimates of the number of fibres contributed by each ramus $T_1 - T_5$ is only slightly greater than the average number of fibres found in control trunks. If axonal sprouting had occurred at the level of the cervical trunk (and had been detected by the silver impregnation method employed) the results of both series of experiments would have been different. However, Geohegan and Aidar's (1942) experiment suggests that axon collaterals can cross the trunks between ganglia and reach neighbouring ganglia. Unfortunately a histological study was not carried out.

The process of collateral sprouting has an interesting medical facet; it could in fact explain surgical cases where recovery of sympathetic activity after denervation seems too quick to be accounted for by regeneration (Simmons and Sheehan, 1939; Monro, 1954), and the failure to obtain a permanent sympathetic denervation even after excision of the appropriate ganglia (Boyd, 1957).

4.5 Post-ganglionic denervation

Section of the post-ganglionic fibres (axotomy) is followed by degeneration of the distal part of the axons (Section 4.5.1) and by changes in the proximal part of the axons and in the ganglion cell bodies (chromatolysis, Section 4.5.2). Ganglionic transmission is impaired (Section 4.5.3). Regeneration of the distal part of the axons and reinnervation of the organs can occur (Section 4.5.4). Comparable effects are obtained by crushing or freezing the post-ganglionic nerves.

4.5.1 *Degeneration of post-ganglionic fibres*
The time course of degeneration of the distal parts of the axons is fairly rapid, but detailed morphological studies of the process have not been made. Failure of nerve conduction and synaptic transmission is certainly not immediate, as the experiments of stimulation on nerves and organs surviving *in vitro* show. *In vivo* uptake of transmitter at the terminals (see p.57) can still be within the normal range 18 h (rat iris; Malmfors and Sachs, 1965a) or 48 h (guinea-pig ileum; Juorio and Gabella, 1974) after the operation. There are wide differences between organs and species and experimental procedures, which might be worth a systematic investigation. The effect of the length of the distal stump on the degeneration time course of adrenergic terminals has not been studied. In skeletal muscles with an increased length of the distal stump of a sectioned nerve there is a longer delay in the onset of failure of neuromuscular transmission (Luco & Eyzaguirre, 1955; Miledi & Slater, 1970).

Cragg (1965) has measured nerve conduction in various unmyelinated nerve fibres of cats and rabbits distally to a cut. Two days after severing the post-ganglionic cervical sympathetic fibres, stimulation of the distal stump elicited no response in the pupil or nictitating membrane of the rabbit or cat, whereas the blood vessels of the ear of the rabbit still responded on the third day and the parotid gland of the cat on the fifth day, failure of conduction in the mesenteric nerve occurred between the third and fourth day after axotomy. Unmyelinated fibres of the vagus nerve maintain a good nerve conduction for longer periods, and complete failure occurs by the seventh post-axotomy day (see p.144).

The degeneration changes of the adrenergic nerve endings are examined in Section 4.5.3.

4.5.2 *Changes in the ganglion cells*

In the ganglion cell bodies the so-called retrograde neuronal cell reaction follows axotomy (De Castro, 1932). Since this reaction has been reviewed recently (Cragg, 1970; Lieberman, 1971), only some data will be reported here. When the post-ganglionic fibres are cut very close to the ganglion (as is usually the case in the superior cervical ganglion) the reaction of ganglion cells is very marked (De Castro, 1932). This reaction has recently been studied in detail in the superior cervical ganglion of the rat, after an axotomy very close to the ganglion (Matthews & Raisman, 1972). There is fragmentation and dispersal of Nissl bodies — as early as 6 h after axotomy, in 25 per cent of the affected neurons and in up to 88 per cent by 24 h. The nuclei, which normally hold a central position, become displaced to the extreme periphery of the cells; they become flat, and later crenated or indented. The number of chromatolytic neurons slowly recedes with time, but after 6 weeks 40—50 per cent of the cells still show clear signs of chromatolysis (Matthews & Nelson, 1975). Some neurons show persistent atrophy even months after axotomy (Matthews & Raisman, 1972), and degeneration of cell bodies can occur (Acheson & Remolina, 1955), and even be very extensive (Levinsohn, 1903; Acheson & Schwarzacher, 1956). (Note 4.2)

Jacobowitz and Woodward (1968) found an increase in catecholamine fluorescence intensity in most of the ganglion cells of the cat superior cervical ganglion after section of the internal and the external carotid nerves very close to the ganglion. There was also a marked increase in the number and size of fluorescent varicosities; however, their conclusion that there is an extensive system of adrenergic terminals on the cell bodies needs to be confirmed at the fine structural level. In the rat superior cervical ganglion Harkönen (1964) and Dahlström and Fuxe (1964) found no increase or even a decrease in the intensity of fluorescence in the cell bodies after axotomy; Krinke, Schnider and Hess (1974) observed a decrease in the fluorescence of small neurons and an increase of that of the large ones. As in most chromatolytic neurons, the acetylcholinesterase activity of axotomized sympathetic ganglion cells is greatly reduced (Taxi, 1965).

4.5.3 *Effects on the ganglionic transmission*

After section of the post-ganglionic fibres there is a reduction in impulse transmission through the superior cervical ganglion of cat and rabbit (Brown & Pascoe, 1954), the inferior mesenteric ganglion of the cat (Acheson & Remolina, 1955), a sympathetic ganglion of the frog (Hunt & Riker, 1966), and the superior cervical ganglion of the rat (Matthews & Nelson, 1975). The decrease in synaptic transmission through the mammalian ganglia begins at about 4 days after nerve section (Acheson & Remolina, 1955; the post-ganglionic nerve was cut about 30 mm from the ganglion) or as early as at the end of the first day, reaching very low levels between 3 and 7 days postoperatively (Matthews & Nelson, 1975; the nerve was cut a few mm from the ganglion). After section of the post-ganglionic fibres the release of acetylcholine from the preganglionic endings is at a normal level, but the ganglion cell membrane becomes less sensitive to intraarterially injected acetylcholine (Brown & Pascoe, 1954).

In the superior cervical ganglion of the rat, from 24 h after the operation onwards, some of the preganglionic nerve ending, showing the usual clustering of synaptic vesicles and apposition of dense material on the axolemma, are no longer apposed to any post-synaptic element and are completely invested by satellite cell processes; by the end of the first post-operative week, these 'detached endings' have become as numerous as the remaining synapses (Matthews & Nelson, 1975). In a very accurate quantitative study of this process Matthews and Nelson (1975) found that the number of synapses was reduced to about a quarter one week post-operatively, while the vesicle-containing profiles showing unapposed presynaptic specializations had risen to a maximum of 7 per cent of all the vesicle-containing profiles. At the same post-operative time only a few vacated post-synaptic membrane sites were seen, indicating that detachment of the preganglionic nerve endings was not accompanied by persistence of this post-synaptic specialization, in striking con-

81

trast with what is observed after preganglionic nerve section (see p.72). Also non-synaptic junctions (desmosome-like attachments, see p.14) between nerve elements became fewer after axotomy concomitantly with the reduction of synapses. At longer survival intervals the incidence of synapses gradually increased, and that of detached nerve endings gradually decreased; recover was well advanced by 42 days (Matthews & Nelson, 1975). A similar process of separation of the nerve endings from the chromatolytic perikarya is also known to occur in motor neurons of the central nervous system (Blinzinger & Kreutzberg, 1968; Sumner & Sutherland, 1973). In the sympathetic ganglia after section of the post-ganglionic nerves, separation of synaptic endings from ganglion cells and decrease in sensitivity to the transmitter seem to concur to reduce transmission through the ganglion, a condition which is probably important for the process of regeneration.

4.6   Heterologous regeneration

A brief account of the hetelogous regeneration is presented. Heterologous regeneration (perhaps better known as heterogenetic regeneration, a term introduced by Boeke, 1917) follows a mismatching of the cut ends of two nerves so that the proximal end of a nerve regenerates in the distal stump of a different nerve. A full account of this problems should take into account the heterologous regeneration in the somatic nervous system, where experiments in more controlled conditions have been carried out.

4.6.1 *Somatic motor nerve and preganglionic sympathetic nerve*
After anastomosis between the hypoglossal and the cervical sympathetic trunk in the cat, reflex stimulation or direct electrical stimulation of the hypoglossal nerve evoke moderate dilatation of the pupil and retraction of the nictitating membrane. The sympathectomy signs persist in the animal at rest, whereas during mastication there is dilatation of the pupil, complete retraction of the nictitating membrane, exophtalmus, vasoconstriction. When both hypoglossal nerve and preganglionic trunk are allowed to regenerate into the superior cervical ganglion, electrical stimulation of either nerve is effective, usually the hypoglossal more than the preganglionic trunk (De Castro, 1934). Near complete functional recovery of the denervation signs

was obtained in cats and monkeys 3 to 4 months after suture of the hypoglossal, the superior laryngeal, the phrenic, or the 5th cervical nerve with the peripheral end of the divided cervical sympathetic trunk (Duel & Ballance, 1932). Wolff, Hare and Cattell (1938) sutured the central end of the phrenic nerve to the distal portion of the cut cervical sympathetic trunk in cats. Stimulation of the phrenic nerve produced retraction of the nictitating membrane. Histologically both the preganglionic and the vagal fibres had regenerated into the superior cervical ganglion. The large fibres of the phrenic ($12-17\,\mu$m in diameter) were seen to branch and end 'synapsing' on ganglion cells.

Regeneration of the hypoglossal or the phrenic nerves into the superior cervical ganglion of rats and rabbits was obtained by Hillarp (1946), but no sign of functional connection and transmission through the ganglion was found. Large regenerated nerve fibres are seen among the ganglion cells but very rarely they form terminal ramifications. Similarly McLachlan (1974) obtained good regeneration of the cut sternohyoid (motor somatic) nerve into the superior cervical ganglion in very young guinea-pigs. However, she observed only minimal extracellular responses to stimulation of the motor fibres which had become preganglionic, and with intracellular recording less than 5 per cent of the impaled cells appeared re-innervated, even after 3 months; in the electron microscope synapses were very rarely seen.

Heterologous re-innervation of the superior cervical ganglion of dogs by the phrenic nerve has been obtained by Taxi and Babmindra (1972). After 1 to 3 years newly formed synapses were found by silver impregnation methods and by electron microscopy. Their fine structure and distribution (entirely on the dendrites of the ganglion cells) were comparable with those in control ganglion. The newly formed synapses were functional since electrical stimulation of the phrenic nerve was followed by dilatation of the pupil and contraction of the nictitating membrane.

4.6.2 *Somatic motor nerve and post-ganglionic sympathetic nerve*
After suturing the proximal stump of the cut hypoglossal nerve and the post-ganglionic nerves of the superior cervical ganglion of the cat the nictitating membrane is re-innervated and the denervation hypersensitivity disappears (Vera, Vial & Luco, 1957). Electrical stimu-

83

lation of the hypoglossal nerve produces a contraction of the nictitating membrane, mediated by a cholinergic mechanism. There is also a ten-fold increase in the acetylcholinesterase content of the nictitating membrane compared with controls (Lennon, Vera, Rex & Luco, 1967).

4.6.3 *Sensory ganglion cells and preganglionic sympathetic nerve*
In two experiments Langley and Anderson (1904) obtained no functional re-innervation of the cat superior cervical ganglion by central or peripheral processes of sensory ganglia. De Castro (1942), on the other hand, reported that a bineuronal reflex arch can be established by nodose ganglion cells the central processes of which are made to synapse one neuron of the superior cervical ganglion. In similar experiments Matsumura and Koelle (1961) obtained functional re-innervation of the de-centralized superior cervical ganglion by the peripheral vagus (sectioned cranial to the nodose ganglion) in 17 out of 44 cats.

4.6.4 *Preganglionic sympathetic nerve and somatic motor nerve*
Preganglionic sympathetic fibres are able to regenerate when united to a somatic motor nerve (phrenic, recurrent laryngeal, spinal accessory, etc.) and to establish some sort of functional connection (Mislavsky, 1902; Langley & Anderson, 1904; Hillarp, 1946). After regeneration electrical stimulation of the preganglionic trunk usually elicits contraction of the re-innervated striated muscle. However, more controlled experiments have recently failed to confirm these early observations. Zalewski (1970) obtained no sign of re-innervation of the denervated sternomastoid muscle of the rat when the cut cervical sympathetic trunk was allowed to grow in it. In spite of the presence of regenerated axons in the muscle, motor end-plates were not seen, and the muscle resembled a chronically denervated muscle.

4.6.5 *Preganglionic sympathetic nerve and post-ganglionic sympathetic nerve*
Ceccarelli *et al.* (1972) excised the superior cervical ganglion of cats and sutured the preganglionic to the post-ganglionic trunk. After 75–120 days most of the cats (14 out of 16) showed clear signs of recovery (the diameter of the pupils was nearly normal and there was

84

retraction of the nictitating membrane). Stimulation of the sympathetic trunk elicited contraction of the nictitating membrane, although not as effectively as in the contralateral unoperated side. The nictitating membrane which had lost its motor supply with the excision of the superior cervical ganglion showed again a rich network of adrenergic fibres, as visualized in fluorescence microscopy. At pharmacological tests the transmission was adrenergic and no evidence for cholinergic fibres was obtained. However, the authors suggestion that these noradrenaline containing axons are preganglionic cholinergic fibres from the spinal cord 'that had been modified so that they could release catecholamines in addition to, or instead of, acetylcholyne', needs further test to exclude regeneration and lateral sprouting, from other adrenergic neurons (e.g. those of the toracic sympathetic chain). The same comment applies to the experiments of Berselli and Rossi (1953), who claimed a successful re-innervation of the eye by preganglionic sympathetic fibres. Experiments of union of the cervical sympathetic trunk with post-ganglionic nerves performed by Langley and Anderson (1904) gave negative results; in the two cases out of eight where a partial recovery was observed, on histological examination it was found that some nerve cells had not been removed.

4.6.6 *Preganglionic parasympathetic nerve and preganglionic sympathetic nerve*

After regeneration of the vagus nerve into the superior cervical ganglion there is an almost complete and persistent remission of the signs of sympathectomy; stimulation of the motor fibres of the vagus produces on the eye the effects of sympathetic stimulation (De Castro, 1934; in another series of experiments by the same author [1937] the results were less clear-cut). Successful regeneration 4½ or months after vagus-sympathetic anastomosis was obtained by Hillarp (1946). Transmission through the ganglion occurred, and many fine nerve endings on ganglion cells, similar to those in control ganglia, were seen by methylene blue staining.

4.6.7 *Preganglionic parasympathetic nerve and somatic motor nerve*

Six to nine months after anastomosis of the recurrent laryngeal and the phrenic nerves of the rat rhythmic contractions and electrical activity was observed in the corresponding hemidiaphragm (in six

85

rats out of eight; Guth, Stoutter, Frank, Campbell & Lloyd, 1960). However, at least in four of the six successful cases contractions continued after section of the vagus high in the neck. In these cases, the authors suggest, the diaphragm may have been re-innervated by accessory nerve fibres joining the phrenic distal to the site of anastomosis or by collateral sprouts from intercostal nerves. Vagal unmyelinated fibres of the thoracic vagus of the frog regenerate within a transplanted (and denervated) sartorius muscle (Landmesser, 1971). Functional contacts are established so that the muscle does not undergo atrophy and electrical stimulation of the vagus produces contractions. Varicosities of unmyelinated vagal fibres make synaptic contacts with the striated muscle fibres, usually at the sites of the old motor end-plates. Transmission, however, is not sensitive to eserine and no acetylcholinesterase activity is histochemically demonstrated at these junctions (Landmesser, 1972).

4.6.8 *Post-ganglionic sympathetic nerve and preganglionic sympathetic nerve*

No functional connection was obtained in a single experiment on a cat where post-ganglionic branches of one side were united with the preganglionic trunk of the other side (Langley & Anderson, 1904). Hillarp (1946) attempted to anastomose post-ganglionic fibres with a preganglionic trunk of the same body side, in order to create synapses between ganglion neurons. All the 63 rats operated on gave negative results: although the post-ganglionic fibres vigorously regenerated forming intercellular nets, no direct intimate connection with the ganglion cells could be demonstrated. However, Hillarp's results are difficult to evaluate since the ganglion cells had also been axotomized (see Section 4.5).

4.6.9 *Post-ganglionic sympathetic nerve and somatic motor nerve*

In one experiment of union of post-ganglionic branches of the superior cervical ganglion to the distal portion of a cut hypoglossal nerve the cervical sympathetic did not acquire any action on the muscles of the tongue (Langley & Anderson, 1904).

4.6.10 *Comment on heterologous regeneration*

The details of the experiments listed above are so various that it is often difficult to compare the results and to reach a conclusion on any type of heterologous regeneration.

The proximal stump of a nerve can regenerate in the distal stump of a different nerve when both have been cut and they have been sutured together. The different diameter of the axons and the Schwann sheaths is not an absolute obstacle to the re-growth of a nerve. In the rabbit when fibres grow from somatic nerves into the unmyelinated anterior mesenteric nerve, myelinated fibres are formed in the latter (although thinner and of smaller diameter than those formed after union of a somatic with a somatic or with a splanchnic [mainly preganglionic] nerve) (Simpson & Young, 1945). When a somatic nerve with large myelinated fibres is made to regenerate into the splanchnic nerve, the myelinated fibres of the latter will be larger than in the control nerve. On the other hand, when unmyelinated fibres of the anterior mesenteric nerve are made to regenerate into a somatic nerve, they will not produce myelinated fibres (Simpson & Young, 1945).

A successful regeneration implies that new neuro-effector junctions or ganglionic synapses are formed. Light microscopy can hardly clarify this point but can establish the extent of terminal arborization of the regenerated fibres. Electron microscopy should establish the closeness and other characteristics of the new junctions. The effectiveness of transmission can be established either by electric stimulation or by reflex activation.

Even when new junctions are formed and effective transmission occurs, it remains difficult to establish the source of the regenerated fibres. Most somatic nerves contain autonomic fibres and the latter can regenerate along new paths. A conclusion on any experiment of heterologous regeneration can be reached only by applying a variety of histological and physiological tests.

Experiments under more controlled conditions and based on the use of a variety of methods are needed to establish the degree of plasticity of the intercellular connections in the autonomic nervous system. The age of the animal is probably a factor which plays a greater role than has been thought. Whether the ability of some nerve fibres to form new, heterologous connections may extend to the release of a different neurotransmitter is an open problem, where experimental evidence is greatly needed. (Note 4.3)

4.7 Effects of denervation during development

Section of the cervical sympathetic trunk in the kitten and rabbit (Note 4.4) a few days after birth did not check the development of the superior cervical ganglion in the following months: size of the ganglion and size and structure of the ganglion cells, stained with methylene blue, were indistinguishable from the controls (Anderson, 1902). In similar experiments on the cat, Tower (1932) found a greatly reduced number of neurons and a decrease in the average neuronal size in the superior cervical ganglion but no effect in the decentralized stellate ganglion. In the rat superior cervical ganglion, preganglionic denervation on the 3rd post-natal day has only a small effect on the biochemical maturation of the adrenergic ganglion neurons (protein content, specific activity of tyrosine-hydroxylase and dopamıne-β-hydroxylase (Thoenen et al., 1972) (a great reduction in the development of the tyrosine hydroxylase activity was however observed by Black et al. [1971] in mice). Inhibition of the bio-chemical maturation was observed in adrenergic neurons of the superior cervical ganglion of mice injected from birth onwards with a pharmacological agent which blocks the preganglionic nerve endings (pempidine and chlorisondamine) (Black & Green, 1973). The experiments of tissue culture (p.89) and organ transplant show that excised sympathetic ganglia are able to develop and grow their processes, in spite of the absence of preganglionic fibres.

Section of the preganglionic nerves in very young kittens has hardly any effect on the following development of the peripheral organs (Tower, 1932). In the experiments with chemical sympa-thectomy in newborn rats and mice the development of the peripheral organs is very close to normal in spite of a sub-total destruction of the sympathetic nerves (p.68).

The experiments above seem to indicate that interruption of nerves, either pre- or post-ganglionic, has little orthograde effect (on the ganglia and on the peripheral organs respectively). On the other hand the retrograde effects (on the preganglionic neurons and on the ganglia respectively) are more obvious. A severe atrophy of the relevant sympathetic ganglia of the chick embryo is observed after an early excision of the limb buds (Levi-Montalcini & Levi, 1944; Simmler, 1949). Section of the post-ganglionic fibres of the superior cervical ganglion in young rabbits and kittens impairs the develop-

88

ment of the corresponding preganglionic tract (Anderson, 1902) and section of the preganglionic fibres has severe effects on the development of the neurons of the intermedio-lateral column (Anderson, 1902). However, Yntema and Hammond (1945) observed a normal differentiation of the preganglionic neuron column and its fibres in chick embryos deprived of sympathetic ganglia by excision of the neural crest. Destruction of sympathetic ganglion neurons by 6-hydroxy-dopamine or nerve growth factor antiserum (see p.66) prevents the development of the choline-acetylase activity (i.e. the preganglionic nerve endings) in the ganglia (Black, Hendry & Iversen, 1972) and greatly reduces the number of axons in the preganglionic nerve trunk (Aguayo, Martin & Bray, 1972).

4.8 Sympathetic ganglia in tissue culture

Sympathetic ganglia from embryonic, young and adult animals have been successfully grown *in vitro*. This field has been reviewed in recent papers (Chamley *et al.*, 1972a, b; Nelson, 1975), and only a few basic data will be reported here.

In cultures of sympathetic ganglia from young rats and guinea-pigs Chamley *et al.* (1972a) observed two types of neurons (Plate 14a–f): small neurons, free of satellite cells (Plate 14a, b), showing a variable and uneven catecholamine fluorescence, and a great ability to migrate out of the cultured ganglion; and larger, non-migrating neurons (accounting for 90–95 per cent of all the neurons) which rarely emerge from the explant, and are closely ensheathed by satellite cells (Plate 14c), with a low and evenly distributed fluorescence reaction. Nerve fibres growing out of the explant are visible within 24 h of culture; axons, particularly when growing singly and not within a bundle, have a varicose appearance, clearly seen in fluorescence and electron microscopy. Granular vesicles, both of the large (70–150 nm) and small (40–60 nm) type, predominate in some varicosities, and small agranular vesicles in others. Mitochondria and tubules of smooth endoplasmic reticulum are also visible, and the microtubules are seen passing through a varicosity from one intervaricose length to the next (Chamley *et al.*, 1972a).

In most of the experiments of tissue culture of sympathetic ganglia, nerve growth factor is added to the medium. Sympathetic neurons of the chick develop better *in vitro* in media without nerve

89

growth factor than do sympathetic neurons of the mouse (Crain, Benitez & Vatter, 1964) or the guinea-pig or rat (Chamley *et al.*, 1972a). In cultures of dissociated embryonic ganglion cells, no neurons survive after 2 or 3 days in the absence of nerve growth factor (Jacobowitz & Greene, 1974). The sympathetic neurons give a fluorescence reaction for catecholamines in the cell bodies after 1–2 days in culture and the fibres give a strong fluorescence as soon as they emerge from the explant (Chamley *et al.*, 1972a). The appearance of the catecholamine fluorescence is slower in explants from ganglia of fetal rats and mice (Sano, Odake & Yonezawa, 1967). The neurons continue to give a specific fluorescence for several weeks *in vitro* (Sano *et al.*, 1967; Chamley *et al.*, 1972a; Silberstein *et al.*, 1971) indicating a maintained synthesis of catecholamines. Sympathetic neurons grown *in vitro* also have the capability to take up catecholamine (neuronal uptake, see p.57) (Goldstein, 1967; Burdman, 1968; England & Goldstein, 1969). Uptake of noradrenaline by superior cervical ganglia rats is actually increased during the first period *in vitro* (4 to 6-fold after 2 days), probably due to a very high uptake by the axonal sprouts of the regenerating adrenergic axons (Silberstein, Johnson, Hanbauer, Bloom & Kopin, 1972). A transient increase in the noradrenaline content occurs during the same period (Webb, Moss, Kopin & Jacobowitz, 1974). The histochemically-demonstrable acetylcholinesterase activity is intense in most of the sympathetic neurons from ganglia of the chick embryo (Kim & Munkacsi, 1972).

In almost all cultures of sympathetic ganglia chromaffin cells are present in varying number (Lever & Presley, 1971; Chamley *et al.*, 1972b; Eränkö *et al.*, 1972a, b). They are readily identifiable with fluorescence histochemistry. Explants of ganglia show, in addition, Schwann cells, satellite cells, connective tissue cells, macrophages, endothelial cells and a few cells resembling astrocytes and oligodendrocytes of the central nervous system (Chamley *et al*., 1972b). In dissociated cell cultures the chromaffin cells survive even in the absence of nerve growth factor and produce extensive ramifications of fluorescent varicose processes (Jacobowitz & Greene, 1974). After several weeks *in vitro* the ramifications of the chromaffin cells formed a network indistinguishable by fluorescence microscopy from that of a sympathetic terminal plexus, e.g. in the rat iris (see p.151).

When the superior cervical ganglion of the rat is cultured alone *in vitro* only very occasionally are synapses formed, whereas if the culture includes a piece of spinal cord synapses on ganglion cells are numerous (Olson & Bunge, 1973); the effect was obtained with both thoracic and cervical spinal cord (the latter usually does not provide preganglionic fibres *in vitro*) but not with a fragment of cerebral cortex. On the other hand in cultures of dissociated sympathetic ganglion cells from newborn rats, ganglion cells appeared free of any cellular ensheathment and after about one week *in vivo* nerve endings synapsing on somata and processes were visible in increasing numbers; with permanganate fixation these endings showed a majority of small dense-core vesicles (endings of this type were not seen in intact ganglia) (Rees & Bunge, 1974). In similar experiments O'Lague *et al.* (1974) observed the formation of large numbers of synapses, which however had pharmacological properties of cholinergic synapses (except for a few where electrical transmission occurred).

The fibres which grow *in vitro* from an excised sympathetic ganglion can penetrate and innervate other excised tissues. This is observed in cultures of chick sympathetic ganglia and heart (Masurovsky & Benitez, 1967) and in rat superior cervical ganglia and iris or pineal gland (Silberstein *et al.*, 1971). The process is not species-specific in the sense that fibres from mouse ganglia grow into rat or guinea-pig iris and fibres from rat ganglia grow into mouse iris (Silberstein *et al.*, 1972b). Fibres from rat sympathetic ganglia grow to explants of normally densely innervated tissues (heart, vas deferens) in preference to explants of normally sparsely innervated tissues (kidney, ureter, uterus, lung) (Chamley, Campbell & Burnstock, 1973).

Note 4.1
The sympathetic system of birds develops through the formation of two ganglionated chains (His, 1897; Tello, 1925). The primary chain is the first to appear, is situated at the posterior aspect of the aorta, and disappears around the 8th day *in ovo*. The secondary chain forms (during the time of disappearance of the primary chain) close to the ventral side of the spinal ganglia and persists in the adult. Tello (1925) recognized that the neurons of the secondary chain originate by centripetal migration of the neurons of the primary chain.

Note 4.2
In the experiments of Acheson and Schwarzacher (1956) on the in-

ferior mesenteric ganglion of the cat, about half of the axotomized cells die in the third post-operative week. Since the inferior mesenteric ganglion cells receive a synaptic input from the periphery (see p.44), in these experiments (section of the hypogastric nerve) they were not only axotomized but also had a reduced synaptic input.

Note 4.3
Evidence suggesting the possibility that some neurons release more than one transmitter has been obtained for some invertebrate species, and some observations on normal development and tissue culture of mammalian neurons pointed to a similar possibility.

Note 4.4
In these experiments functional regeneration was usually impeded by excising a length of the nerve trunk.

Note 4.5
Ptosis is due to paralysis of the smooth muscle component of the levator palpebrae muscle.

5   PARAVISCERAL GANGLIA

Other, more peripheral autonomic ganglia lie in close proximity to the viscera that they innervate: the heart and the pelvic viscera. The pelvic ganglia are connected to the prevertebral ganglia by an intricate plexus, whose pattern varies among different individuals and different species even more than other parts of the vegetative nervous system. Moreover, the plexuses for the pelvic viscera are different in male and female subjects (Fig. 3). Many pelvic ganglia contain pre- and post-ganglionic fibres of both the sympathetic and parasympathetic pathways. The cardiac ganglia are part of the vagal efferent pathway, but contain also sympathetic fibres.

5.1   Ganglia and plexuses of the heart

Numerous ganglia lie close to the heart or in the cardiac walls, and they are connected by nerve tracts to form a plexus. The cardiac branches of the vagus nerves and the cardiac sympathetic branches are the extrinsic nerves contributing to the cardiac plexus (Note 5.1); in man this is divisible into two components, a superficial and a deep cardiac plexus around the great vessels. Some of the ganglia can be up to 1 mm in diameter, but most of them are microscopic entities, demonstrable only by histological methods. They are mainly found in relation to the atria, usually lying under the epicardium (Francillon, 1928), and to the roots of the great vessels (Perman, 1924; Smith, 1971). Only few ganglia are present in the ventricles, usually in the regions closest to the atria (Smith, 1971): only in Artiodactyla and Cetacea are ventricular ganglia a consistent finding (Davies, Francis and King, 1952).

There are approximately 11 000 ganglion cells in the cardiac ganglia of the mouse (Klingman & Klingman, 1967). Mammalian cardiac ganglia contain unipolar, bipolar and multipolar neurons (Davies, Francis & King, 1952). The ganglia of the cardiac plexus contain many fibres in transit, including a number of sensory fibres, and fibres which originate from, or are directed towards, other ganglia. The neurons of the cardiac ganglia receive preganglionic fibres, the cardio-inhibitory fibres, most or all of which are unmyelinated (Mizeres, 1957), from the vagus nerves and give rise to the post-ganglionic fibres of the parasympathetic pathway to the heart. The cardiac ganglion cells are acetylcholinesterase-positive (although the reaction shows considerable variation between cells [Osborne & Silva, 1970]) and there is pharmacological evidence that they are cholinergic.

With fluorescence microscopy adrenergic neurons have not been found in cardiac ganglia of mammals (Ehinger, Falck, Persson & Sporrong, 1968; Jacobowitz, 1967). However, numerous adrenergic fibres run through the plexus. In the cat these post-ganglionic sympathetic fibres (thoracic nerves) originate mainly from neurons of the stellate ganglion (Aiken & Reit, 1968). In the dog most of them originate from neurons situated in the inferior cervical ganglion, which in this species is separate from the stellate ganglion (Wacksman, Farr & Grupp, 1969). Adrenergic fibres to the heart are also supplied by several of the thoracic paravertebral ganglia with a certain degree of asymmetry between left and right side. In the cat the thoracic cardiac nerves comprise approximately 2800 fibres on each side, three quarters of which are sympathetic and one quarter afferent; nearly three quarters of the latter are unmyelinated (Saccomanno, 1943).

In the cat, rat, rabbit and guinea-pig a number of fluorescent terminal varicosities of adrenergic fibres impinge upon ganglion cells of the cardiac plexus (Jacobowitz, 1967; Nielsen & Owman, 1968). These fluorescent terminals, which are very small and whose detection requires optimal technical conditions, lie between and around the ganglion neurons, and Jacobowitz (1967) suggests that they form axo-somatic and axo-axonic synapses (particularly on the axon hillock). However the occurrence of synapses is difficult to ascertain using fluorescence microscopy alone. Dahlström, Fuxe, Mya-Tu & Zetterstrom (1965) and Osborne and Silva (1970) did not observe adrenergic terminals around the cardiac ganglion cells of dog and monkey.

The cardiac ganglia also contain small cells giving an intense yellow fluorescence characteristic of catecholamines (chromaffin cells, see p.23). As with the sympathetic ganglia, these cells also react positively to the chromaffin reaction in some species (e.g. the cat), but not in others (rat, mouse, guinea-pig) (Jacobowitz, 1967). Chromaffin cells are also present in the nerve trunks of the cardiac plexus, in the pericardial connective and fat tissues, and among atrial myocardial cells (Ehinger *et al.*, 1968). Some chromaffin cells, particularly in the cat and guinea-pig, have short, stout, branching processes with the same fluorescence that the cell body (Ehinger *et al.*, 1968), and some have varicose and relatively long processes (Jacobowitz, 1967). Acetylcholinesterase-positive nerve fibres, usually arising from neurons of the same ganglion, are seen ending onto the chromaffin cells, and this is interpreted as a synaptic relation (Jacobowitz, 1967). The function of these chromaffin cells is still unknown. It is possible that they release a biogenic amine which affects the ganglion neurons or diffuses to the cardiac muscle cells; their secretion could also be released into the blood stream (to or from the musculature?), since clusters of intensely fluorescent cells are frequently found close to blood vessels. They were not observed in the cardiac ganglia of dogs and rabbits (Angelakos, King & Millard, 1969).

In summary, cardiac ganglia are composed of cholinergic neurons innervated by preganglionic vagal efferent fibres. In some species noradrenergic fibres are observed to come close to ganglionic neurons, and it is therefore possible that some integration of the cranial parasympathetic and the thoracic sympathetic outflows takes place at the level of the cardiac ganglia. Neither the details of this convergence, nor a possible interaction between ganglion cells (among which multipolar neurons are known to occur) have been investigated. Studies of the fine structure of the cardiac ganglia, and quantitative analyses of data on the distribution of interneuronal connections may help to clarify these points.

5.2 The pelvic plexus

Another group of ganglia, lying farther from the spinal cord and closer to the peripheral organs than the paravertebral ganglia, are associated with the pelvic organs. They form the pelvic plexus, bilaterally represented, situated in a sagittal plane (hence also described as a laminar ganglionated plexus) beside the rectum and the adjacent genital organs (Fig. 3). The pelvic ganglia are considered as a separate group from the paravertebral and prevertebral ganglia because of their position (Langley & Anderson, 1895), including the fact that

95

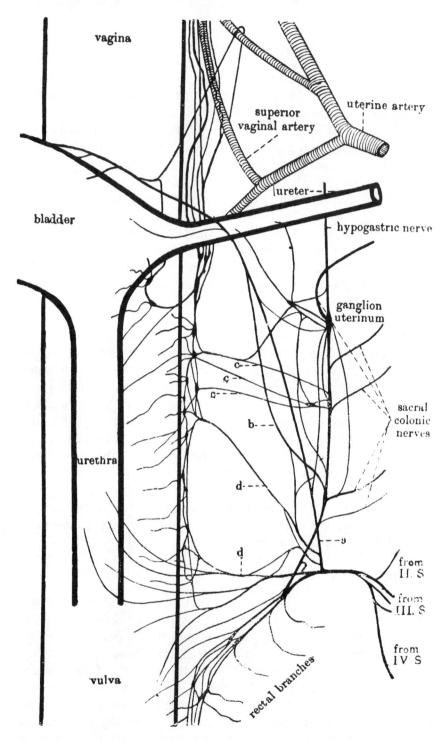

Figure 3a. Arrangement of the pelvic plexus in a female rabbit. (From Langley & Anderson, 1896.)

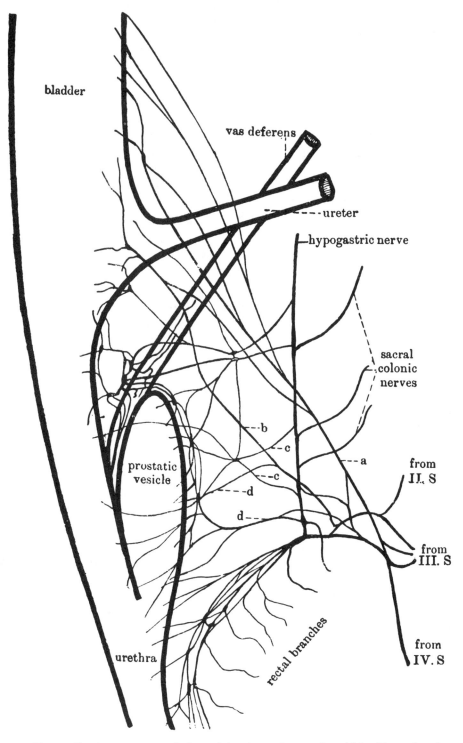

bladder

vas deferens

ureter

hypogastric nerve

sacral
colonic
nerves

b

c

a

from
II. S

prostatic
vesicle

c

d

d

from
III. S

urethra

rectal branches

from
IV. S

Figure 3b. Arrangement of the pelvic plexus in a male rabbit. (From Langley & Anderson, 1896.)

they lie very close to the viscera they innervate, and because they are structurally different from the sympathetic ganglia examined above, at least in one important aspect: they receive a sacral parasympathetic output and a lumbar sympathetic output, and contain both adrenergic neurons and neurons of the parasympathetic pathways (Kuntz & Moseley, 1936). In addition to the topographical difference, the adrenergic neurons present in the pelvic plexus are in a different category from those of the sympathetic ganglia described above, and are labelled 'short adrenergic neurons', since their axons travel a much shorter distance before reaching their target organs (Owman & Sjöstrand, 1965; Sjöstrand, 1965). The differences between short adrenergic neurons and 'long' ordinary adrenergic neurons are mainly pharmacological (see Swedin, 1971), and some of them appear related to the characteristic mode of termination of these fibres in the viscera. Why the neurons of the pelvic ganglia are less sensitive than other adrenergic neurons to 6-hydroxydopamine and largely insensitive to immunosympathectomy (see p.66) is not yet known.

The nomenclature for these ganglia and their nerves varies slightly among the authors. Detailed descriptions of the gross anatomy of the pelvic plexus can be found in Langley and Anderson (1895), Trumble (1934), Mitchell (1953), Wozniak and Skowronska (1967), Pick (1970). The plexus is obviously different in male and female subjects, and has also a great variability among species (Wozniak & Skowronska, 1967).

In man the pelvic ganglionated (Frankenhauser's) plexuses are situated on both sides of the rectum and the inferolateral surface of the bladder (in the male) or on both sides of the rectum and uterus (in the female). The plexus is formed by branches from (a) the hypogastric nerves (or plexuses), originating from the inferior mesenteric nerve; (b) small nerves (splanchnic nerves) from the sacral sympathetic ganglia (this contribution is consistent in the female, whereas in the male some authors were unable to find them [Pick, 1970]); (c) nerves (nervi erigentes) emerging from the sacral spinal nerves (they contain, sometimes as separate nerves, afferent fibres originating from dorsal root ganglia — branches of the pudendal nerves — and preganglionic sacral parasympathetic fibres or pelvic nerves, see Chapter 9). In man, macaque and rabbit (but not in cat and dog) the pelvic plexuses of the two sides are connected by branches passing dorsal to the rectum, so that a sort of horse-shoe-shaped plexus is formed (Wozniak & Skowronska, 1967). In man and also the cat the hypogastric nerves contain nerve cells scattered along their entire length (Trumble, 1934; Vanov & Vogt, 1963).

The small ganglia lying within 10 mm of the vas deferens and seminal vesicle (described as the 'hypogastric plexus', and corresponding to part of what is here described as the 'pelvic ganglia') of the guinea-pig contain angular ganglion cells, about 30–40 μm in diameter sheathed by satellite glial cells (Wantanabe, 1971). The neurons are multipolar, and their axons appear in the electron microscope thicker than preganglionic axons. Small protrusions (1–2 μm × 0·2–0·4 μm) or spines from the surface of the cell body usually invaginate into a nerve ending. Numerous axo-somatic, axo-axonic and axo-dendritic synapses are observed, which contain either agranular vesicles, 50 nm in diameter, with a few large granulated vesicles, or large numbers of small granulated vesicles, with a few small agranular and large granulated vesicles.

The large granular vesicles have a denser and more irregularly shaped granule in the latter type of synapse. Endings of the first type are more numerous and represent the preganglionic (cholinergic) nerve endings. The second type represents adrenergic nerve endings (issuing from other ganglion cells), which are seen in fluorescence microscopy as pericellular nests around some of the ganglion cells.

Based on fluorescence histochemical studies the neurons of the guinea-pig pelvic plexus are said to be monopolar, to have no dendrites, and to be supplied by few varicose adrenergic axons (Costa & Furness, 1973); associated with the ganglia and nerves of the plexus many chromaffin cells were observed, brightly fluorescent and with one or two long, often varicose, processes. In the electron microscope ganglia of the pelvic plexus of the guinea-pig show less structural complexity than ganglia of the sympathetic trunk (Blackman, Crowcroft, Devine, Holman & Yonemura, 1969). Preganglionic fibres, which are varicose, synapse mainly on short intracapsular processes, less frequently on long dendrites or on perikarya.

In the pelvic plexus of the male guinea-pig Sjöstrand (1965) found large clusters of ganglion cells. The neurons were rather uniform in size and showed varying degrees of fluorescence, from faint to very intense; groups of non-fluorescent cells also occurred (most of the non-fluorescent neurons and none of the fluorescent ones showed intense acetylcholinesterase activity [Bell & McLean, 1967]). Around

99

a minority of the neurons, both of the fluorescent and non-fluorescent type, adrenergic terminals were seen. Ganglion cells were also found very close to the genital organs, and within the prostate and the coagulating glands. Ganglia similar to those described in the guinea-pig were observed also in other species (Sjöstrand, 1965). In the rat, pericellular fluorescent nests were rarely found; in the rabbit, most of the cell bodies emitted no or a very faint fluorescence; in the cat, the ganglia consisted either of non-fluorescent cells only, or of a mixture of non-fluorescent and fluorescent cells, the latter predominating in number (the smaller cells had a stronger fluorescence); in the dog and macaque there were only a few fluorescent neurons. Chromaffin (small intensely fluorescent, small granule-containing) cells are present in the pelvic ganglia. They were seen by fluorescence microscopy in ganglia associated with the male genital organs in many species (Sjöstrand, 1965).

The paracervical ganglion (ganglion cervicale uteri) is bilaterally situated close to the uterine cervix. In the mouse the number of neurons varies, in each ganglion, between 1800 and 5200. In other species the number of neurons is as follows: rat 5700, rabbit 5000, cat 5000, dog 4100, hyena 9800, rhesus monkey 12 700 (newborn) and 14 400 (adult) (Blotevogel, 1927). The average cell diameter is about 15 μm in the mouse, and it is greater in species of larger body size. In the mouse after castration the neuron number is unchanged but the average cell diameter falls below 11 μm (Blotevogel, 1928). About one third of the neurons of the rat paracervical ganglion show the specific fluorescence for catecholamines, but fluorescent fibres are only occasionally encountered close to ganglion cells (Kanerva, Lietzén & Teräväinen, 1972). Pericellular nests of fluorescent endings have been reported in the paracervical ganglia of man (Owman, Rosengren & Sjöberg, 1967), cat (Rosenberg & Sjöberg, 1967), and guinea-pig (Furness & Malmfors, 1971). The adrenergic neurons of the paracervical ganglion contribute most of the adrenergic fibres to the genital tract (see p.159).

Chromaffin cells are found among the paracervical ganglion cells. In the mouse they amount to about 3 per cent of the number of ganglion cells (Blotevogel, 1927) but consistently decrease to less than 0·5 per cent following castration (Blotevogel, 1928). Chromaffin cells are less numerous in the paracervical ganglion of other species: 1·6 per cent in the rat, 1·2 in the rabbit, 1·4 in the dog, 1·3 in the cat, 1·1 in the hyena, 0·9 in the monkey (Blotevogel, 1927). These cells display an intense formaldehyde-induced fluorescence (Sjöberg, 1967) and in the electron microscope appear filled with vesicles 80—140 nm in diameter with an electron-dense granule and a clear-cut halo between granule and membrane; a minority of chromaffin cells contain instead vesicles 200—300 nm in diameter, less regular in shape and without a clear-cut halo (Kanerva & Teräväinen, 1972). Efferent synapses from chromaffin cells were never seen and afferent synapses were very rare (Kanerva & Teräväinen, 1972); the latter are not affected by section of the sympathetic or the parasympathetic input to the ganglion, and are considered to arise from neurons of the same ganglion (Mustonen & Teräväinen, 1971).

In the electron microscope the neurons of the rat paracervical ganglion show the usual organelles of the ganglion neurons (Kanerva & Teräväinen, 1972). By fixing the tissue with potassium permanganate the neurons could be classified as presumably adrenergic (containing small and large granular vesicles) and presumably cholinergic (containing virtually no dense core vesicles) (Hervonen, Kanerva & Teräväinen, 1972). Numerous nerve endings, containing agranular vesicles, synapse on the cell bodies (including those of vacuolated neurons, see below), sometimes deeply embedded in them, are present in the rat paracervical ganglion, but synapses of endings with small granular vesicles were not seen (Kanerva & Teräväinen, 1972; Hervonen et al., 1972). In spite of the results of degeneration experiments (Mustonen & Teräväinen, 1971) it seems that the rat paracervical ganglion has few if any adrenergic fibres synapsing on ganglion cells. The same is true for other ganglia of the rat pelvic plexus (Sjöstrand, 1965) and is at variance with the results obtained in fluorescence microscopy in other species.

A minority of neurons in the paracervical ganglion (less than 1 per cent in the rat, localized chiefly in the apical part of the ganglion) are bigger than neighbouring ganglion cells (up to 60 μm in diameter) and are characterized by one or a few large cytoplasmic vacuoles (vacuolated neurons) (Lehmann & Stange, 1953). The vacuoles measure up to 20 μm in diameter, are membrane-bounded and show, within an amorphous content, microvilli and lamellar inclusions (Becker, 1968; Kanerva & Teräväinen, 1972). Vacuoles are not recognized in immature animals (Takahashi, 1960), whereas during pregnancy they become more numerous — from 0·13 per cent in control rats to 0·8 per cent in pregnant rats (means of 9 and 7 cases) (Lehmann & Stange, 1953). It remains to be proved whether such vacuoles are related to a neurosecretory activity, as suggested by Takahashi (1960).

Ganglia associated with the bladder form the uretero-vesical plexus. The ganglia are situated, in the dog and rabbit, close to the terminal part of the ureter and to the base of the bladder. Individual neurons, usually in a perivascular position, are found within the vesical musculature of the base of the bladder and around the intramural part of the ureters (El-Badawi & Schenk, 1968; Schulman, Duarte-Escalante & Boyarsky, 1972). The majority of the neurons are intensely positive for the acetylcholinesterase reaction, and a minority (among both the ganglion neurons and the individual intramural neurons) show the specific fluorescence for catecholamines (Hamberger et al., 1965; Schulman et al., 1972). The presence of adrenergic endings in close proximity to the cholinergic parasympathetic neurons of these ganglia has prompted the suggestion of a sympathetic control on the ganglionic transmission (Hamberger & Norberg, 1965). It has in fact been shown that catecholamines administered intra-arterially or released by electrical stimulation of the hypogastric nerves of the cat elicit a depression of the vesical musculature (via a β-adrenoceptor) and a depression of transmission in vesical ganglia (via an α-adrenoceptor) (De Groat & Saum, 1972). In addition it has been shown electrophysiologically that in the rat pelvic ganglion there are afferent perikarya, which are synaptically associated with efferent ganglion neurons (Puriton et al., 1971) (see Section 2.10).

Note 5.1
Some authors (e.g. Klingman, 1970) use the term 'cardiac ganglion' to indicate part of the abdominal plexus (with the coeliac and superior mesenteric ganglia).

6 THE CILIARY GANGLION

6.1 The ciliary ganglion in mammals

The ciliary ganglion is a small ganglion, up to 2 mm in its antero-posterior diameter in man, situated behind the eyeball, lateral to the optic nerve. It receives nerves (its *roots*) from the aculomotor nerve (radix brevis, generally from the branch to the inferior oblique muscle), and sends nerves (the short ciliary nerves) to the eyeball. In man and a few other species it also contains sensory fibres from the trigeminal nerve (radix longa, from the naso-ciliary nerve) and sympathetic post-ganglionic fibres (radices sympathicae) from the superior cervical ganglion (via the internal carotid plexus); both these orders of fibres pass through the ganglion without interruption. Sensory and sympathetic fibres are absent in the ciliary ganglion of the cat (Whitteridge, 1937; Skok, 1973). In the small rodents the ganglion is composed of microscopic clusters of neurons in the proximity of the optic nerve (Malmfors & Nilsson, 1966 [rat]; Watanabe, 1972 [guinea-pig]).

Ganglion neurons are spheroidal and measure about 25—36 μm in diameter in man, 11—15 μm in the mouse, 34—50 μm in the dog (Slavich, 1932), 30—40 μm in the guinea-pig (Wantabe, 1972) (Plate 15c, e—g). In the cat the number of ganglion cells ranges between 4250 and 5100 (four cases) (Wolf, 1941). Neurons are closely packed and individually sheathed by satellite cells. In all species investigated ciliary ganglion neurons are larger than the neurons of the corresponding sympathetic ganglia (for example those of the superior cervical ganglion). Moreover, they never show accumulation of pigment, not even in old (human) subjects, where the diameters increase to 35—40 μm (Slavich, 1932).

Slavich (1932) has studied the processes of the ciliary ganglion cells in several mammalian species using silver impregnation methods. A few ganglion cells, particularly in human ganglia have long dendrites (usually 2 or 3), whereas the majority of cells have only short processes confined within the pericellular sheath and usually ending with terminal knobs (Plate 15f). These short, intracapsular processes become thicker and coarser in old subjects and, notably in man and the dog, form pericellular nests together with the preganglionic fibres. Fenestration (i.e. cell processes resembling cup-handles and stout dendritic branches which anastomose repeatedly) (Plate 15c) are found in ciliary ganglion neurons, particularly in the dog (Slavich, 1932). The axons from the ganglion cells are clearly identifiable in silver preparations: they cross the sheath and proceed undivided among other neurons. The initial tract of the axon sometimes shows fine short collaterals. Carpenter (1912) found no ganglion cells with long dendrites in the sheep ciliary ganglion stained with methylene blue and only a few extracapsular dendrites were seen: of course it is not possible to assess to what extent this result was due to refractoriness of the cell processes to staining with methylene blue. Pines (1927) classified the neurons of the human ciliary ganglion in eight groups, including neurons with subcapsular or extracapsular processes only or with both, unipolar and bipolar neurons, unipolar neurons with a T-shaped process, fenestrated neurons and degenerating neurons. Whitteridge (1937) and Nishi and Christ (1971) obtained electrophysiological evidence that there are two types of neuron in the ciliary ganglion of the cat, B- and C- neurons. There are therefore two transmission pathways through the ganglion; one characterized by a higher excitability of the preganglionic fibres, a shorter synaptic delay and a higher post-ganglionic conduction than the other. In the monkey, only the fast transmission pathway is found (Whitteridge, 1937). Obviously the morphological studies available are too few to allow a subdivision of ciliary ganglion cells on structural bases.

The histochemical reaction for acetylcholinesterase is positive in all neurons of the ciliary ganglion of the cat and in their pericellular nests (preganglionic terminals and short processes) (Koelle, 1951; Koelle & Koelle, 1959; Fredricsson & Sjöqvist, 1962; Taxi, 1965). The intensity of the acetylcholinesterase activity is similar in all the ganglion cells in histochemical preparations and when measured by microgasometry on isolated cells is higher than in any ganglion cell of the rat (Giacobini, 1959). Choline acetylase activity per unit weight is more than twice that found in the stellate and lumbar sympathetic ganglia (Buckley et al., 1967).

In the electron microscope the ganglion cells of the ciliary ganglion

ERRATUM

Due to an error in binding, it is regretted that the Plates occur between pages 104 and 105, and their legends between pages 128 and 129.

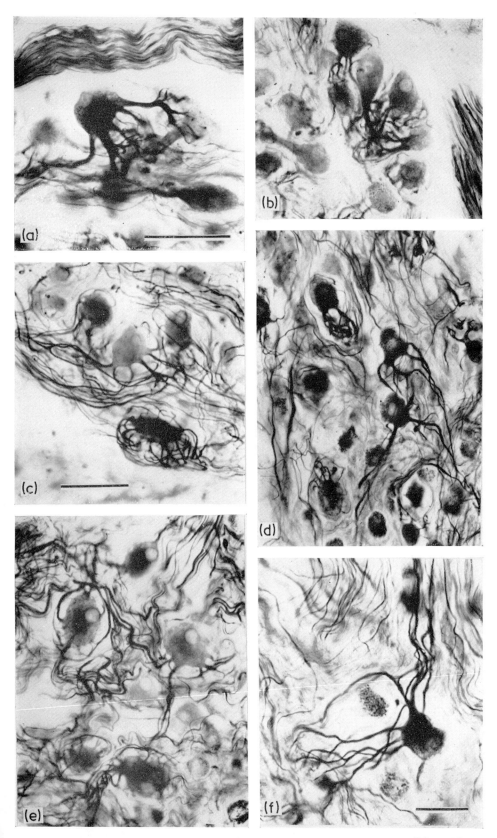

Plate 1

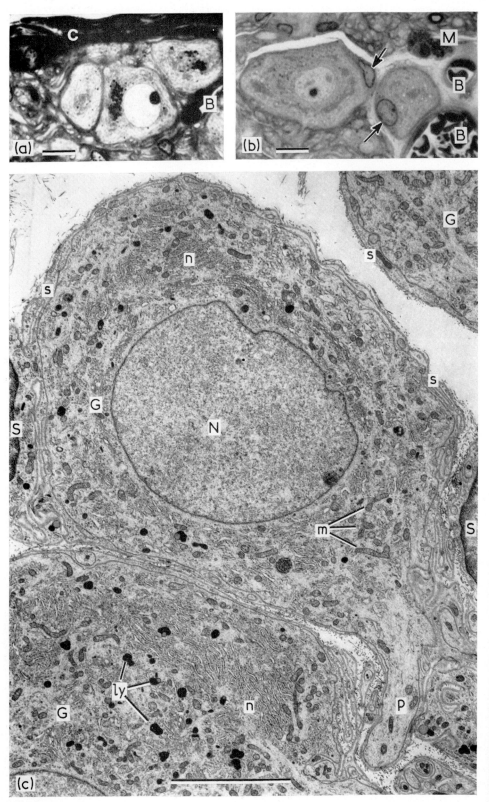

Plate 2

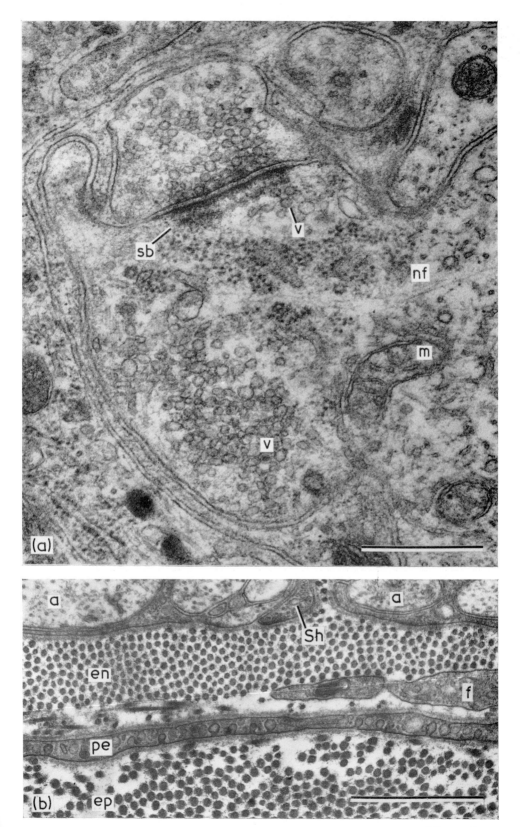

Plate 3

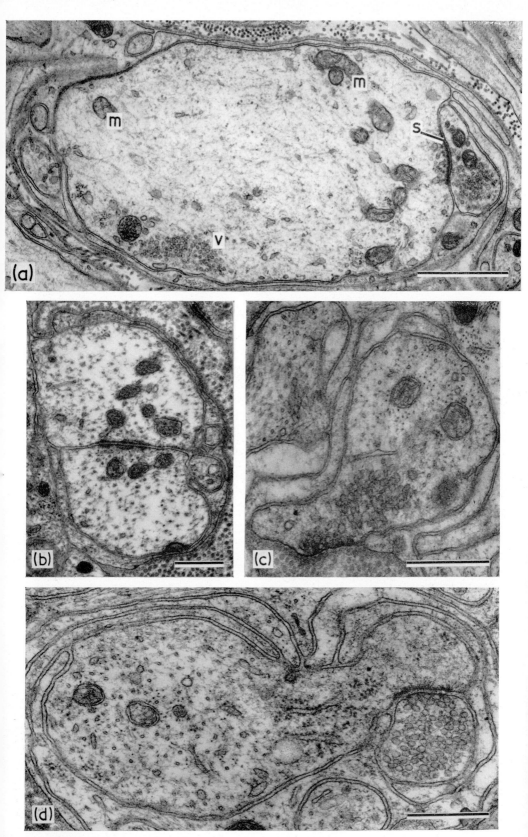

Plate 4

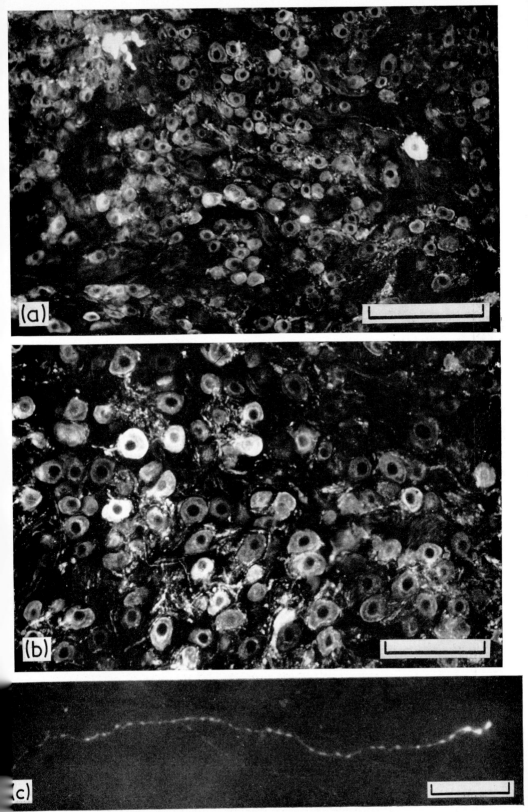

(a)

(b)

(c)

Plate 5

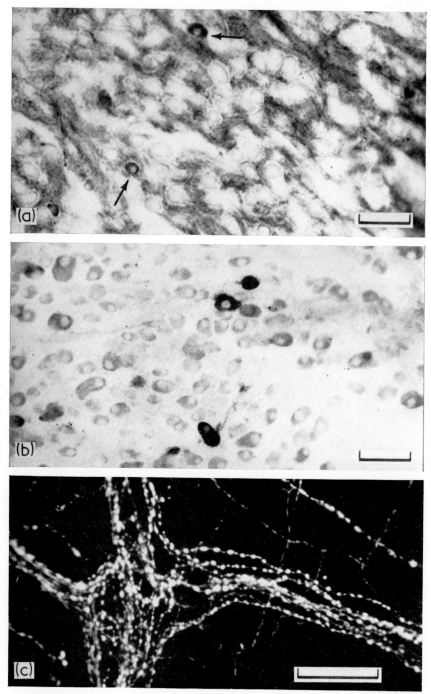

Plate 6

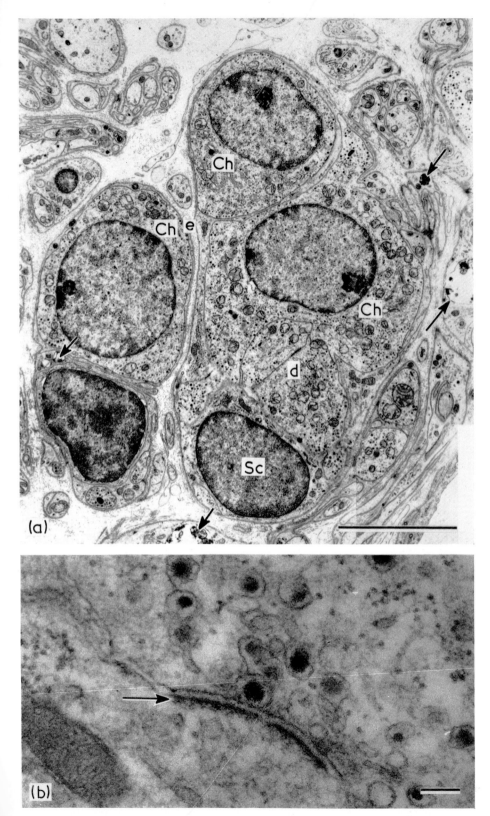

Plate 7

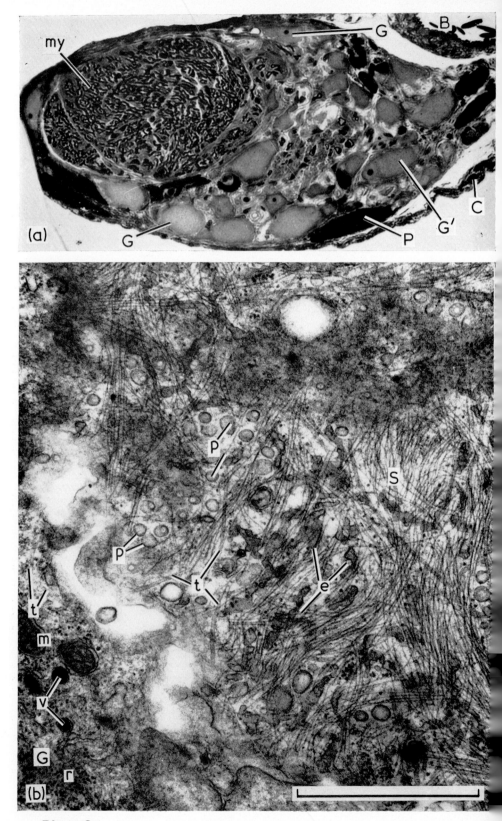

Plate 8

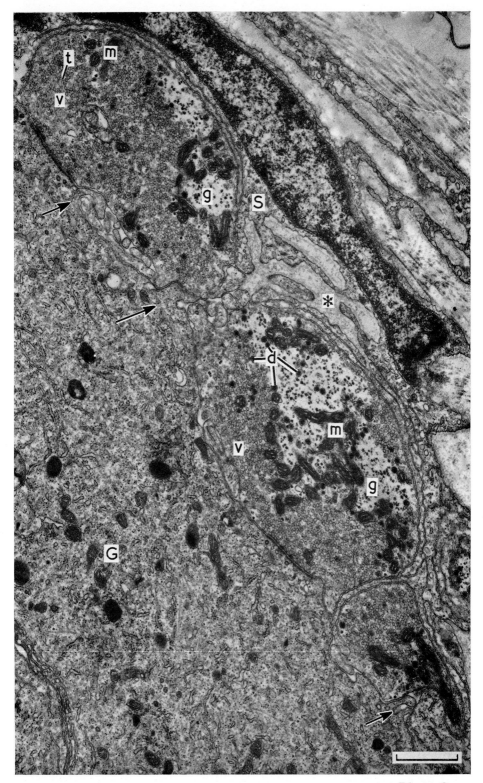

Plate 9

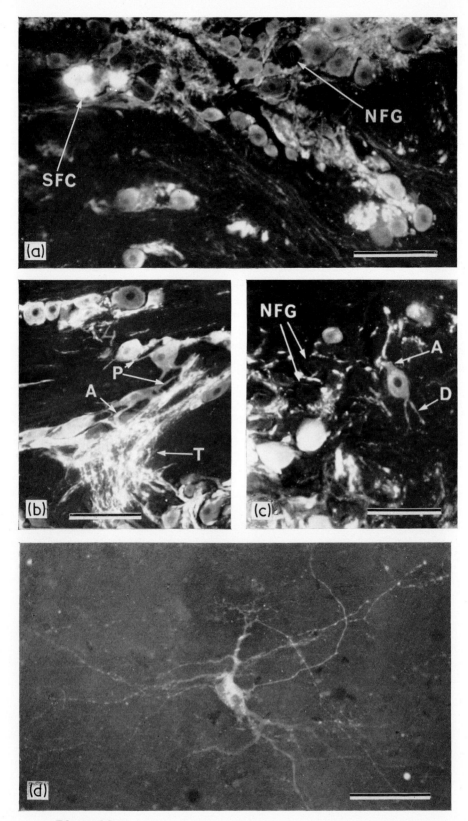

Plate 10

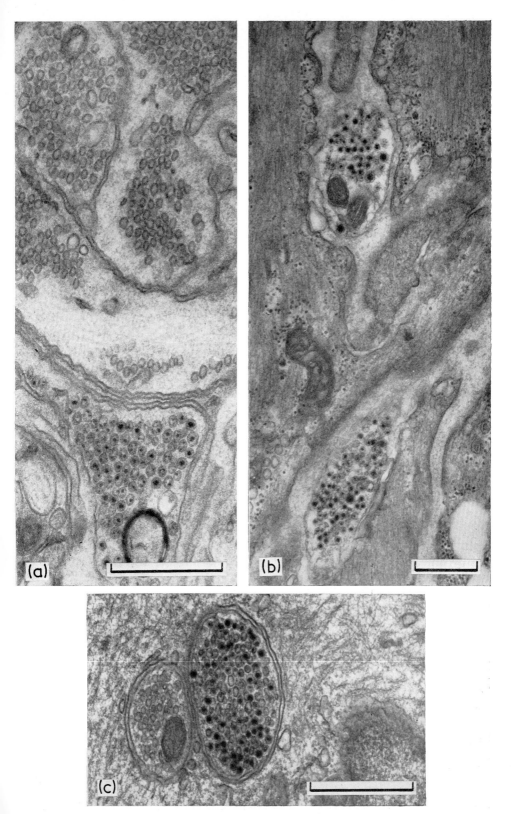

Plate 11

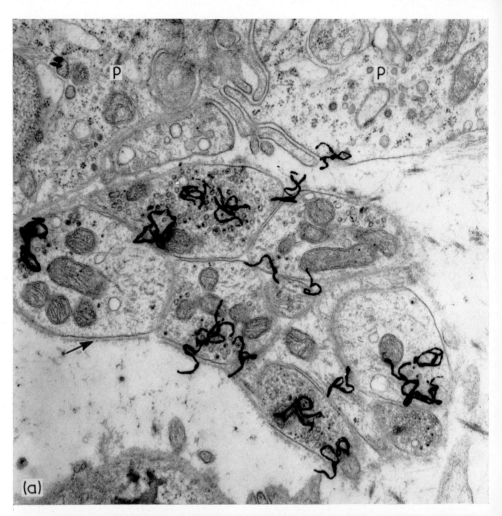

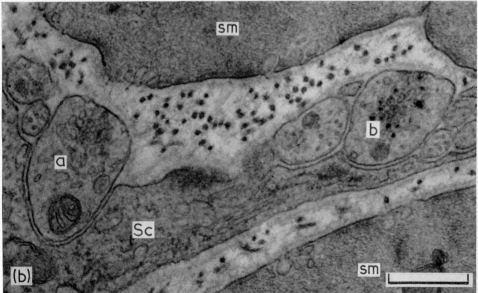

Plate 12

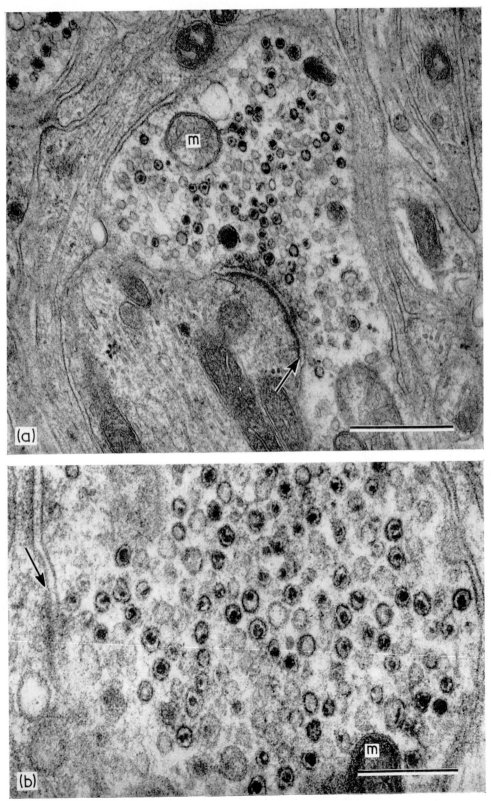

Plate 13

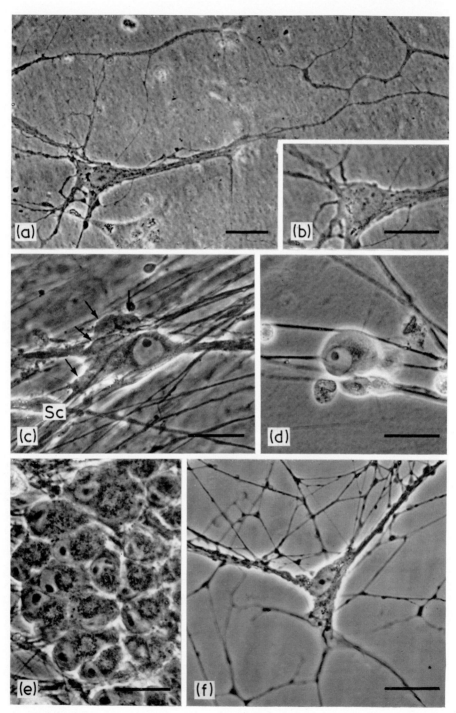

Plate 14

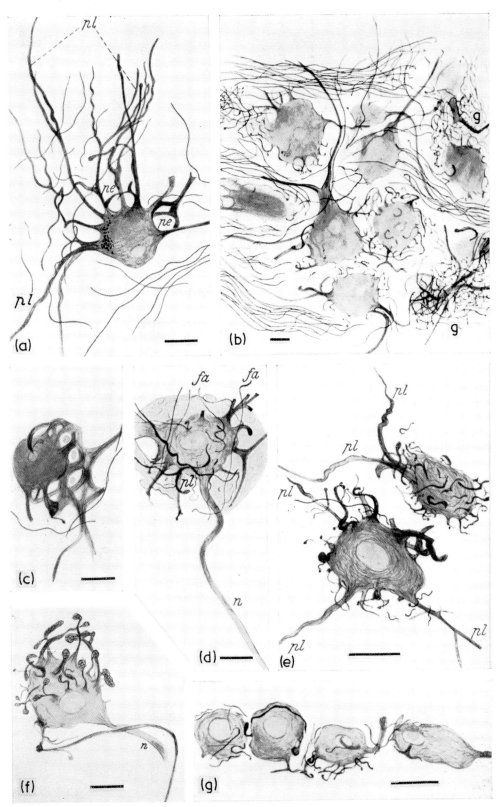

Plate 15

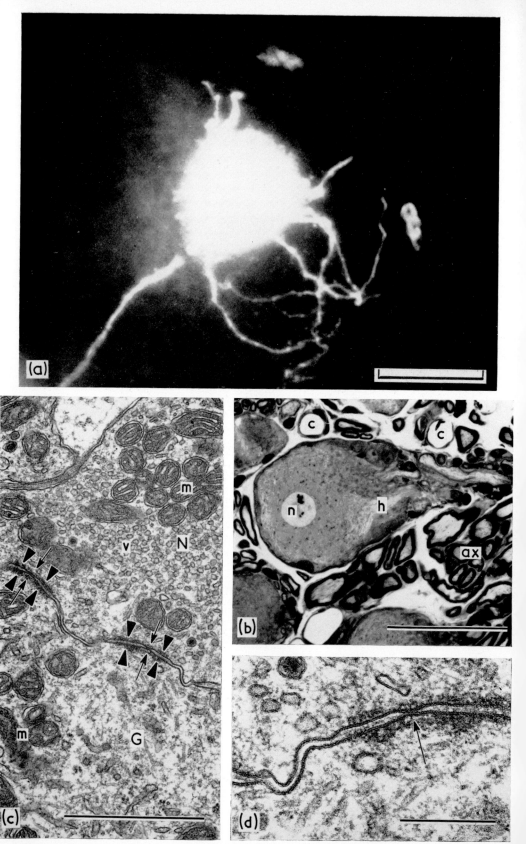

Plate 16

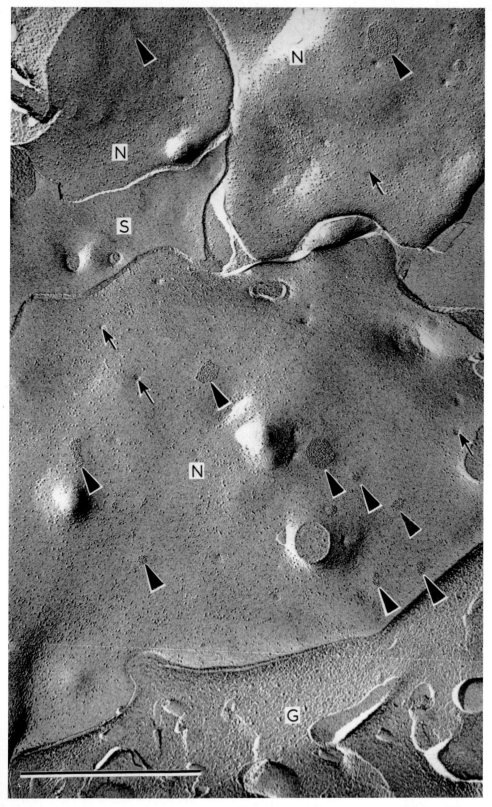

Plate 17

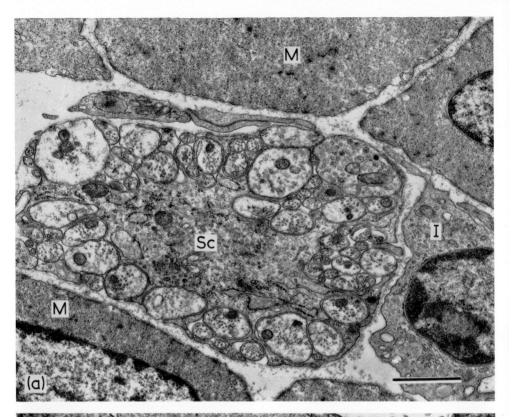

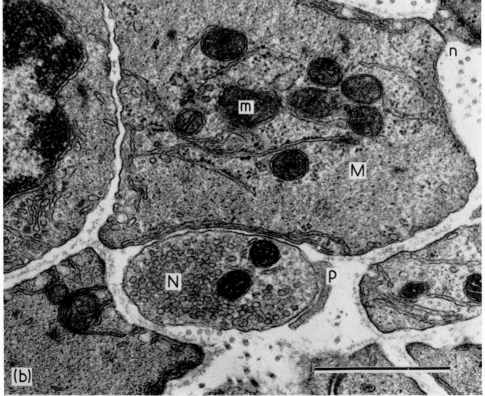

Plate 18

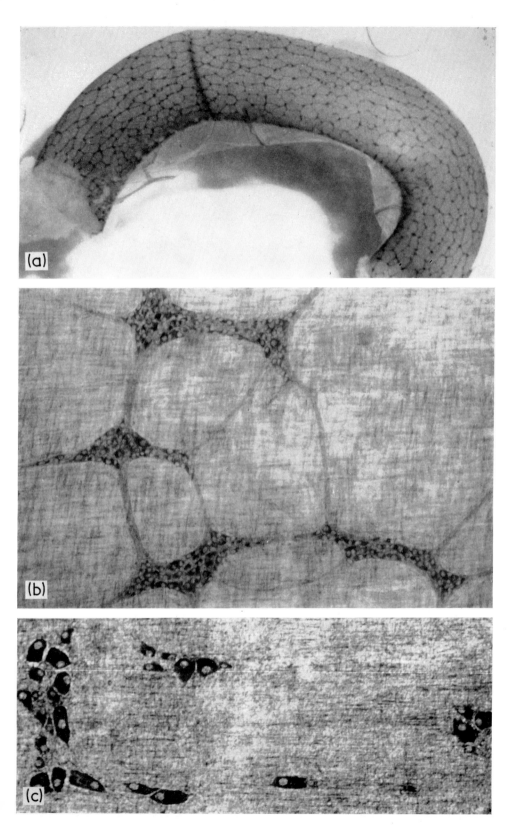

Plate 19

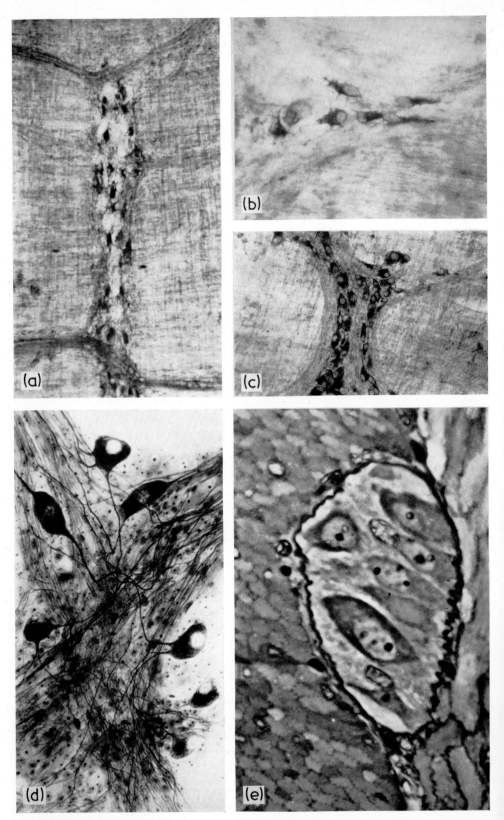

Plate 20

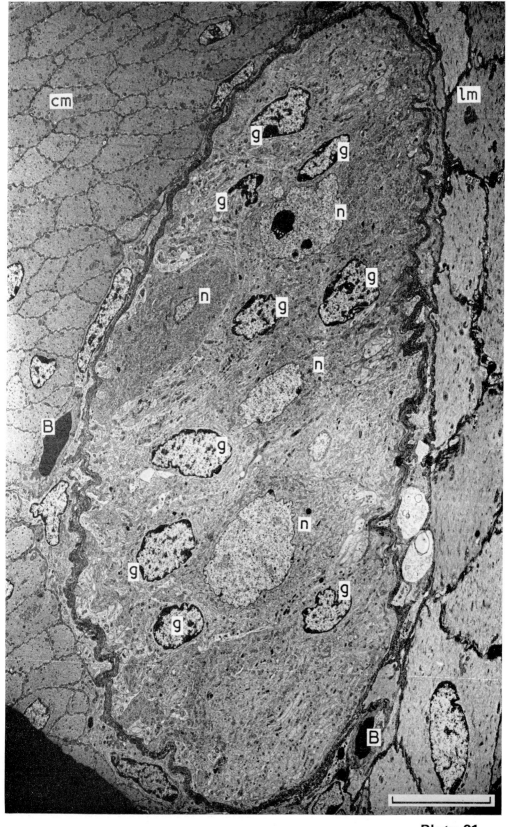

Plate 21

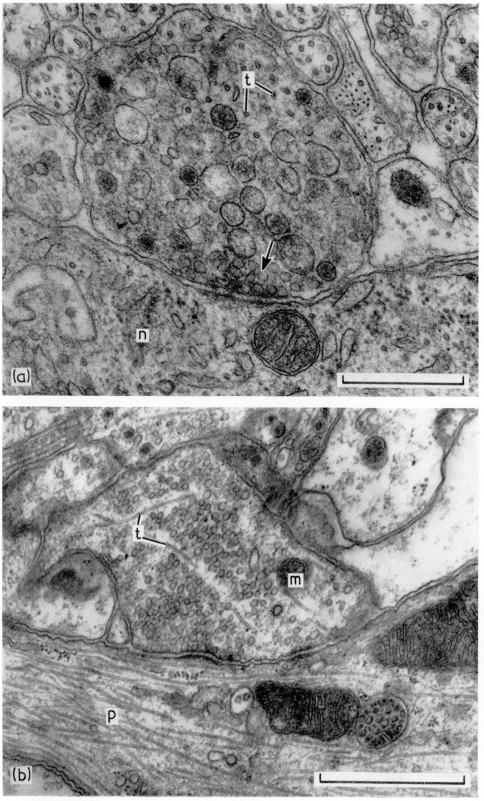

Plate 22

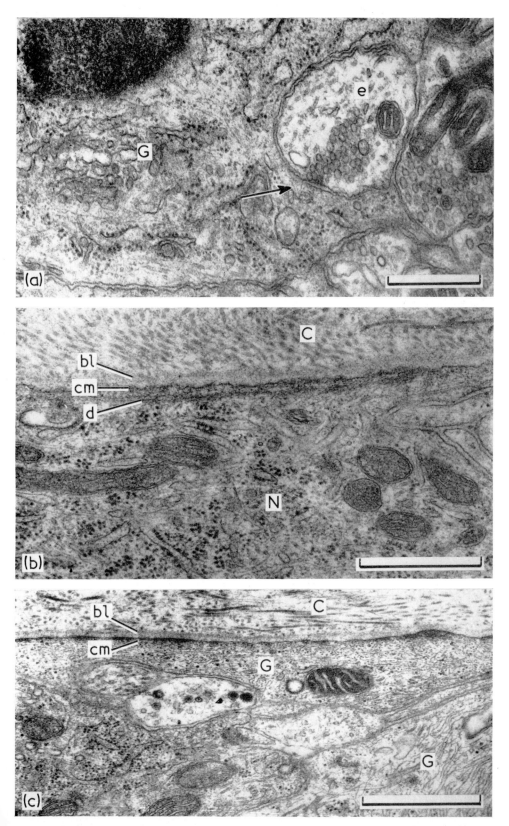

Plate 23

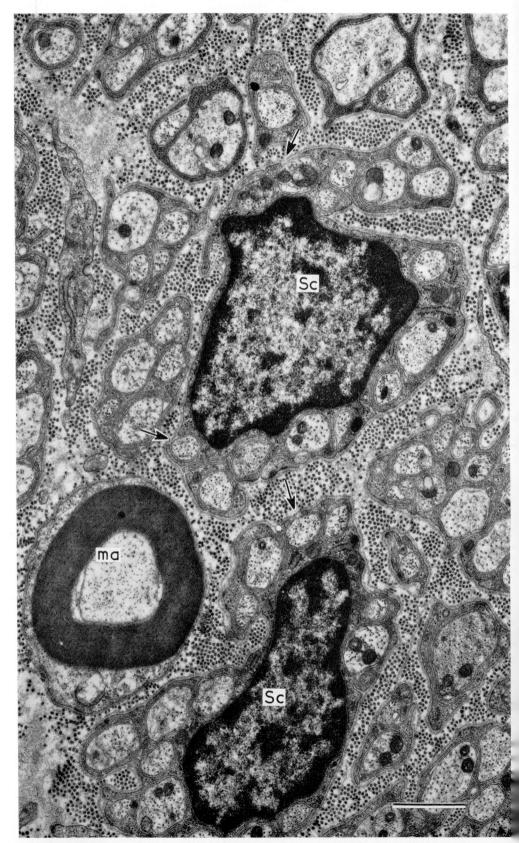

Plate 24

show a few long dendrites (shorter however than those found in sympathetic ganglia) and many intracapsular processes, or pseudo-dendrites, $0\cdot1-2\cdot0\,\mu m$ long and $0\cdot2-0\cdot5\,\mu m$ wide. (See also Plate 16a, showing a ciliary ganglion cell and its numerous and long processes after intracellular injection of a fluorescent dye.) All nerve cell bodies and processes are ensheathed by satellite cells, characterized by abundant bundles of filaments about 10 nm in diameter and often containing a cilium (Watanabe, 1972).

The endings of the preganglionic fibres in the guinea-pig ciliary ganglion contain agranular vesicles 50 nm in diameter and synapse on the cell body and the short intracapsular processes (Watanabe, 1972). It is not yet clear whether the dendrites receive a significant synaptic input. In man, using silver impregnation and Golgi methods, preganglionic fibres are seen to form complicated terminal nests around the great majority of neurons (Slavich, 1932). In the cat most of the neurons are innervated by two or more preganglionic fibres, but B-neurons are exclusively innervated by B fibres and C-neurons by C fibres (Nishi & Christ, 1971). In this species the ratio between preganglionic fibres and ganglion neurons ranges between $1:1\cdot7$ and $1:2\cdot6$ (Wolf, 1941), a ratio which is much higher than that calculated for sympathetic ganglia (see p.39). The synapses between preganglionic fibres and ganglion neurons are cholinergic (nicotinic) (Perry & Talesnik, 1953). A few preganglionic fibres cross the ciliary ganglion, giving off collateral branches to the ganglion cells, and terminate more distally in the accessory ciliary ganglion (Skok, 1973), situated closer to the eyeball along the length of the ciliary nerves.

No adrenergic perikarya are present in the ciliary ganglia of rats, cats, guinea-pigs, goats and monkeys (Ehinger & Falck, 1970b; Watanabe, 1972). Only a few varicose fibres with specific fluorescence for catecholamines are found in mammalian ciliary ganglia (Hamberger et al., 1965), and they are probably perivascular adrenergic fibres (Ehinger & Falck, 1970b; Watanabe, 1972). However, neurons showing specific fluorescence for catecholamines were found in animals that had died under severe stress (Ehinger & Falck, 1970b), and also following Nialamide or L-dopa injection. Without excluding the possibility that a different transmitter is involved, these authors suggest that some neurons in the ciliary ganglion may be adrenergic cells operating with an unusually low concentration of noradrenaline. Suden, Hart, Lindenberg & Marrazzi (1951) showed that the ciliary ganglion of the dog contains adrenergic receptors, and that adrenaline inhibits the transmission through the ganglion; however, their suggestion that adrenergic neurons extensively synapse on ganglion neurons has not been confirmed with histological methods. Wantanabe (1972) found no fluorescent perikarya in the ciliary ganglion of the guinea-pig even after Nialamide and L-dopa injection. Chromaffin (small intensely fluorescent) cells were occasionally observed by Ehinger and Falck (1970) in mammalian ciliary ganglia.

Preganglionic fibres are myelinated and originate in the mesencephalon in the nucleus of Edinger—Westphal (noyau superieur à petites cellules of Cajal). This has multipolar neurons, $15-26 \mu m$ in diameter in the monkey, with few Nissl bodies (Warwick, 1954). In the rat these neurons all show an intense acetylcholinesterase activity (Koelle, 1954). A high density of fine noradrenaline containing nerve endings is seen by fluorescence microscopy around the neurons of the Edinger—Westphal nucleus in the rat (Dahlström, Fuxe, Hillarp & Malmfors, 1964; Fuxe, 1965); fluorescent fibres are absent in the main nuclei of the oculomotor complex. Warwick (1954) observed chromatolysis in the neurons of Edinger—Westphal nucleus and its cephalic prolongation in monkeys 8—16 days after removal of the ciliary ganglion. Similar observations were made by Crouch (1936) in the cat, but only after enucleation of the content of the orbit (and not after excision of the ciliary ganglion only); chromatolysis was also present in a number of neurons of the contralateral side.

6.2   Other parasympathetic ganglia of the head

Other parasympathetic ganglia, besides the ciliary ganglion, are present in the head, but there are relatively few studies of their structure and function. The main ganglia of this group are the otic, spheno-palatine, and submandibular ganglia.

The otic ganglion is situated in man beneath the foramen ovale, and is topographically related to the mandibular nerve. Its preganglionic fibres belong to the glosso-pharyngeal nerve and reach the ganglion by the lesser superficial petrosal nerve. The post-ganglionic fibres mainly join the auriculo-temporal nerve supplying secretory fibres to the parotid. Sympathetic fibres (post-ganglionic) and afferent fibres pass through the ganglion without being interrupted.

The spheno-palatine ganglion is situated in man ventral to the pterygoid canal in close topographical relation with the maxillary nerve. Its preganglionic fibres belong to the facial nerve. Its post-ganglionic fibres provide secretory fibres to the lacrimal gland through many branches and the glands of the nasal cavity, pharynx and mouth.

In man the submandibular ganglion measures one millimetre or less in diameter, is situated under the lingual nerve, usually at an equal distance from the submandibular and sublingual glands. A detailed description of the topography of this ganglion in several mammals can be found in Catania (1924). This author could not find a macro-scopic submandibular ganglion in the dog, while in the goat and the Equides he observed several ganglia constituting a complex sub-mandibular plexus. The preganglionic fibres originate from the facial nerve and reach the ganglion by the chorda tympani and lingual nerves. The post-ganglionic fibres are mainly secretory fibres for the submandibular and sublingual glands.

In methylene blue preparations of the spheno-palatine, otic and submandibular ganglia of sheep the ganglion cells are multipolar, with long, slender, sometimes branching dendrites, some of which have a long course among the neurons (Carpenter, 1912) (see also Plate 15). In the optic ganglion of the rabbit, nerve cells are multi-polar with 3—4 dendrites, which are relatively short and thin and are never seen branching (Olivieri-Sangiacomo, 1969); the cells are quite different in size with the small ones frequently located near the ganglion surface. In all the parasympathetic ganglia of the head in man ganglion neurons lack or have a few long dendrites (Plate 15d), while short, intracapsular processes are consistently present (Müller & Dahl, 1910). In the spheno-palatine and otic ganglia of horse and cattle (Plate 15b), neurons with long dendrites are more common than in human ganglia, but short processes always predominate (Slavich, 1932) and make these neurons readily distinguishable from those of the sympathetic ganglia. A fenestrated apparatus is also common and typical of these ganglion cells. In silver preparations these neurons are said to constitute a population of heterogeneous appearance, unlike the neurons of sympathetic ganglia (Slavich, 1932).

A sheath of satellite cells enwraps each neuron, as in other ganglia. In the otic ganglion of the rabbit Dixon (1966) observed small gaps in such sheaths, where the neuron surface is directly apposed to the

107

basal lamina. Between neurons and satellite cells there are occasional zonulae adherentes (desmosome-like) (Dixon, 1966; Olivieri-Sangiacomo, 1969).

Axo-somatic synapses are extremely rare in the otic ganglion of the rabbit. The great majority of synapses are axo-dendritic, and it seems that they are more numerous on small-sized dendrites and on dendritic spines (Olivieri-Sangiacomo, 1969).

Although the spheno-palatine ganglion and the other ganglia mentioned above are part of the cranial parasympathetic, it is not clear to what extent they can be considered similar to the ciliary ganglion, in spite of the fact that several authors have pointed out morphological similarities (Müller & Dahl, 1910). The spheno-palatine ganglion of the cat for example contains a mixed population of cholinergic and non-cholinergic neurons (as shown histochemically) whereas in the ciliary ganglion all the neurons have an intense acetylcholinesterase activity (Koelle & Koelle, 1959). Adrenergic neurons are absent (Sano et al., 1969). One would expect that the control of the relatively fast contractions of the muscles of the iris and the lens would impose different requirements on the nerve pathways than on those controlling the lacrimal and salivar secretion

Other smaller parasympathetic ganglia are present in several organs of the head. For example, Chorobski and Penfield (1932) described in the macacus monkey a constant small ganglion and scattered ganglion cells in the nerve trunk between the greater superficial petrosal nerve and the carotid plexus. Preganglionic fibres of the 7th cranial nerve end in this ganglion: the post-ganglionic fibres provide the vaso-dilator fibres to the cerebral vessels. (In the cerebral vessels of this species also the sympathetic innervation is provided by intra-cranial ganglia.)

6.3   The ciliary ganglion in birds

The ganglion contains about 6000 neurons in the turkey (Terzuolo, 1951) and pigeon (Marwitt, Pilar & Weakley, 1971) and 3000 in the chicken (Landmesser & Pilar, 1974), subdivided into two populations occupying different parts of the ganglion and differing in the average cell body size (Carpenter, 1911; Terzuolo, 1951; Hess, 1965). The large neurons (ciliary neurons) provide the motor innervation to the striated muscle fibres of the ciliary body and the iris, whereas the

108

small neurons (choroid neurons) form the choroid nerves and innervate the smooth muscle cells of the choroid (Marwitt *et al.*, 1971). In
the turkey the choroid neurons are less numerous, more tightly
packed, and occupy the upper and more distal part of the ganglion
(Terzuolo, 1951); in the pigeon and chicken the choroid neurons represent half of the ganglion cells (Marwitt *et al.*, 1971; Landmesser &
Pilar, 1974). Many myelinated fibres are seen in the ganglion.

Ganglion cells are ensheathed by glial satellite cells. In the ciliary
neurons the sheath consists of 3–20 lamellae of loose, semi-compact
or compact myelin (Hess, 1965); this myelin sheath is provided by
satellite glial cells, many of which are present around each ganglion
cell. All ganglion cells are spherical, have one axon and only short,
intracapsular dendrites (unipolar neurons); the nucleus is often
eccentric (De Lorenzo, 1960; Takahashi & Hama, 1965b). The axon
emerges from the opposite pole of the neuron (hilar pole), which is
usually proximal, i.e. the axon is first directed proximally, and very
close to the preganglionic fibres, then it bends and heads distally
(Lenhossek, 1911; Terzuolo, 1951; Cantino & Mugnaini, 1975)
(Plate 16b).

The characteristic synapse of the avian ciliary ganglion, first described by Carpenter (1911), is formed by a calyciform (cup-shaped)
nerve terminal (De Lorenzo, 1960) around the hilar pole of each ciliary
neuron (Hess, 1965), covering as much as 65 per cent of the ganglion
cell surface in 1-month-old chickens (De Lorenzo, 1966). Later the
calyciform terminal breaks into many short endings which appear
like a brush around the emerging axon. At around six months few
calyces remain, but on the majority of cells numerous, bouton-like
synapses are seen in their stead. Each calyx, and the numerous
boutons which are made as a result of its cleavage, are formed by one
preganglionic fibres only and constitute the only synaptic input to
the perikaryon.

The short intracapsular dendrites originate during post-hatching
life as interdigitations between the nerve endings and the perikarya
(Koenig, 1967). Rarely, the perikaryon protrudes into the calyciform
nerve terminal with a process about 1 μm long and 1·5 μm in diameter, having an expanded end and post-synaptic differentiations on
the lateral aspects of what can be considered a somatic spine (Takahashi & Hama, 1965a; Koenig, 1967). The short dendrites and the
arborization of the preganglionic fibres around the large neurons

109

show a remarkable increase in complexity throughout life (Terzuolo, 1951; Szentágothai, 1964).

In adult chicken ciliary neurons (studied in detail in a recent paper by Cantino and Mugnaini, 1975) the dendrites, about 3 per cell, follow a sinous course, measure about 15 μm in length and 2–8 μm in diameter, and have spine-like evaginations. The axon at its emergence from a typical axon hillock (in this conical portion the cytoplasm lacks conspicuous Nissl bodies) measures up to 8 μm in diameter, then it progressively tapers to 3 μm at about 40 μm from the cell body, where it becomes myelinated and again attains a larger diameter. Before acquiring a myelin sheath the axon show the characteristics of the axonal initial segment: it contains mainly microtubules, which in transverse section appear linked to each other by cross bridges, and has an electron-dense undercoat on the cytoplasmic aspect of the axolemma. An initial segment with these specializations is present in the neurons of the central nervous system (Palay, Sotelo, Peters & Orkard, 1968) but has not been previously observed in autonomic ganglia. The initial segment of the ciliary neurons is smooth-surfaced, receives no synapses and is covered by Schwann cytoplasmic processes. The axon hillock, the dendrites and the rest of the hilar pole of the neuron show spines and receive preganglionic nerve endings (they cover about 85 per cent of the surface area available, 10 per cent being covered by glial profiles and 5 per cent facing directly the extracellular space).

All the nerve endings on the ganglion cells contain agranular veiscles 30–60 nm in diameter, together with a few large granulated vesicles (Plate 16c). Preganglionic nerve terminals store and release acetylcholine, more than half of the total content of acetylcholine, measured by gas-chromatography, being in the presynaptic nerve terminals, and less than a quarter in the ganglion cells (Pilar, Jenden & Campbell, 1973). Acetylcholinesterase activity of medium intensity is histochemically detectable in all ganglion cells (Szentágothai, Donhoffer & Rajkovits, 1954; Taxi, 1965; Koenig, 1965). In 20–30 per cent of the ganglion cells one pole of the cell is capped by an area with intense acetylcholinesterase activity, corresponding to the calyciform terminal.

Between nerve endings and ciliary neurons there are also frequent desmosome-like contacts (puncta adherentia), with symmetrical thickenings of the membrane, no clustering of vesicles, and an intercellular cleft of approximately 30 nm (Takahashi & Hama, 1965b). Gap junctions, or areas where the membrane to membrane distance is reduced to 2−3 nm (sometimes described in the past under different names) have also been observed between nerve endings and ciliary neurons (Takahashi & Hama, 1965b; De Lorenzo, 1966; Koenig, 1967). They are rather rare in electron microscopy sections (Plate 16d), and more readily identified in freeze-fractured preparations where they appear as aggregates of membrane particles 9 nm in diameter (McNutt & Weinstein, 1973) (Plate 17). On the ciliary neurons they appear more numerous than it was thought from ordinary electron micrographs, and it has been calculated that the total area of the gap junctions on one neuron is about $28 \mu m^2$ or 0·7 per cent of the total appositional area at the hilar pole (Cantino & Mugnaini, 1975). They are elongated or round patches, with diameter ranging between a twentieth and a third of a micron.

As regards the choroid neurons, the preganglionic fibre branches some distance from the ganglion cell and ends in numerous small terminal knobs which all contact the cell body (De Lorenzo, 1960; Hess, 1965; Landmesser & Pilar, 1972).

Preganglionic impulses to the large and myelinated ciliary neurons are transmitted by a dual mechanism, electrical and chemical (Fig. 4). The small choroid neurons receive only chemically transmitted impulses. Chemical transmission is cholinergic in both cases, although the mechanisms are not pharmacologically identical, the choroid cells being more susceptible to blocking by hexamethonium that are the ciliary neurons. The two systems of cells appear connected to two separate sets of preganglionic fibres (Merwitt et al., 1971); at 7 ms⁻¹ , the preganglionic fibres for the ciliary neurons conduct twice as fast as those for the choroid neurons (Landmesser & Pilar, 1970). Moreover, the axons (post-ganglionic fibres) of the large neurons are myelinated, whereas those of the small neurons are unmyelinated.

The electrical synaptic transmission in the ciliary neurons of the chick and pigeon has been studied by Martin and Pilar, (1963) and Marwitt et al. (1971) An interesting difference between the two species is that in the chicken, unlike the pigeon, the electrical transmission can occur in both directions (Hess, Pilar & Weakley, 1969). It was first suggested that the close apposition of pre- and post-ganglionic membranes explained the occurrence of electrical transmission (De Lorenzo, 1966), since in several tissues, both nervous

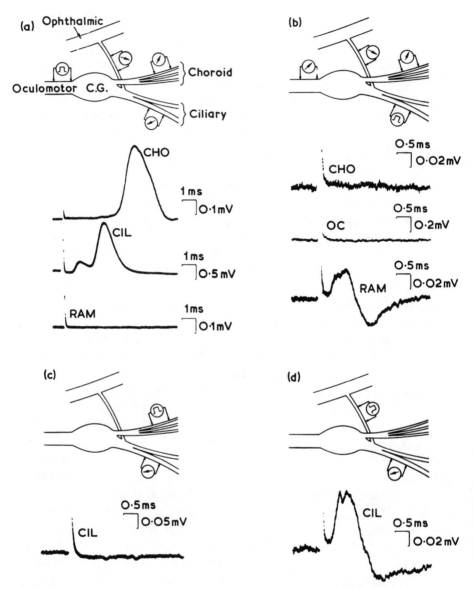

Figure 4. Electrical responses obtained under various recording and stimulation conditions in the pigeon ciliary ganglion. (Reproduced by courtesy of Dr G. Pilar, from Marwitt, Pilar & Weakley, 1971.) All records were obtained from the same preparation. Each diagram shows the position of the stimulating and recording electrodes. (a) Stimulation of the oculomotor nerve produces the characteristic bimodal compound action potential in the ciliary nerves (CIL); a unimodal response with a longer latency is recorded from the choroid nerve (CHO); no

and non-nervous, appostion of junctional membranes has been thought to provide a low resistance pathway for electrical coupling. Hess *et al.*, (1969) have shown, however, that the time of appearance of electrical coupling (before hatching in the chick; during the second post-hatching week in the pigeon) correlates better with the presence of myelin lamellae than with the occurrence of close junctions. Although it is not known to what extent the rather loose myelin around ganglion cells has electrical properties (resistance value) comparable to those of myelin in peripheral nerves, the authors suggest that 'the so-called saltatory conduction of nerve impulses that occurs in myelinated nerve fibres might also occur though the ciliary ganglion. That is, the synaptic apparatus with its myelin envelope may behave as an *internode*.' However, the number of gap junctions, as recently estimated on freeze-fracture preparations, seems to. be sufficient to provide for an effective electrotonic coupling (Cantino & Mugnaini, 1975). The significance of these mixed synapses, *i.e.* synapses capable of chemical and electrical transmission, examples of which are known to occur in the central nervous system (see Pappas & Waxman, 1972), is still obscure..

Preganglionic fibres for the ciliary ganglion originate in the oculomotor nuclear complex of the midbrain, including the so-called accessory nucleus which is thought to be homologous with the Edinger–Westphal nucleus of mammals (Ariens Kappers, Huber & Crosby, 1936). Chromatolysis appears in neurons of the oculomotor nuclear complex of the fowl after excision of the ciliary ganglion (Isomura, 1974). Terzuolo (1951) found degeneration of all preganglionic fibres to ciliary ganglion of the duck after a rather extensive thermocoagulation of the oculomotor nuclear complex.

---

response is obtained from the communicating ramus (RAM) between the ophthalmic branch of the trigeminal nerve and the ciliary nerves. (b) Stimulation of the ciliary nerves produces no response in the oculomotor nerve (OC), i.e. there is no antidromic electrical coupling (this, however, is present in the chicken); the response in the communicating ramus shows that ophthalmic nerve fibres run in the ciliary nerves (this is confirmed in (d)). Stimulation of the ciliary nerves elicits no response in the choroid nerve and vice versa (c), which indicate that axons of the ciliary ganglion neurons do not split to reach both nerves, but travel exclusively either in the ciliary or in the choroid nerve.

Ehinger (1967) found fine varicose non-vascular adrenergic terminals throughout the ganglion in the chick, pigeon and duck. They were particularly numerous in the region of the small (choroid) neurons and occasionally such adrenergic fibres formed a pericellular nest around a ganglion cell, but adrenergic perikarya were absent. Cantino and Mugnaini (1974) confirmed these observations, and found by electron microscopy that adrenergic fibres, whose varicosities are filled with dense-core vesicles, are never in direct contact with the ganglion neurons beneath the glial satellite cells.

6.4   Post-ganglionic fibres

The post-ganglionic fibres of the mammalian ciliary ganglion innervate the ciliary muscle and the muscles of the iris. It is not known whether they also innervate the smooth musculature of the choroid blood vessels. Some of the post-ganglionic fibres, probably most of them, are myelinated for some of their length, although it is not known where they loose their myelin sheaths: by the time they reach their muscles all nerve fibres are unmyelinated. The mean conduction velocity of these fibres in the cat is $3-9\,ms^{-1}$ (Skok, 1973).

In the sphincter pupillae the terminal arborization of the ciliary fibres is very extensive; the fibres are varicose, contain agranular synaptic vesicles about 50 nm in diameter of cholinergic type, and come in close relation with the muscle cells (see p.151). A few endings are also found in the region of the dilator pupillae.

In birds the post-ganglionic fibres issuing from ciliary neurons are myelinated and innervate the striated musculature of the ciliary body and the iris. The axons end in motor endplates the areas of which are very large (especially when compared with the small size of the muscle fibres (diameter $1\cdot5-24\,\mu m$, length $280-1700\,\mu m$)) (Zenker & Krammer, 1967). Unlike the motor endplates of other striated muscles, the post-junctional membrane of these muscle fibres has no fold (Hess, 1966; Zenker & Krammer, 1967) and the axolemma to sarcolemma distance is only $15-20\,nm$ (Zenker & Krammer, 1967). Each neuron innervates about four muscle fibres. The axons contain agranular vesicles about 50 nm in diameter, and some large (55–120 nm) granular vesicles (Zenker & Krammer, 1967).

6.5   Studies on development

According to Hammond and Yntema (1958) in the chick the parasympathetic ganglia of the head arise from the neural crest of the midbrain and anterior hindbrain regions. Other authors have suggested an origin in·common with the corresponding cranial nerves and from the semilunar ganglion (Kuntz, 1914) or from the local mesenchyme (Levi-Montalcini & Amprino, 1946). In the rat differentiation of the ciliary ganglion is already recognizable in embryos of 14 mm (18 mm in human embryos) and preganglionic fibres from the oculomotor nerve are visible in embryos of 17 mm (Hogg, 1964). A quantitative study of the human submandibular ganglion has revealed a decrease in the number of ganglion cells from 12 000 at the 17th week to 6000 at term (Crouse & Cucinotta, 1965). A reduction of 50 per cent is also observed in the neurons of the chick embryo ciliary ganglion between the 9th and 13th day (Landmesser and Pilar, 1974b).

Landmesser and Pilar (1972) have studied the onset of transmission and the development of synapses in the ciliary ganglion of chick embryos, and found that at the earliest stage when transmission occurs through all the neurons (8 days *in ovo*) synaptic contacts recognizable in the electron microscope are very rare; the first synapses, however, formed at the onset of transmission through the ganglion (5 days). At the time of formation of synapses, the neurons send out extensive dendritic processes, which receive the synapses in the form of boutons (Landmesser & Pilar, 1974a). Around the 10th day all these processes are retracted, and the calyciform endings form on the ciliary neurons; later on these are invested by glial cells. During the same period the number of ganglion neurons (in both the ciliary and choroid groups) is reduced to half the original value (Landmesser & Pilar, 1974b). Since cell death occurs at the same time as the formation of peripheral connections with the iris musculature, the authors suggest that the neurons which die do so because they have failed to form adequate peripheral connections.

6.6   Axotomy and other experiments on the ciliary ganglion

Preganglionic denervation (de-centralization) of the ciliary ganglion of birds causes a great fall in the acetylcholine content of the nerve terminals as might be expected, but the acetylcholine in the ganglion

115

cells and in the post-ganglionic nerves also falls to as little as one tenth of the control values. The acetylcholine levels of the ganglion cells tend to return to their control values upon re-innervation (after about 15 days) (an example of a trans-synaptic orthograde influence) (Pilar *et al.*, 1973). The section of the oculomotor nerve causes all the preganglionic terminals to disappear (Terzuolo, 1951; Pilar *et al.*, 1973). On the other hand, no degenerating fibres are found in the ciliary nerves after section of the oculomotor nerve, i.e. all fibres from the oculomotor nerve which reach the ganglion end in it (Terzuolo, 1951). The number of neurons in the ciliary ganglion of adult turkeys is reduced to one half, or less, of that on the control side, 3—8 months after de-centralization (Terzuolo, 1951). The average neuronal size also decreases, but this change is reversible and disappears when regenerated fibres re-innervate the ganglion cells (Terzuolo, 1951). The effects of de-centralization of the ciliary ganglion appear more noticeable than those observed in sympathetic ganglia (p.72).

In some ganglion cells of the pigeon ciliary ganglion post-synaptic membrane thickenings are still visible when presynaptic terminals have disappeared some 3—5 days after denervation (Pilar *et al.*, 1973), and post-synaptic structures were clearly seen by Koenig (1967) as late as 12 days after preganglionic denervation in the chick. Such structures may correspond to the spots of intense acetylcholinesterase activity seen on the surface of ciliary ganglion neurons after preganglionic nerve section (Taxi, 1965). The regeneration of the preganglionic fibres to the ciliary ganglion of adult pigeons is highly specific, so that each group of cells, ciliary and choroid, is re-innervated by its original class of preganglionic fibres (Landmesser & Pilar, 1970).

7 INTRAMURAL GANGLIA

7.1 The intramural ganglia

Ganglia situated inside the same organ that they innervate are characteristically associated with the alimentary tract and constitute the 'enteric nervous system' (Langley, 1921). (Note 7.1) The intramural ganglia lie so close to their target tissues that they are directly exposed to the effects of the mechanical activity which they themselves control. Intramural ganglion neurons are therefore unique among the mammalian neurons in that they are exposed to enormous mechanical stress and deformation during the motor activity of the intestinal wall.

The ganglia are coextensive with the smooth musculature of the alimentary tract, including that of the biliary extrahepatic pathways. They are connected by nerve strands of various thickness, forming meshworks or plexuses whose pattern is characteristic of the various portions of the alimentary canal and varies from species to species. There are two ganglionated plexuses, one situated between the two muscle layers of the muscularis externa (myenteric or Auerbach's plexus), the other situated in the submucosa (submucous or Meissner's plexus) (Note 7.2); they are interconnected and send branches to the muscle layers, to the blood vessels and to the mucosa. The ganglia are thin and spread with their major surface parallel to the intestinal outer surface (Plate 19a). In the rat and guinea-pig (when the gut is relaxed) they are one-cell thick; when the longitudinal musculature is peeled off *in toto* and mounted as a lamina (Plate 19b, c), the myenteric plexus usually remains attached to it and appears as a monolayer of ganglion cells and nerve processes, and the neuronal circuit can be imagined to be laid down almost in two dimensions only. The two plexuses extend as uninterrupted structures from the lower part of the oesophagus to the anal canal. Each ganglion, containing from a few to tens of neurons (Plate 19b), is sheathed by a thin collagen capsule which does not penetrate into the ganglion nor around individual ganglion cells (Taxi, 1965). Neurons can also occur singly, apposed to an interganglionic connecting strand (Stöhr, 1932).

7.2   Number and size of neurons

The number of neurons in the intestinal intramural ganglia is considerable, but varies from species to species, with different densities of neurons per unit surface in the various segments of the alimentary canal (Table 7.1). In the myenteric plexus of the guinea-pig ileum about 7500 neurons have been counted in the ganglia within a region corresponding to $1 cm^2$ of serosal surface (Irwin, 1931; Matsuo, 1934). Higher values were found in the colon (15—19 000), rectum (18 000) and pyloric part of the stomach (20 000). In the caecum, neurons are nearly three times more numerous beneath the taeniae than between the taeniae. In the rat it has been calculated that nearly two million neurons are present within the wall of the alimentary canal (Gabella, 1971). In the two plexuses of the cat small intestine there can be as many as 6 million neurons (Sauer & Rumble, 1946). According to the latter authors the submucous plexus of the cat small intestine has two to three times more neurons than the myenteric plexus; in the guinea-pig ileum I found that the myenteric plexus has about twice as many neurons as the sub mucous plexus.

Although quantitative studies have been done on few species only, from them and other qualitative data it appears that the packing density of intramural neurons is higher in species of small body size, whereas the average perikaryon size is larger in larger species.

The range of neuron sizes in the enteric ganglia is wider than in other autonomic ganglia (Gabella, 1971). In the rat the range is widest in the myenteric plexus of caecum, where a number of very large neurons are visible; in the ileum there are fewer large neurons and there is a large population of small neurons, which were interpreted as being cells capable of further development in adult animals. The neurons of the submucous plexus of the small intestine are on average smaller and less variable in size than those of the myenteric plexus (Hill, 1927; Gabella, 1971); in the latter the small neurons are more abundant in the part of the gut near the mesenteric attachment (Leaming & Cauna, 1961; Maslennikova, 1962; Gabella, 1971). In the frog intestine, on the other hand, the large neurons are found only along the line of attachment of the mesentery; neurons

118

Table 7.1

Number of neurons in the myentric plexus of various portions of the alimentary tract in several species. Figures are number of neurons per cm² of outer surface of the organ.

Species	Region of alimentary tract	Neurons cm⁻²	Staining method	References
guinea pig	oesophagus	1 370	Methylene blue ('spread' preparations)	Irwin (1931)
	stomach (cardia)	3 500		
	(pylorus)	20 000		
	duodenum	10 000		
	ileum	7 500		
	caecum			
	(beneath taenia)	12 000		
	(between taenia)	4 500		
	colon	15 000		
		19 000		
	sigmoid	17 000		
	rectum	18 000		
guinea pig	oesophagus	1 300	Methylene blue ('spread' preparations)	Matsuo (1934)
	stomach (pylorus)	16 500		
	duodenum (upper)	9 300		
	(middle)	98 000		
	ileum	7 200		
	caecum	4 100		
	colon	14 800		
	sigmoid	14 800		
	rectum	16 000		

Species	Region of alimentary tract	Neurons cm^{-2}	Staining method	References
monkey	stomach (cardia)	2 500	Methylene blue ('spread' preparations)	Ohkubo (1936a)
	(fundus)	1 100		
	(pylorus)	3 500		
	duodenum	1 700		
	jejunum	2 700		
	ileum	2 400		
	caecum	1 300		
	colon	1 400		
	rectum	3 500		
guinea pig	stomach (cardia)	2 200	Methylene blue ('spread preparations)	Ohkubo (1936b)
	(body)	9 500		
	(pylorus)	16 250		
	duodenum	6 700		
	ileum	5 300		
	colon	12 500		
	rectum	15 600		
cat	duodenum	49 081	Thionine (sections)[1]	Sauer and Rumble (1946)
	ileum	15 411		
dog	ileum	7 786	Thionine (sections)[2]	Filogamo and Vigliani (1954)
guinea pig	ileum	1 421	Toluidine blue ('spread' preparations)[3]	Tafuri (1957)
	caecum	929		
	colon	3 557		

Animal	Region	Count	Method	Reference
mouse	ileum	2 960	Toluidine blue ('spread' preparations)[3]	Tafuri and De Almeida Campos (1958)
	caecum	5 020		
	large intestine	9 080		
brown trout (Salmo trutta)	oesophagus	2 500	Methylene blue ('spread' preparations)	Burnstock (1959)
	stomach	5 100		
		11 600		
	duodenum	18 000		
	ileum	11 000		
		15 900		
cat	duodenum	12 170	Bielschowski (tangential sections)[4]	Leaming and Cauna (1961)
rabbit	duodenum (mes.)	3 500	Methylene blue	Maslennikova (1962)
	(antimes.)	2 280		
	jejunum (mes.)	2 900		
	(antimes.)	2 088		
	ileum (mes.)	2 500		
	(antimes.)	2 000		
	caecum	1 760		
	rectum (mes.)	2 940		
	(antimes.)	2 840		
	anus	2 640		
rat	small intestine	9 405	Tetrazolium stain ('spread' preparations)[5]	Gabella (1971)

[1] About 45 000 neurons were counted (from 5 cats).   [2] About 23 000 neurons were counted (from 3 dogs).
[3] The actual figures given in this paper are one hundred times bigger, due to an error in the transformation of square surfaces. The counts were carried out on a total surface of 0·011 cm² (guinea pig) and 0·015 cm² (mouse).
[4] The counts were carried out on a total surface of 0·067 cm².
[5] The counts were carried out on a total surface of 11·60 cm² (from 3 rats). The standard deviation was ± 677.

121

are scattered along the meshes of the myenteric plexus, and do not form clear-cut ganglia (Gunn, 1951).

In conditions of intestinal hypertrophy proximal (oral) to an experimental stenosis a large increase in the neuron sizes and an increase in the number of the readily stainable ganglion cells occur in rat (Benninghoff, 1951) and dog (Filogamo & Vigliani, 1954). A three-fold increase in the average neuron size is found in the myenteric plexus of the caecum of rats grown in germ-free conditions (these produce a more than six-fold increase in volume of the caecum; Dupont, Jervis & Sprinz, 1965).

An increase in the morphological complexity of neurons of the human intestine occurs throughout life, but senescence changes are said to be less prominent than in paravertebral ganglia (Cavazzana & Borsetto, 1948; Lorenz, 1962). Accumulation of lipofuscin pigment is usually present in myenteric neurons of guinea-pig of about one year, and in guinea-pigs over two year old there is a remarkable reduction in the number of neurons (Plate 20a, b).

7.3 Cell types

According to Dogiel's (1896) classification there are two types of neurons in the enteric ganglia (mainly of man and guinea-pig) stained by methylene blue: type I, with one long axon and many short dendrites anastomosing with those issuing from other neurons, are motor neurons; type II, with long processes only (the long branched dendrites ending as sensory receptors, the axon arborizing within the ganglion), are sensory neurons. Later (Dogiel, 1899) a type III neuron, with dendrites of medium length that branch around other ganglion cells was described. Many authors working with silver impregnation methods have elaborated and modified but substantially accepted this classification (e.g. Müller, 1921; Lawrentjew, 1931; Stöhr, 1932; Gunn, 1959, 1968). Others have denied the validity of Dogiel's classification (Johnson, 1925; Kuntz, 1922; Schofield, 1968). Kuntz (1922) thought that Dogiel's cells do not represent distinct cell types since all the morphological gradations are found between them. Hill (1927) recognized Dogiel's cell types in the intramural plexuses of guinea-pig, but she also considered type II to be motor; the enteric neurons would constitute a purely motor system, part of the parasympathetic pathway, whilst sympathetic fibres end directly on the muscle cells. The latter view was widely held until the development of the fluorescence histochemical method for detection of adrenergic fibres (see p.15). In the oesophagus the proximal part of the stomach and the terminal rectum of the dog only cells of type I were found by Lawrentjew (1931); type I cells predominated in the distal part of the stomach, in the duodenum and in the rest of the rectum, whereas type II predominated over type I in the jejunum and ileum. In the colon and caecum type I and II neurons were in approximately equal numbers. Preganglionic parasympathetic fibres (from the vagus and the nervi erigentes) were found associated only with type I neurons. A similar arrangement was described in the cow (Sokolowa, 1931). According to Jabonero (1953) the sympathetic post-ganglionic fibres synapse only on type II neurons, and the preganglionic parasympathetic fibres only on type I neurons. Gunn (1959, 1968) found that the enteric neurons of cat, sheep and goat conform to Dogiel's types, but within each type a distinction between small and large neurons was introduced; it was suggested that the large ones represented an intrinsic enteric nervous system developed *in situ*, which, independent of extrinsic nerves, is responsible for the myenteric reflex activity. Schofield (1968) suggests that a better classification of enteric neurons could be based on the number of their processes.

In spite of a great deal of work done on this problem, a clear-cut classification of intramural neurons has not yet emerged. Cells responding to Dogiel's description, for example, are visible in the gut of some species; the same ganglia, however, show neurons which do not fit in either category, or are too small to be classified or are refractory to the silver impregnation. Species variations were widely overlooked by those who worked on this problem, and the pitfalls of silver impregnation were obscured by the visual appeal of some silver preparations. It is, however, certain that the intestinal intramural neurons constitute a heterogeneous population, in term of size of neurons, types and patterns of cell processes (Plate 20d), types of nerve endings; electrophysiological studies have shown the existence of different neuronal types (Nishi & North, 1973; Hirst, Holman & Spence, 1974), and models of the nerve circuit are being developed, involving inhibitory and excitatory neurons, interneurons and sensory neurons (for example Hirst and McKirdy, 1974). However, morphological studies have so far failed to exactly localize and identify these different categories of neurons.

7.4   Structure of neurons, nerve processes, glial cells

In the electron microscope the intramural neurons show the ultra-structural features common to most neurons. The nuclei are large, often eccentrically placed, with a prominent nucleolus and finely granular karyoplasm. Ribosomes, smooth and rough endoplasmic reticulum and mitochondria are well in evidence in the cytoplasm; microtubules and bundles of neurofilaments are also common.

Since the connective tissue does not penetrate within the ganglia, these are made by ganglion cell bodies embedded in a thick neuropil formed by their dendrites, by axons extrinsic and intrinsic in origin, and by glial cells and their processes. The ganglia appear as compact structures where the only 'extra-cellular' space is a gap of 20–30 nm between adjacent structures (Fig. 5). At first glance an electron micrograph of the myenteric plexus might be taken for a section of an area of the central nervous system. Each ganglion is invested by a basal lamina, around which bundles of collagen fibrils and processes of fibroblasts and interstitial cells are visible (Plate 21).

The surface of ganglion cell bodies is: (a) partly occupied by the emerging processes; (b) partly covered by glial cells; (c) partly lying directly at the surface of the ganglion; (d) partly covered by synaptic endings impinging upon it (see Section 7.5). Although all these are permanent contacts, which are seen in ganglia in contracted or relaxed intestine, the mechanical activity of the intestinal wall alters the shape of ganglia and it is probable that when this occurs there is extensive readjustment in the shape of neurons and of the elements of the neuropil.

Long dendrites often originating as a continuation of the pole of a neuron, run preferentially at the surface of the ganglia. Some neurons, and some of the larger dendrites, have a number of short finger-like evaginations (pseudodendrites). Sites of origin of the axons, either from the cell body or from a dendrite, have not yet been identified in electron microscopy.

Glial cells are numerous in the intestinal plexuses (Plate 21). In the guinea-pig and rat they outnumber the ganglion cells by about three to one. They cover part of the surface of the ganglion cells and penetrate among various axonal and dendritic processes, moulding their shape on the spaces left among them. Nuclei of glial cells are smaller than those of neurons, show indentations and large patches of dense

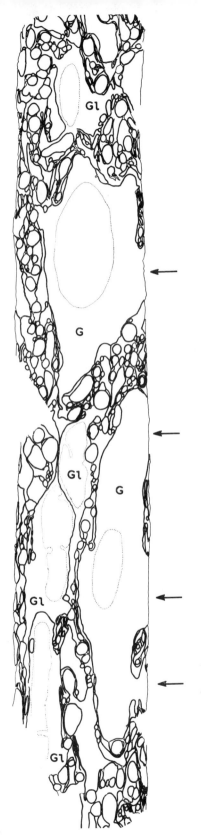

Figure 5. Profiles of nerve cell bodies, glial cells and cell processes outlined from a montage of electron micrographs. Ganglion of the myenteric plexus of the rat stomach. Several glial cells (Gl) and two ganglion cells (G) are visible. The latter have parts of their surface (arrows) lying at the very surface of the ganglion, immediately underneath basal lamina and collagen fibrils.

material attached to the inner side of the nuclear envelop. The cytoplasm of glial cells is rich in ribosomes, endoplasmic reticulum, microtubules and bundles of gliofilaments; there is often a pair of centrioles, sometimes with a cilium. In spite of obvious structural differences among the numerous glial cells of the intramural plexuses, these cells have not yet been classified in different types. Some glial cells are, so to speak, wrapped around a nerve cell and cover a large part of its surface. Other glial cells have so many processes (particularly rich in gliofilaments) that the shape of the cell body is ill-defined. Glial processes are very irregular in size and shape; some of them reach the ganglion surface and lie for some length directly under the basal lamina. In these areas patches of electron-dense material line the inner side of the glial cell membrane and gliofilaments seem to merge in them (Gabella, 1972).

In the rat and guinea-pig ileum a substantial part of the surface of some perikarya and of some large dendrites has no glial covering and lies directly under the basal lamina. Some neurons are exposed at both the surfaces of a ganglion, i.e. towards the circular and the longitudinal musculature. In these areas the plasma membrane appears thicker and more electron dense. An ill-defined band of electron-dense material, 40–80 nm thick and showing a thick microfibrillar texture, is situated in the cytoplasm about 30 nm beneath the plasma membrane (Gabella, 1972) (Plate 23a). The significance of these unique features of intramural neurons — naked surface and corresponding sub-surface dense lamina — is still obscure.

7.5 Nerve endings

With few exceptions (see p.130) the intramural neurons are not adrenergic, but they receive abundant supply of adrenergic fibres (containing noradrenaline), mainly from the prevertebral ganglia.

The sites of termination of adrenergic fibres in the alimentary canal, which had been interpreted in contrasting ways when studied by means of silver impregnation methods, have been clarified by the fluorescence microscopy method for catecholamines. Numerous adrenergic fibres are seen by fluorescence microscopy in the myenteric and submucous plexuses (Norberg, 1964; Jacobowitz, 1965). Individual varicose fluorescent fibres can be followed in the connecting meshes, while in the ganglia they form thick networks, sometimes in the form of pericellular nests, and they cannot be followed as individual fibres (Plate 5c). A similar distribution of adrenergic fibres has been seen throughout the entire length of the alimentary canal by using whole mount preparations of the longitudinal muscle with myenteric plexus and of other layers of the intestinal wall (Gabella & Costa, 1967). A wealth of histochemical studies have been published on the distribution of adrenergic fibres in the intestinal plexuses (Baumgarten, 1967, on human intestine; Bennett, 1969, on avian gizzard; Read and Burnstock, 1968, on large intestine in several vertebrates; Silva, Ross and Osborne, 1971, on cat ileum; Furness, 1970, on guinea-pig ileum; Costa and Gabella, 1971, on guinea-pig alimentary tract; and others). The submucous plexus of the stomach in rat (Muryobayashi, Mori, Fujwara & Shimamoto, 1968), cat, guinea-pig and rabbit (Furness & Costa, 1974) appears to be lacking adrenergic fibres.

In the electron microscope adrenergic nerve endings, identified by the presence of dense core vesicles (see Section 3.3), are seen within the ganglia of the myenteric plexus (large intestine of rhesus, guinea-pig and man: Baumgarten et al., 1970; guinea-pig: Gabella, 1972). In the guinea-pig ileum adrenergic endings are seen to synapse on perikarya and processes of ganglion cells, with the characteristic junctional specialization: clustering of vesicles, pre-synaptic dense projection and sub-synaptic thickening (Gabella, 1972) (Plate 13a, b). In agreement with the observations in fluorescence microscopy, the majority of the neurons of the myenteric plexus of guinea-pig ileum seem to receive adrenergic synapses. It is however not known whether each varicosity of the long terminal part of the axon is in synaptic contact with a ganglion neuron. In the myenteric ganglia of the large intestine of the monkey, guinea-pig and man, no membrane specializations were observed at sites of close contacts of adrenergic endings with ganglion cells (Baumgarten et al., 1970), whereas a few were found in the submucous plexus of the rat duodenum (Wong et al., 1974). In the last two papers experiments with false transmitters are reported, which show uptake of 5-hydroxydopamine followed by increase in the numbers and electron density of small granulated vesicles, and uptake of 6-hydroxydopamine followed by degeneration of the presumed adrenergic endings. Uptake of tritiated noradrenaline is shown by some endings of the intramural plexuses (Marks, Samorajski & Webster, 1962; Taxi and Droz, 1966b); the labelling, however, is less intense than it would be expected on the basis of fluorescence microscopy observations. Ross and Gershon (1970) failed to observe any effect of 6-hydroxydopamine on nerve endings synapsing in the myenteric plexus of guinea-pig. It would be interesting to know whether to adrenergic endings which are deeply embedded within the intramural ganglia are less accessible to exogenous drugs than other adrenergic endings.

Histochemical (Norberg, 1964; Jacobowitz, 1965), cytofluorimetric (Ahlman and Enerbäck, 1974), and biochemical studies (Juorio & Gabella, 1974) have shown that the transmitter of the sympathetic fibres to the myenteric plexus of the guinea-pig is noradrenaline, in agreement with the histochemical observation above quoted, carried out in a number of mammalian species (Note 7.4). After extrinsic denervation all fluorescent fibres (including those associated with the smooth musculature, the blood vessels and the mucosa, disappear (Jacobowitz, 1965; Furness, 1969) and, in the guinea-pig ileum, the noradrenaline content falls close to zero (Juorio & Gabella, 1974).

The adrenergic synapses of the gut are considered to be inhibitory, since catecholamines inhibit acetylcholine output from the myenteric plexus of the guinea-pig both in resting conditions and after stimulation (Schaumann, 1958; Paton & Vizi, 1969; Kosterlitz, Lydon & Watt, 1970), and noradrenaline reduces the amplitude of evoked potentials (Holman, Hirst & Spence, 1972; Nishi & North, 1973). Evidence has been obtained showing that noradrenaline depresses intestinal activity by inhibiting the intramural nerve network (McDougal & West, 1954; Kosterlitz & Robinson, 1957; Paton & Vizi, 1969).

Another type of nerve ending synapsing on myenteric neurons contains a heterogeneous population of agranular and granular vesicles (Baumgarten et al., 1970, in the large intestine of the rhesus monkey, guinea-pig and man; Gabella, 1972, in the small intestine of the guinea-pig) (Plate 22a): most of the vesicles are about 100 nm in diameter and are filled with a material of medium electron density around which there is no clear-cut halo. In the guinea-pig, ileum nerve endings of this type (which were labelled HGV, heterogeneous granular vesicle containing endings) synapse on ganglion cell bodies and dendrites, and, characteristically, adjacent to the presynaptic membrane only agranular vesicles about 50 nm in diameter are found (Gabella, 1972). These endings do not degenerate following extrinsic denervation of the ileum, and are therefore considered of intrinsic

PLATES 1–24

Plate 1 (a–f). Various aspects of the human superior cervical ganglion, silver impregnated with the Gros method. (Courtesy of Professor R. Amprino.) Note the variety in size, arborization and length of the cell processes. (a and b): 15 year old woman, Marker: 50 μm; (c): 42 year old man, Marker: 100 μm; (d) 81 year old man; (e): 35 year old woman; (f) 81 year old woman, Marker: 50 μm.

Plate 2. Superior cervical ganglion of the rat.
(a) and (b). Plastic sections stained with toluidine blue. In (a) part of the fibrous capsule of the ganglion is visible (C). In the centre a neuron with large, vesicular nucleus, shows an accumulation of pigment granules. In (b) nuclei of satellite cells are indicated by arrows. M is a mast cell and B are blood vessels. Marker: 10μm.
(c) Electron micrograph showing parts of three ganglion neurons (G). N is a neuron nucleus poor in electron-dense material. In the cytoplasm the most prominent organelles are mitochondria (m), and stacks of cisternae of rough endoplasmic reticulum (Nissl bodies, n) and lysosomes (ly). p is a cell process. Lamellae of satellite cell cytoplasm (s) invest the neurons and the nuclei of two satellite cells are also visible (S). In the upper part of the figure the extracellular space is increased due to a slight shrinkage of the ganglion cells. Collagen fibrils are present in the extracellular space. (Courtesy of Dr Margaret Matthews.) Marker: 5 μm.

Plate 3. (a) Superior cervical ganglion of a rat (fixed by immersion in glutaraldehyde). A preganglionic nerve ending synapses on a cell process containing ribosomes, neurofilaments (nf) and a large collection of electron-lucent vesicles (v). An ill-defined band of electron-dense material lies beneath the post-synaptic membrane (sub-synaptic bar, sb); m, mitochondrion. Marker: 0·5 μm.
(b) Small mesenteric nerve of a guinea-pig. The capsule of this small nerve consists of epineurium (ep), a single perineural lamella (pe), within which collagen fibres of the endoneurium (en) can be seen. Sh, Schwann cell process; a, axons; f, fibroblast-like cell. Note that the collagen fibrils of the endoneurium are smaller than those of the epineurium (and the ordinary connective tissue). Marker: 1 μm.

Plate 4. (a) Superior cervical ganglion of a rat. A large dendrite invested by satellite cell processes. (s) indicates a synapse of a preganglionic nerve ending. Note the prominent post-synaptic thickening beneath which are a few vesicles and a row of electron-dense particles. The dendrite has a large collection of agranular vesicles (v) and a few mitochondria (m). (Courtesy of Dr M. Matthews.) Marker: 1 μm. (b–d) Superior cervical ganglion of a rat (fixed by immersion in glutaraldehyde). (b) A specialized symmetrical contact between two dendrites. The dendrites contain microtubules, neurofilaments and mitochondria. Marker: 0·5 μm. (c) A dendrite with a large number of vesicles which lie directly underneath its surface. The cell membrane appears thickened and has some dense projections; it lies directly underneath the basal lamina without any satellite cell sheath intervening. Marker: 0·5 μm. (d) A dendrite with a spine-like projection upon which a small preganglionic nerve ending synapses. Marker: 0·5 μm.

Plate 5 (a—b). Rat superior cervical ganglion photographed in fluorescence microscopy (Falck-Hillarp method for catecholamines). (Courtesy of Dr Lars Olson, from Olson & Malmfors, 1970.) (a) The nerve cell bodies are closely packed together and almost all of them show specific fluorescence, although with varying intensities. A group of intensely fluorescent cells is visible at the top left. Marker: 200 μm. (b) Among the densely packed fluorescent ganglion cells a few varicose fluorescent fibres are visible. Marker: 100 μm. (c) An individual varicose fibre in the mesentery of a guinea-pig, photographed in fluorescence microscopy (Falck-Hillarp method). Note that the varicosities at the very end of the fibre are larger and have a brighter fluorescence. Marker: 50 μm.

Plate 6 (a and b). Cat superior cervical ganglion stained for the histochemical detection of acetylcholinesterase (Koelle method). Markers: 100 μm. (Courtesy of Professor J. Taxi, from Taxi, 1965.) (a) Normal ganglion showing only few positive cells (arrows); most of the acetylcholinesterase activity is in the tissue among the ganglion cells. (b) The ganglion 8 days after section of the preganglionic nerve fibres. The activity which was present among the ganglion cells has disappeared (and it can therefore be assumed that it was localized in the preganglionic fibres). The activity in the ganglion cells appears more intense than in control ganglia. (c) A ganglion of the myenteric plexus of the rabbit ileum, photographed in fluorescence microscopy (Falck-Hillarp method). (From Gabella & Costa, 1969.) Nerve cells are not fluorescent; they appear as round dark areas within the ganglion, and are surrounded by a thick network of varicose fluorescent fibres. Size and brightness of varicosities vary within and between nerve fibres. Marker: 100 μm.

Plate 7. Rat superior cervical ganglion (Courtesy of Dr Margaret Matthews. (a) from Matthews & Ostberg, 1973; (b) from Matthews & Raisman, 1969). (a) A group of chromaffin cells (Ch) 14½ hours after section of the cervical sympathetic trunk. Arrows indicate degenerating preganglionic axons. d is an attachment area between apposed membranes of two chromaffin cells; Sc is the nucleus of a Schwann cell; e is an area of the surface of a chromaffin cell separated only by a basal lamina from the interstitial space. Marker: 5 μm. (b) An efferent synapse from a chromaffin cell body onto a spine-like projection arising from a dendrite. The chromaffin cell contains numerous dense-cored vesicles. In this example the specialization of the post-junctional membrane is particularly prominent (arrow). Marker: 0·1 μm.

Plate 8. Lumber sympathetic ganglion of a frog (*Rana temporaria*) (fixed by immersion in glutaraldehyde). (a) Plastic section stained with toluidine blue. G, ganglion cells (G′ shows an eccentric nucleus); P, pigment cells; C, capsule of the ganglion; B, blood vessel; my, a myelinated nerve, 300x. (b) Tangential section through a ganglion neuron (g) and a satellite cell (S). Ribosomes (r), microtubules (t), mitochondria (m), large granular vesicles (v) and sacs of endoplasmic reticulum are present in the ganglion neuron. The satellite cell show large numbers of gliofilaments, microtubules, sacs of endoplasmic reticulum (e), ribsomes and micropinicytotic vesicles (p). Marker: 1 μm.

Plate 9. Lumbar sympathetic ganglion of a frog (*Rana temporaria*) (fixed by immersion in glutaraldehyde). Two preganglionic nerve endings synapse on a ganglion neuron (G). The surface of the neuron has a number of finger-like projections (arrows). The nerve endings are packed with mitochondria (m), small agranular vesicles (v), large granular vesicles (d) and glycogen granules (g). Microtubules (t) are sometimes visible among the vesicles. A satellite cell (S) of complicated shape invests nerve endings and ganglion-cell, but spaces are left between its lamellar processes (*). Marker: 1 μm.

Plate 10. Autonomic ganglia of adult chickens. Histochemical detection of catecholamines in fluorescence microscopy. (Courtesy of Dr Terry Bennett. (a–c) from Bennett & Malmfors, 1970; (d) from Bennett *et al.*, 1973). Markers: 100 μm. (a) Sympathetic ganglion of the abdominal paravertebral chain. Ganglion cells of different sizes and fluorescence intensities are present. There are also a few non-fluorescent ganglion cells (NFG) and a cluster of chromaffin (small intensely fluorescent) cells (SFC). (b) Same tissue as in (a). Processes of ganglion cells tentatively identified as axons (A) and dendrites (P) display a bright catecholamine fluorescence. A meshwork of brightly fluorescent terminal fibres (T) is present. (c) Same tissue as (a). Processes identified as axons and dendrites display specific fluorescence. Non-fluorescent ganglion cells are also present (NFG). (d) Myenteric plexus of the gizzard. The chick was injected with 6-hydroxy-dopamine 48h previously and all the adrenergic nerve endings of the plexus have disappeared, while the fluorescent cell body and processes of an intrinsic adrenergic neuron show up particularly clearly.

Plate 11. (a) Dilator pupillae muscle of the rat iris, fixed by immersion in potassium permanganate. Adrenergic (bottom) and probably cholinergic (top) nerve endings are readily identified by the presence of small granular vesicles and agranular vesicles respectively. Marker: 0·5 μm. (Courtesy of Dr T. Hökfelt, from Hökfelt, 1973.) (b) Outer muscle coat of the vas deferens of a rat, fixed by immersion in acrolein and sodium dichromate. With this procedure most of the vesicles of adrenergic endings show a highly electron-dense content. Marker: 0·5 μm. (Courtesy of Mr P. Gordon-Weeks.) (c) Vas deferens of a guinea-pig, incubated in vitro with 5-hydroxy-dopamine. Two nerve fibres (varicosities) tunnelling through a muscle cell: one of them is filled with dense-cored vesicles, the other contains only agranular vesicles. Marker: 0·5 μm. (Courtesy of Dr J.B. Furness.)

Plate 12. (a) Pineal gland of a rat, fixed 30 minutes after injection of tritiated noradrenaline. Autoradiographic preparation. Silver 'grains' are visible superimposed on axons containing small granular vesicles. The nerve bundle is surrounded by a basal lamina (arrow). p: pinealocytes. (Courtesy of Professor J. Taxi & Droz, 1966b.) Marker: 1 μm. (b) Axons in the muscular coat of the rectum of a rat (fixed by immersion in glutaraldehyde). sm: smooth muscle cells with caveolae; Sc: Schwann cell; a: an axon with electron-lucent vesicles (probably cholinergic). b: an axon with small granulated vesicles (probably adrenergic). Characteristically the preservation of dense cores in adrenergic fibres of the rat is rather poor in glutaraldehyde-fixed tissues. Collagen fibrils and a wide intercellular space lie between nerve endings and smooth muscle cells. Marker: 0·5 μm.

Plate 13. Myenteric plexus of the guinea-pig ileum (fixed by immersion in glutaraldehyde). Adrenergic nerve endings synapse on a process (a) and the perikaryon (b) of a ganglion cell. The endings show mitochondria (m) and a large number of small granular vesicles. The cores vary in size and shape, and are sometimes eccentrically located. The membrane of the vesicles is often highly electron-dense, even in some of the vesicles which do not show a dense core. Some large dense-cored vesicles are also observed (a). Arrows point to the post-synaptic membrane. Markers: (a) 0·5 μm; (b) 0·25 μm.

Plate 14. Tissue cultures of sympathetic ganglia photographed alive *in vitro*. (Courtesy of Dr J.H. Chamley. From Chamley *et al.*, 1972.) Markers: 25 μm.
(a) From 18 day old rat superior cervical ganglion, 9 days *in vitro*. Type 1 neuron.
(b) Same neuron as in (a), photographed a few minutes later. Note change in the appearance and position of the nucleus.
(c) From 7 day old rat sympathetic chain, 21 days *in vitro*. Type 2 neuron. Satellite cells (arrows) closely apposed to the cell body. Sc, Schwann cell.
(d) From 5 day old rat sympathetic chain enzyme-dispersed, 21 days *in vitro*. Type 2 neuron with no closely applied satellite cells.
(e) From newborn guinea-pig sympathetic chain. Type 2 neuron in explant.
(f) From 5 day old rat sympathetic chain, 7 days *in vitro*. Neurons with characteristics of both type 1 and 2.

Plate 15. Camera lucida drawings from silver preparations of autonomic ganglia. (From Slavich, 1932. By permission of Springer-Verlag) Markers: 10 μm.
(a) Human superior cervical ganglion (man of 48 years). pe: intracapsular processes; pl: long dendrites.
(b) Otic ganglion from 4-year-old cattle. Ganglion cells with many short processes, some of which form dendritic glomeruli (g).
(c) Ciliary ganglion from 4-year-old cattle. A ganglion cell showing a fenestrated apparatus (arrow).
(d) Human spheno-palatin ganglion (man of 22 years). fa: preganglionic fibres; n: axon; pl: long dendrites.
(e) Ciliary ganglion cells from an adult cat showing both short and long (pl) processes.

(f) Human ciliary ganglion (man 60-year-old). The ganglion cell has many short bulbous processes. n: axon.

(g) Ciliary ganglion from a mouse.

Plate 16. (a) Ciliary ganglion of a cat. Ganglion cell with its dendrites and axon, stained by intracellular injection of the fluorescent dye Procion Yellow. Photographed in fluorescence microscopy. (Courtesy of Dr S. Nishi.) Marker: 50 μm.

(b) Ciliary ganglion of an adult chicken. Araldite section stained with toluidine blue. A ciliary ganglion neuron invested by a compact glial sheath. At (h), the hilar pole of the neuron with the emerging axon is surrounded by the incoming preganglionic fibres. n, nucleus; ax, myelinated axons; c, capillary. Marker: 50 μm.

(c) Ciliary ganglion of an adult chicken. A contact between a preganglionic nerve ending (N) and the perikaryon of a ciliary ganglion neuron (G). The arrowheads point to desmosomial complexes between nerve ending and perikaryon. Within these junctions there is an area of closer apposition (gap junction). m, mitochondria; v, synaptic vesicles. Marker: 1 μm.

(d) Detail of (c) showing a desmosomial complex and a gap junction (arrow). Marker: 0·24 μm.

(b–d, Courtesy of Dr E. Mugnaini. From Cantino & Mugnaini, 1975.)

Plate 17. Ciliary ganglion of an adult chicken. Freeze-fracture preparation of the hilar pole of a ciliary neuron. The fracture plane has cut across the peripheral cytoplasm of a ganglion neuron (G) and has exposed the cytoplasmic half ('A face' or 'P face') of the membrane of the pre-ganglionic nerve endings (N) and the external face ('B face' or 'E face') of glial process (S). The arrowheads indicate clusters of 'particles' (9 nm in diameter, centre-to-centre distance 10 nm), which correspond to gap junctions. The arrows indicate possible sites where synaptic vesicles open. (Courtesy of Dr E. Mugnaine. From Cantino & Mugnaini, 1975.) Marker: 1 μm.

Plate 18. (a) Circular muscle of the guinea-pig ileum. A group of axons partly invested by a Schwann cell (Sc) runs between smooth muscle cells (M) without making close contacts with any of them. Some of the axons lie in direct contact with each other, and some contain synaptic vesicles. Some of the axons are less than 0·2 μm in diameter. A thin basal lamina surrounds the nerve bundle and the smooth muscle cells. I, interstitial cell with its nucleus. Marker: 1 μm.

(b) Iris of the guinea-pig. Transverse section of the sphincter pupillae. Smooth muscle cells (M) are rich in mitochondria and sarcoplasmic reticulum, and are connected by nexuses (n). An axon (N), filled with cytoplasmic vesicles (and microtubules, endoplasmic reticulum, and mitochondria) runs accompanied only by a thin Schwann cell process (p). The neuro-muscular gap is about 20 nm, and the muscle cell has a sub-surface cisterna of sarcoplasmic reticulum immediately underneath the area of apposition. (From Gabella, 1974.) Marker: 1 μm.

Plate 19. (a) An intestinal loop from a chick, histochemically stained *in toto*. The myenteric plexus with its ganglia and connecting meshes is visible in the otherwise unstained wall. The lumen of the intestine with some of the mucosa is visible at the left-hand side.

(b) A preparation similar to the one in (a), from the rectum of a guinea-pig. After the histochemical reaction for NADH-diaphorase activity was carried out on the intestine *in toto*, this was cut in lengths and the longitudinal muscle with the attached myenteric plexus was peeled off and mounted in glycerol. The smooth muscle is almost unstained and well individualized ganglia and strands of the myenteric plexus are visible, 125X.

(c) A similar preparation from the myenteric plexus of rat. This species lacks clear-cut ganglia, and the neurons are spread in rows parallel to the longitudinal muscle. Note the great variability of cell sizes, and the eccentric position of some nuclei (which appear as round unstained areas), 400X.

Plate 20. (a–c) Preparation using the same method as in Plate 19b, from the myenteric plexus of the ileum. (a) and (b) from a guinea-pig over 2 years old, (c) from a guinea-pig about 5 months old. The ganglia of the ageing animal are characterized by a reduced packing density of the neurons and by large 'empty' spaces in the ganglia. The neurons show a more irregular and horny surface, compared with those of the young adult guinea-pig.

(d) Ganglion of the myenteric plexus of a cat, stained by the silver impregnation method of Bielschowsky-Gros. (Courtesy of Dr D.H.L. Evans.) Bipolar and multipolar neurons are visible. Only some of the neurons of the ganglion are stained.

(e) Section from a plastic embedded myenteric plexus ganglion of a guinea-pig. The circular muscle is to the left and the longitudinal muscle to the right. In the ganglion large neurons and glial cells are visible (compare with Plate 21).

Plate 21. Low-power electron micrograph of the same ganglion as that shown in Plate 20e. The ganglion is surrounded by connective tissue and small blood vessels (B); the circular (cm) and the longitudinal musculature (lm) are at the left and the right respectively. The ganglion cells (n) are recognized by their bigger size and large nucleus poor in chromatin. The neurons are embedded in a neuropil formed by glial cells (g) and numerous nerve processes. Marker: $10 \mu m$.

Plate 22. (a) Myenteric plexus of the guinea-pig ileum. A nerve ending characterized by a heterogeneous population of granular vesicles synapses on an intramural neuron (n). In the presynaptic region mainly small agranular vesicles are observed (arrow). Note that the large vesicles contain electron-dense material which is not surrounded by a clear-cut halo. t, microtubules. Axons and glial processes are visible around the nerve ending. Marker: $0.5 \mu m$.

(b) Myenteric plexus of the guinea-pig colon. A nerve ending filled with small agranular vesicles synapses on a process (p) of an intramural neuron, showing a large number of microtubules. Microtubules (t) and mitochondria (m) are also visible in the nerve ending. Marker: 1 μm.

Plate 23 (a—c). Myenteric plexus of the guinea-pig ileum (from Gabella, 1972). (a) A nerve ending (e) is closely associated to a glial cell. Clustering of vesicles and a dense projection suggest the occurrence of a specialized neuro-glial contact. Marker: 0·5 μm.
(b) Portions of the surface of a ganglion cell (n) are not covered by glial cells: they lie directly underneath the basal lamina (bl) and the collagen fibrils (C). A dense layer of microfibrillar material (d) is visible under the cell membrane (cm). Marker: 1 μm.
(d) A process of a glial cell (G) at the surface of the ganglion, lying under the basal lamina (bl) and collagen fibrils (C). At this level, on the inner side of the cell membrane (cm) there are patches of dense material where glyofilaments are attached. Marker: 1 μm.

Plate 24. Transverse section of the abdominal portion of the vagus of a rat. Two Schwann cells, investing a number of (unmyelinated) axons, are cut at the level of their nuclei (Sc); the other axons are wrapped up by thin processes of Schwann cells. A basal lamina surrounds each Schwann cell with its satellite axons. The Schwann cell provide a complete sheath to each individual axons; only rarely the latter come into contact with each other or with the basal lamina (arrows). Abundant collagen fibrils (in transverse section) and microfibrils are present in the extracellular space. The axons mainly show microtubules and small mitochondria. ma: an axon with a thick myelin sheath. (From Gabella & Pease, 1973). Marker: 1 μm.

origin. It is not known what relationship exists between the various types of vesicles of these endings, nor indeed what is the neurotransmitter or whether they belong to motor or sensory neurons. Besides cholinergic and adrenergic neurons, at least one other type of fibre has been identified in the intestinal plexuses, which is inhibitory and of intrinsic origin (Burnstock, Campbell, Bennett & Holman, 1964), and evidence has been obtained that its transmitter may be ATP (Burnstock, Campbell, Satchell & Smythe, 1972; see Burnstock, 1972). However, these intramural inhibitory fibres have not yet been identified histologically, although the endings with heterogeneous granular vesicles are an obvious candidate.

A third type of nerve ending synapsing on intramural neurons contains only agranular vesicles 40–60 nm in diameter (apart from occasional large granulated vesicles) (Taxi, 1958, 1965; Baumgarten et al., 1970; Gabella, 1972) (Plate 22b). They are considered to be cholinergic and to originate mainly from other intramural neurons. In the myenteric plexus of the guinea-pig, ileum nerve endings with agranular vesicles are the more numerous endings and are found not only synapsing on intramural neurons but also at the surface of ganglia, directly underneath the basal lamina (Gabella, 1972). In the former case the typical pre- and post-synaptic specializations are observed, in the latter case vesicles can be seen in clusters close to points of the membrane adjacent to the basal lamina, sometimes around densities reminiscent of the presynaptic dense projections. In fact the content in acetylcholine of the myenteric plexus is higher than that of any other mammalian nervous tissue (Welsh & Hyde, 1944), and large amounts of acetylcholine are released from the plexus upon stimulation (Feldberg & Lin, 1950; Paton & Zar, 1968). The great majority of these presumably cholinergic endings are intrinsic in origin, since they do not disappear after extrinsic denervation; moreover Feldberg and Lin (1950) showed that the release of acetylcholine from the myenteric plexus is not dependent on the integrity of the extrinsic nerves.

Other nerve endings are characterized by flat agranular vesicles (Gabella, 1972). Some of them synapse on intramural neurons, others lie at the surface of the ganglia. It is still not clear whether these flat vesicles arise from round vesicles during the histological preparation procedure (as has been experimentally obtained, for example, in the motor end-plates, Korneliussen, 1972), but it may be

129

possible that in the myenteric plexus they characterize a different type of ending.

A number of varicosities in the myenteric plexus, usually containing agranular vesicles, do not synapse on intramural neurons, but show contact specializations with glial cells (Gabella, 1972): clustering of vesicles, thickening of an area of the axolemma, wider and more regular intercellular gap (Plate 23b). The significance of these neuro-glial junctions is unknown. Symmetrical contacts (attachment plaques) are also found between glial and nerve elements, without clustering of vesicles.

Intramural neurons are not adrenergic and the experiments of extrinsic denervation (see p.128) show that the adrenergic innervation to the mammalian gut is extrinsic in origin, i.e. from the prevertebral ganglia. The only well-established example of intrinsic adrenergic neurons in the mammals is the myenteric plexus of the guinea-pig colon (Costa, Furness & Gabella, 1971; Furness & Costa, 1971). It is estimated that in the whole length of the proximal colon there are about 10 000 adrenergic neurons; their axons are finely varicose and lie within the plexus or in the circular musculature (Furness & Costa, 1971). Pharmacologically they resemble the adrenergic neurons of sympathetic ganglia, although they appear less sensitive to depletion by reserpine, guanethidine and 6-hydroxydopamine (Costa & Furness, 1971). No studies have yet been made on the fine structure of such neurons and their synaptic input. The content of noradrenaline of the myenteric plexus in the colon is more than twice that in the ileum and the depletion obtained by extrinsic denervation is only about 75 per cent (Gabella & Juorio, 1975). (Note 7.3.) Intrinsic adrenergic neurons within the intestinal plexuses have been observed in non-mammalian species, notably the chick gizzard (Bennett, Malmfors & Cobb, 1973) (Plate 10d), the lizard large intestine (Baumgarten, Bjorklund, Lachenmayer, Nobin & Rosengren, 1973) (the latter species also contains dopaminergic neurons).

7.6 The 'post-ganglionic' fibres

Axons of the intramural neurons are difficult to recognize in silver impregnated preparations, and the emergence of an axon from the cell body or a dendrite has not yet been identified in electron microscopy. Most of the axons of the plexuses, a large number of synapses and most of the intramuscular axons of the guinea-pig survive an operation of extrinsic denervation and originate, therefore, from intramural neurons (Juorio & Gabella, 1974). The fibres issuing from intramural neurons can project on other ganglion neurons (see Section 7.5), to prevertebral ganglion cells as afferent fibres (see Sections 2.3 and 2.10) and to the muscle tissue as excitatory or inhibitory fibres. Some intrinsic fibres (in addition to the adrenergic fibres) can innervate the blood vessels of the intestinal wall of cat (Biber, Fara & Lundgren, 1973).

7.7 Studies on development

A series of detailed experiments on the origin of the intramural ganglia in the chick embryo have been published by Andrew (1964, 1969, 1970), and the author also reviewed all the previous experiments on this vexed question (Andrew, 1971). Her conclusion is that intramural neurons *can* derive from the vagal neural crest and from the trunk neural crest, and that the vagal neural crest *does* give rise to at least some enteric neurons. Mesoderm and endoderm are discounted as possible sources of enteric ganglion neurons. Recently Le Douarin and Teillet (1973) by applying an original experimental technique were able to demonstrate that in the chick embryo the enteric ganglion neurons arise from two levels of the neural axis, which correspond to the vagal and the lumbo-sacral parasympathetic centres. From the vagal source (which is the more important of the two) ganglion cells migrate to the whole length of the gut (the migration to the hind-gut can take six or more days). The lumbo-sacral source gives rise only to ganglion cells of the post-umbilical part of the gut.

Well-defined ganglia are already recognizable in the small intestine of a 12 mm human embryo (Kubozoe, Daikoku & Takita, 1969). The adrenergic innervation of the small intestine of rat, as studied in fluorescence microscopy, seems to develop earlier than that of the iris or vas deferens (Champlain *et al.*, 1970). Thus at birth the myenteric and submucous plexuses show a well-developed network of adrenergic fibres around the ganglion cells. By a combined histochemical and pharmacological study Gershon and Thompson (1973) were able to show that in rabbit embryos the intrinsic cholinergic excitatory innervation and the intrinsic inhibitory innervation develop several days before the adrenergic innervation.

131

In the myenteric plexus of the newborn rat the number of neurons per unit surface is much greater than in the adult, although the total number of neurons in the small intestine is only a quarter (Gabella, 1971); when during the post-natal life this increase in number occurs has not been ascertained. An increase in the distances between ganglia and in the average neuronal size parallels the increase in diameter and length of the intestine.

Note 7.1
Solitary neurons found for example in the human tongue (Chu, 1968) or in the salivary glands (Alm, Bloom & Carlsöö, 1973) are not part of the intramural plexuses, but parasympathetic neurons displaced peripheral to the ganglia, with which they remain connected. Similarly, small ganglia found within the pancreas (e.g. Watari, 1968, in the monkey and bat; Kudo, 1971 in the chicken) show structural similarity to the prevertebral ganglia rather than to the intestinal intramural ganglia.

Note 7.2
Some authors (e.g. Schabadasch (1930) and Ohkubo (1936a)) describe two plexuses in the submucosa: the plexus entericus internus of Henle, close to the circular muscle layer, and the plexus submucosus of Meissner, distributed throughout the submucosa.

Note 7.3
Oosaki and Sugai (1974) have described adrenergic neurons (measuring about $15 \times 10\,\mu m$) associated with the meshes of the myenteric plexus in the rat small intestine; they were visualized by fluorescence microscopy on stretch preparations of the ileal wall. Whether the structure illustrated by Oosaki and Sugai are cells at all, remains, in my opinion, an open question. Kyösola and Rechardt (1973), in their study of the adrenergic innervation of the choledoco-duodenal junction of the cat and dog, also claimed that adrenergic cell bodies are present in this part of the alimentary tract.

Note 7.4
Robinson and Gershon (1971) have described in the myenteric plexus of the guinea-pig ileum nerve endings containing 5-hydroxytryptamine, originating from neurons of the submucous plexus.

132

8 THE VAGUS NERVE

8.1 The vagus nerve

The vagus nerve, the 10th cranial nerve, has a superficial origin from the medulla oblongata with several rootlets which merge together while passing through the jugular foramen. It has two obvious bulges, a smaller one called the jugular (or superior) ganglion and a larger one immediately caudal to it called the nodose (or inferior) ganglion. It passes along the neck to the thorax and the abdomen, and its main branches are the auricular, pharyngeal, laryngeal, cardiac, pulmonary, oesophageal and abdominal branches.

Some of the fibres of the vagus are somatic motor and innervate striated voluntary musculature of the pharynx and larynx. Some afferent fibres are present in the auricular branch and reach the external auditory meatus. The experimental evidence for the visceral and cardio-vascular afferent activity in the vagus nerve will not be reviewed here (see for example Harper, McSwiney & Suffolk, 1935; Paintal, 1973). The autonomic efferent functions of the vagus have also been extensively studied e.g. Jansson, 1969.

8.2 Structure of the vagus nerve

The vagus nerve has a complex structure as one would expect from its wide distribution and the variety of functions it controls. Table 8.1 reports the data of quantitative studies on the vagus nerve at various levels, its rootlets and the nodose ganglion. Most of the work has been done in the cat, the rabbit and man, by the pyridine silver impregnation method; more recently some counts were done by using the electron microscope. There is in general good agreement between the authors. A great variability in axon numbers was found between individuals of the same species, but no apparent correlation with the age of the subjects was detected.

The nerve contains a wide spectrum of myelinated and unmyelinated fibres (Evans & Murray, 1954) (Plate 24). Both efferent and afferent fibres can be either myelinated or unmyelinated. The size-frequency distribution is particularly wide in the cervical vagus. Most of the large myelinated fibres ($> 10\,\mu$m) contribute to the formation of the recurrent laryngeal nerve. In sheep and goats, though the total number of fibres has not been counted, the abdominal vagus charac-teristically contains thousands of myelinated axons with a wide spec-trum of diameters (Iggo, 1956). For the topography of various bundles in the rootlets, the trunks and the main branches of the vagus see DuBois and Foley (1935), Evans and Murray (1954), Agostoni, Chinnock, Daly and Murray, (1957), and Kerr, Hendler and Bowron, (1970).

By combining studies on fibres degeneration and retrograde chromatolytic changes in cell bodies DuBois and Foley (1935) analysed the main branches of the vagus of the cat as follows: auricular nerve: 6000—8000 fibres, approximately three-quarters of which are unmyelinated (cells of origin in the jugular ganglion); pharyngeal nerve: 1100—1600 fibres, mainly myelinated (from the jugular ganglion); superior laryngeal nerve: 2400—2900 fibres, myelinated, largely sensory (cells of origin in the nodose ganglion); recurrent laryngeal nerve: 300—400 large myelinated motor fibres and 600—1000 small myelinated sensory fibres (cells of origin in the nodose ganglion). In the laryngeal bundle of the recurrent laryngeal nerve of the cat and the rabbit about 450 and 260 myelinated fibres respectively, mainly in the range 8—14 μm in diameter, and up to 80 unmyelinated fibres (which were unaffected by infranodose vagotomy) were counted (Evans & Murray, 1954; Murray, 1957). The superior laryngeal nerve has about 670 myelinated fibres in the rat (Andrew, 1956), 2500 in the cat (Dubois & Foley, 1935) and 15 000 in man (Ogura & Lam, 1953).

In many species (including man, dog, cat, rabbit) right and left vagus merge in the thorax forming a plexus around the oesophagus, usually condensed in an anterior and a posterior group. Since, after unilateral infranodose vagotomy in the rabbit and dog one half of the fibres degenerate in both the anterior and the posterior trunks, the right and left vagus nerves seem to contribute evenly to both trunks (Evans & Murray, 1954; Kemp, 1973). About 5—10 per cent of the fibres in the abdominal vagus did not degenerate after bilateral vagotomy (left infranodose vagotomy plus right upper thoracic

134

Table 8.1

Quantitative studies on the vagus nerve

(Numbers are mean ± standard deviations, number of cases in brackets)

Species	Staining methods	Region of count	Number of neurons and/or fibres	References
cat	azur-eosin (for cell counts). pyridine-silver impregnation	nodose ganglion	number of ganglion cells[1]: 26 000 ± 750 (13)	Foley and Dubois, 1937
		upper cervical level	total number of fibres[2]: 34 300 ± 1300 (9)	
			number of myelinated fibres: 8500 ± 200 (9)	
			total number of fibres after section of the roots of the X and XI (right side): 20—35 per cent less than in the left (control) nerve[3][4]	
cat	azur-eosin (for cell counts). pyridine-silver impregnation	nodose ganglion	number of ganglion cells[5]: 29 600 ± 1050 (10)	Jones, 1937
		proximal to the nodose ganglion	total number of fibres[5]: 28 900 ± 2600 (9)	
		distal to the nodose ganglion	total number of fibres[5]: 34 300 ± 1300 (13)	
rabbit	pyridine-silver impregnation osmic acid	lower cervical level	total number of fibres: 23 000 ± 960 (6)	Evans and Murray, 1954
			number of myelinated fibres: 2900 ± 200 (5)	

Species	Staining methods	Region of count	Number of neurons and/or fibres	References
		diaphragmatic level (anterior and posterior abdominal trunks)	total number of fibres after intracranial vagotomy or supranodose vagotomy[6]: 18 000 ± 1300 (6)	
			total number of fibres: 26 200 ± 1300 (6)	
			number of myelinated fibres: less than 75 (4)	
			total number of fibres after either right or left infra-nodose vagotomy: about 50 per cent of the fibres degenerate in both trunks (6)	
			total number of fibres after intracranial or supranodose vagotomy[7]: a few degenerating fibres, but total number of fibres still within the normal range (4)	
sheep, goat	osmic acid	diaphragmatic level	total number of fibres after left cervical infranodose vagotomy and right upper thoracic vagotomy[8]: 1200 ± 200 (3)	
			number of myelinated fibres[9]: 'several thousands'	Iggo, 1956

cat	pyridine-silver impregnation osmic acid	cervical level	total number of fibres: $30\,500 \pm 700$ (6)	Agostoni, Chinnock, Daly and Murray, 1957
			total number of fibres after supranodose (intra- or extracranial) vagotomy $24\,000 \pm 1200$ (6)	
		abdominal level (both sides)	total number of fibres: $31\,000 \pm 950$ (3)	
			total number of fibres after unilateral (either right or left) infranodose vagotomy[10]: $16\,000 \pm 300$ (5)	
			total number of fibres after cervical infranodose vagotomy and upper thoracic vagotomy on the opposite side: 3000 ± 500 (3)	
			total number of fibres after supranodose vagotomy (intra- or extracranial): $31\,000 \pm 650$ (6)	(6)
man	sudan black	mid-cervical level	number of myelinated fibres[11] [12]: left: $16\,500 \pm 1650$ (17) right: $20\,000 \pm 1350$ (17)	Schnitzlein, Rowe and Hoffman, 1958
		recurrent laryngeal nerve	number of myelinated fibres: left: 2500 ± 250 (14) right: 2300 ± 150 (13)	
		diaphragmatic level (both sides)	number of myelinated fibres[13]: 2050 ± 1000 (12)	(12)

Species	Staining methods	Region of count	Number of neurons and/or fibres	References
cat	osmic acid	cervical level	number of myelinated fibres: range 3100–4600	Cottle and Mitchell, 1966
rat	electron microscopy	diaphragmatic level	total number of fibres 9500 ± 350 (6) number of myelinated fibres: 83 ± 10 (6)	Gabella and Pease, 1973
dog	electron microscopy	abdominal level	total number of fibres[17]: ventral trunk: 12 500 dorsal trunk: 13 200	Kemp, 1973
		abdominal level (both sides)	total number of fibres after unilateral supranodose vagotomy[18]: 24 600	
			total number of fibres after ulilateral infranodose vagotomy: 13 100	
			total number of fibres after unilateral supranodose vagotomy and contralateral sub-hilar vagotomy: 2250	

[1] In most cases there are more cells in the left than in the right ganglion (average excess : 5 per cent).

[2] There are on average 3 per cent more fibres in the left than in the right nerve.

[3] Therefore 20–35 per cent of the fibres at the upper cervical level are efferent.

4 From counts of myelinated and unmyelinated fibres in the control and operated sides, the authors calculated that of the myelinated fibres 36–46 per cent are sensory and 54–64 per cent are motor (or, 10–20 per cent of all sensory fibres and 48–71 per cent of all motor fibres are myelinated).

5 The average ratio between proximal fibres, ganglion cells, and distal fibres is 85·6 : 85·8 : 100. In view of the excess of fibres distal to the ganglion over those proximal, Jones suggested that some of the cells of the nodose ganglion are motor; the discrepancy, however, can be explained by sensory fibres contributed to the vagus nerve by the jugular ganglion (DuBois and Foley, 1937).

6 20–25 per cent of the fibres have degenerated and may therefore be considered efferent. Degeneration affects both myelinated and unmyelinated fibres. Among the myelinated fibres degeneration is nearly complete in the group of 12–14 μm, 75 per cent in the group 10–12 μm, 50 per cent in the group 0–4 μm; hardly any change in the group 4–10 μm.

7 Most of the fibres (well over 90 per cent) are therefore afferent.

8 The surviving fibres are interpreted as either sympathetic fibres reaching the vagus from the thoracic sympathetic chain or visceral afferent fibres reaching the spinal cord.

9 Size range: 2–4 μm : 80 per cent; 4–6·5 μm : 14 per cent; 7–12 μm : 3 per cent.

10 The right and left cervical vagus nerves each contribute an approximately equal number of fibres to the abdominal vagus nerves.

11 Great variability between individuals. Individuals with a high number of myelinated fibres on one side also had a high number of fibres on the other side. No correlation between number of fibres and age of the subjects (range 2–86 years).

12 Up to 88 per cent of the myelinated fibres are less than 3 μm in diameter, but there is also a number of myelinated fibres larger than 10 μm, which all contribute to the recurrent laryngeal nerve.

13 Right and left vagus nerves merge in the thorax forming a plexus around the oesophagus, usually condensed in an anterior and a posterior group. At the diaphragmatic level the number of myelinated fibres is about 6 per cent of that found at mid-cervical level; they are almost all less than 3 μm in diameter.

14 No correlation between number of fibres and age of the subjects (range 2–86 years). The right cervical vagus has significantly more fibres than the left. On average 81 per cent of the fibres are unmyelinated.

15 About 66 per cent of the fibres are unmyelinated.   16 About 97 per cent of the fibres are unmyelinated.

17 About 50 per cent of the fibres terminate in the acid-secreting portion of the stomach.

18 Not significantly different from the control value (25 700); therefore the contribution of efferent fibres from the medulla is very small.

vagotomy) in the rabbit (Evans & Murray, 1954), the cat (Agostoni *et al.*, 1957), and the dog (Kemp, 1973).

In small rodents the abdominal part of the vagus is accompanied by small groups of cells structurally similar to the carotid and aortic body tissue (Goormaghtich, 1936; Hollinshead, 1941, 1946; Chen & Yates, 1970; Mascorro & Yates, 1974; Deane, Howe & Morgan, 1974). Between 4 and 46 such paraganglia were counted in the region of the gastro-oesophageal junction in the rat (Deane *et al.*, 1974). They are formed by cells with specific fluorescence for catecholamines and numerous dense core vesicles in the cytoplasm; they do not show the chromaffin reaction and are said to be smaller in size than the cells in the sympathetic paraganglia (Goormaghtich, 1936). Some paraganglia also contain neurons. Although their function is unknown a chemoreceptor role has been suggested for them (Hollinshead, 1946).

8.3   The nodose and jugular ganglia

The nodose (or inferior or plexiform) ganglion of the cat contains about 30 000 neurons (Jones, 1937; Foley & DuBois, 1937). (The number of neurons in individual spinal ganglia of the same species seldom exceeds 7000 (Duncan & Keyser, 1936)). Most of the neurons in the nodose ganglion of the cat are $35-40 \mu$m in diameter, but some are only $20-30 \mu$m (Mohiuddin, 1953). The ganglion cells are unipolar neurons, whose axons have at first a convoluted course around one pole of the cell (Cajal, 1909). Many neurons are fenestrated (Cajal, 1909; Ranson, Foley & Alpert, 1933); fusiform or bipolar neurons are occasionally observed (Cajal, 1909).

The axons divide, like those of the spinal ganglia, into a peripheral and a central branch, the latter always being the thinner of the two, often not more than a third the diameter of the former (Ranson *et al.*, 1933). The ganglion cells issue both myelinated and unmyelinated fibres, and for some neurons a myelin sheath is present only on the distal process (Jones, 1937). The fibres originating from the ganglion cells usually run in the centre of the ganglion, while the motor fibres run along one side of it (Cajal, 1909).

The nodose ganglion of the cat contains sparse chromaffin cells similar to those described in the superior cervical ganglion (see p.23) (Jacobs & Comroe, 1971; Grillo, Jacobs & Comroe, 1974); they were

140

seen receiving synapses from endings with agranular vesicles, but had no efferent synapses (Grillo *et al.*, 1974). Chromaffin cells (or chemoreceptor-like cells, as they were called because of their similarity to the carotid body cells) in the nodose ganglia were first observed in birds (Muratori, 1932; confirmed in fluorescence microscopy by Bennett, 1971) and in man (White, 1935). The possible significance of such cells in the nodose ganglion has been discussed by Jacobs and Comroe (1971). A few fluorescent (adrenergic) fibres, some of which are perivascular, have been seen in the nodose ganglion of the dog and the cat (Muryobayashi *et al.*, 1968; Nielsen, Owman & Santini, 1969), and the chick (Bennett, 1971).

Although the structural details of the vagus nerve in birds are not examined here, it is worth mentioning that a peculiar feature of the avian vagus nerve is the presence of a large ganglion in the upper thoracic part of the nerve (thoracic ganglion of the vagus). Terni (1924) has shown that in the chick embryo the ganglion develops around the fourth day at the level of the first cervical nerve, whence it gradually descends to reach its definitive position at the level of the fifteenth cervical and first thoracic nerves around the 10th day *in ovo*. Most of its neurons, and of those of the jugular ganglion, are also bipolar in the adult, the central process being smaller and more intensely stained with silver methods. The cells measure about 50μm in diameter (about 30μm in the pigeon). In spite of its position the ganglion is homologous to the nodose ganglion of mammals. A distally located vagal ganglion is present also in reptiles (Ranson, 1915).

The jugular (or superior) ganglion is smaller than the nodose ganglion and lies above it. In the cat it contains 8700 ± 190 ($N = 6$) ganglion cells (DuBois & Foley, 1937). It contributes between 1700 and 3500 sensory fibres to the main trunk of the vagus (about 15 per cent of the ganglion cells showed chromatolysis after section of the vagus trunk), and the great majority of the sensory fibres of the auricular nerve (about 73 per cent of the ganglion cells showed frank chromatolysis after section of this nerve). The auricular nerve of the cat, which is one of the smallest branch of the vagus nerve, arises directly from the jugular ganglion and contains no less than 8800 ± 725 ($N = 5$) fibres, mostly of the smallest unmyelinated variety (DuBois & Foley, 1937).

8.4 Origin of the axons of the vagus nerve

After intracranial vagotomy 20–25 per cent of the fibres in the vagus of the rabbit at the lower cervical level degenerate and can be con-considered to originate from the medulla (efferent fibres) (Evans & Murray, 1954). The degeneration is nearly complete in the recurrent laryngeal of the rabbit (apart from a few myelinated fibres which also survive an infranodose vagotomy), composed mainly of large and myelinated fibres (Evans & Murray, 1954), whereas less than 10 per cent of the total number of fibres degenerate in the abdominal vagus of rabbit and cat and they are probably unmyelinated (Evans & Murray, 1954; Agostoni *et al.*, 1957). Following section of the vagus below the origin of the pulmonary branches (the lower-most thoracic branches), retrograde chromatolytic changes were seen in about half of the large cells of the dorsal nucleus of the vagus and in about one fifth of the cells of the nodose ganglion of the cat (Mohiuddin, 1953). Few of the fibres of the main vagus trunk and most of those of the auricular nerve are contributed by the jugular ganglion cells (DuBois & Foley, 1937). For the composition and origin of various vagal branches in the cat and rabbit see DuBois and Foley (1935) and Evans and Murray (1954).

It has been mentioned (p.134) that a number of fibres in the abdominal vagus of rabbit, cat and dog, do not degenerate after bilateral vagotomy. Such fibres may be sympathetic fibres reaching the vagus from the sympathetic chain, or visceral afferent fibres from spinal ganglia, or fibres issuing from scattered 'ganglion' cells. In fact small anastomotic trunks between vagus and the sympathetic chain have been illustrated by several authors, but the actual exchange of nerve fibres is more difficult to demonstrate. A few adrenergic fibres, as evidenced in fluorescence microscopy, are seen in the vagus nerve of dogs (Muryobayashi *et al.*, 1968) and cats (Nielsen, Owman & Santini, 1969). They originate in the superior cervical ganglion (Muryobayashi *et al.*, 1968; Nielsen *et al.*, 1969). At least part of these fibres terminate in the heart (Nielsen *et al.*, 1969), but they are also found in the abdominal vagus (Muryobayashi *et al.*, 1968). Chromaffin cells with very long processes are scattered along the length of the vagus of the rat (Gabella & Costa, 1968), and they are in intimate contact with unmyelinated axons.

As regards visceral afferent vagal fibres reaching the spinal cord

142

there is not yet anatomical evidence that they exist, but Harper, McSwiney and Suffolk (1935) have shown by physiological means that a group of afferent fibres from the abdominal vagus of the cat leave the thoracic vagal trunk, accompany the intercostal arteries, join the intercostal nerves close to their exit from the intervertebral foramina, and enter the spinal cord by the dorsal roots from the second to the eighth thoracic levels inclusive. As regards the occurrence of scattered 'ganglion' cells along the length of the vagus nerve, there is abundant evidence for it. In five cats Dolgo-Saburov (1935) found on average 404 neurons in the right vagus and 303 in the left vagus (36 and 16 at the cervical level, 310 and 254 in the thoracic part, and 58 and 23 in the abdominal part). Some of these cells were indistinguishable in shape from the cells situated in the nodose ganglion, some were multipolar cells, on which endings of axons (presumably preganglionic) could be seen. Since in man, dog and cat most of these neurons lie in the branches of the vagus leading to the respiratory apparatus, Botar, Afra, Moritz, Schiffman and Scholz (1950) regard them as equivalent to the extramural and intramural post-ganglionic neurons of the heart and the stomach respectively. In man (one case) they found about 1700 neurons in the trunk and the branches of the vagus of each side.

8.5   The preganglionic neurons

The efferent fibres of the vagus nerve for the smooth muscles of the respiratory apparatus and the stomach and for the heart (cardio-inhibitory fibres) are generally considered to originate from the dorsal vagal nucleus, situated in the medulla oblongata, under the floor of the fourth ventricle, lateral to the hypoglossal nucleus. The nucleus is common also to the glosso-pharyngeal and accessory nerves, and measures in man 10–11 mm in length (Tomasch & Ebnessajjade, 1961). In the dorsal vagal nucleus of each side there are about 3000 neurons in the cat (Mohiuddin, 1953) and 9400 in man (Etemadi, 1961). The anatomical studies are reviewed and discussed by Mitchell and Warwick (1955).

In the dorsal vagal nucleus of the rabbit obvious chromatolytic changes follow vagotomy. Performing vagotomy at various levels along the nerve Getz and Sirnes (1949) were able to find within the nucleus a topographical representation of the innervated organs (most caudal portion of the nucleus: trachea, bronchi, oesophagus; central part: heart and gut; cranial part: gut and lungs). A topographical representation was also found by Mitchell and Warwick (1955) in monkeys. They also observed, particularly at the outer border of the nucleus, numerous small neurons without chromatolytic changes following vagotomy, and suggested that these were sensory elements, the nucleus being therefore of a mixed type. Dramatic chromatolytic changes in the dorsal vagal nucleus following crushing of the vagus were observed by Lewis, Blundell Jones, Breathnach and Navaratnam, (1972) in the rat.

There is, however, strong physiological evidence that in the cat the dorsal nucleus contains neither motor nor cardio-inhibotory neurons. In fact its electrical stimulation does not produce bradycardia (Achari, Dowman & Wibster, 1968; Borison & Domjan, 1970; Calaresu & Pearce, 1965; Gunn, Sevelius, Puiggari & Myers, 1968), and destruction of the nucleus does not abolish vagal cardio-inhibitory reflexes (Borison & Domjan, 1970) nor effect the responses obtained by stimulation of the vagus (Kerr, 1969). Kerr suggests that the dorsal vagus nucleus provides secretomotor fibres.

Thomas and Calaresu (1974) have obtained evidence that efferent vagal fibres for the heart (cardio-inhibitory) originate in the nucleus ambiguus. Efferent fibres from the nucleus ambiguus to the vagus nerve were clearly described in the cat by Winkler and Potter (1914), Papez (1929) and Windle (1933), but only a few authors have stated, on anatomical grounds, that the nucleus ambiguus contains cardio-inhibitory (Kosaka, 1909) and visceromotor (Hudovernig, 1908; Szabo & Dussardier, 1964) neurons. Anatomical (Morest, 1967) and physiological (Thomas & Calaresu, 1974) evidence suggests that excitation of the neurons of the nucleus ambiguus probably involves an interneuron located in the nucleus of the tractus solitarius.

8.6   Degeneration and regeneration of the vagus nerve

After cutting the vagus nerve of the rabbit and the cat (below the nodose ganglion) the electrical conduction of the myelinated fibres fails between the end of the third day and the fourth day (Cragg, 1965). Failure of electrical conduction along the unmyelinated fibres occurs later, and electrical responses over short distances were still detectable at the end of the sixth day — but not after (Cragg, 1965).

The cross-sectional area of the vagus distal to the cut increases in the first days after operation (170 and 140 per cent the control values on the 5th and 7th day) and is again within the normal range after 10 days (Cottle & Mitchell, 1966). Unlike the axons of the central nervous system, fragmented axons persist for relatively short periods in the degenerating vagus (Cottle & Mitchell, 1966).

Lewis *et al.* (1972) studied the changes in the neurons of the vagal dorsal nucleus of rat after section of the cervical vagus, and compared them with the changes in motor neurons of the spinal cord and the medulla after axotomy. The disappearance of AChE activity (described also by Dargent, 1963) and the increase of acid phosphatase activity occur within a few days from the operation; the disappearance of AChE activity is much quicker and more complete than in somatic motoneurons of the hypoglossal nucleus and the spinal cord, and the recovery is much slower and never complete. There is an extensive cell atrophy so that 18 months after the operation the cell population is reduced to about a quarter of that on the control side.

A slow regeneration and functional recovery follows a crush of the abdominal vagus nerves of the rabbit. On the other hand, following a crush of the cervical vagus, no evidence of functional recovery of the stomach was found even after survival periods of 600 days; only a few unmyelinated fibres had succeeded in regenerating to the stomach (Evans & Murray, 1954). The cardio-inhibitory fibres also regenerate slowly, and in most cases the regeneration is incomplete (Cameron, 1933). For the experiments of heterogeneous regeneration of the vagus nerve see Section 4.6.

Studying the propagation of action potentials *in vitro* at various times of regeneration after cervical vagotomy in the cat, Guth and Jacobson (1966) found a regeneration rate very similar to that of somatic nerves. The rate reached a maximum of 5·2 mm per day during the 5th week.

145

9 AUTONOMIC EFFERENT NEURONS IN THE CENTRAL NERVOUS SYSTEM

9.1 Sympathetic preganglionic neurons

The preganglionic neurons of the sympathetic pathway (visceral motor neurons) are located in the spinal cord, at the base of the ventral horn. They constitute a cellular column, the intermediolateral column (or nucleus), which in man reaches from the 1st thoracic to the upper lumbar segment and corresponds to the lateral horn. The rostral end of the intermediolateral nucleus of the rat (Navaratnam & Lewis, 1970), cat (Rexed, 1954; Henry & Calaresu, 1972) and man (Massazza, 1923, 1924; Gagel, 1928; Bok, 1928) is located at the limit between the cervical and thoracic spinal cord (Fig. 6). The caudal end of the cellular column is located by most authors between the first and third lumbar level. Henry and Calaresu (1972) found that the intermediolateral nucleus in the cat becomes less distinct in the lumbar levels but can be followed as far down as the fourth lumbar segment. Massazza (1923, 1924) and Bok (1928) reported that in man the intermediolateral column becomes thin in the midlumbar segments, but it extends down to the sacral spinal level where it merges with the sacral parasympathetic column.

About 88 000 neurons were counted in one human intermediolateral column (Bruce, 1908). In the cat the total number of neurons of this column ranges from 33 000 to 53 000, with no difference between right and left side; however, female cats have on average 35 000 ± 1400 [$N = 4$] neurons, while male cats have 46 000 ± 2500 [$N = 4$] (Henry & Calaresu, 1972). The significance of this sex difference in the number of neurons in cats of the same body weight (but probably not of the same age) is obscure. Petras and Cummings (1972) state that in the cat the visceral motor neurons appear in far greater number than somatic motor neurons. The neurons of the cat intermediolateral nucleus are substantially smaller than the corresponding somatic motorneurons (Henry & Calaresu, 1972). In the

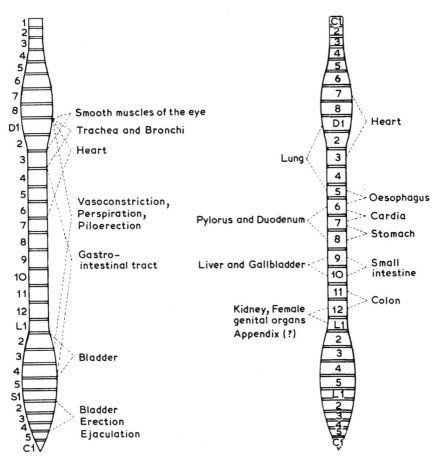

Figure 6. Schematic representation of the human spinal cord. (From Greving, 1928.) Left. Segmental distribution of the preganglionic neurons related to various peripheral organs. Right. Segments of the spinal cord where sensory fibres related to various peripheral organs reach the central nervous system.

monkey, however, many autonomic motor neurons are as large as somatic motor neurons (Petras & Cummings, 1972).

The distribution of preganglionic sympathetic neurons is more complex than it appears from the above description. Many authors have reported on other preganglionic cell nuclei (see Pick, 1970) and in a detailed study Petras and Cummings (1972) have identified several nuclei in the so-called 'zona intermedia' of the spinal cord of the rhesus monkey. These authors also observed that visceral afferent

147

fibres from the dorsal roots do not synapse on the visceral motor neurons; the visceral reflex pathway always includes at least one interneurone, probably situated in the intermediolateral nucleus or in the nucleus proprius cornus dorsalis.

In the cat the neurons of the intermediolateral column are elongated, with a long diameter of 25—35 µm, and oriented longitudinally (Réthelyi, 1972). Most of the dendrites originate from the poles of the cells and run in a longitudinal direction, giving the intermediolateral column, when stained with the Golgi method, a fence-like appearance in longitudinal sections. The axons emerge with conspicuous axon-hillock from the soma or more often from a dendrite. In electron microscopy three types of nerve endings are seen synapsing on these neurons (Réthelyi, 1972): small endings containing spherical electron-lucent vesicles and synapsing on spine-like dendrite projections; relatively large endings containing flat electron-lucent vesicles and synapsing on perikarya; and large dendrites and endings containing a preponderance of large dense-cored vesicles and synapsing on large and medium-sized dendrites. Different types of nerve ending have also been observed in the intermediolateral nucleus of the rat, where they form synaptic glomeruli with the dendrites (Wong & Tan, 1974).

Abundant noradrenaline-containing endings are seen by fluorescence microscopy forming pericellular nests around the neurons of the intermediolateral nucleus of rat, mouse, guinea-pig, rabbit, cat and dog (Dahlström and Fuxe, 1965b). Other, less numerous endings contain 5-hydroxy-tryptamine. Both types of ending (in the rat) completely disappear caudal to a spinal cord transection (Dahlström and Fuxe, 1965b). The neurons have an intense acetylcholinesterase activity (Navaratnam and Lewis, 1970).

The preganglionic fibres (see Section 2.8) emerge from the spinal cord with the somatic motor fibres. In addition to the main autonomic outflow (cholinergic preganglionic fibres from the intermediolateral nucleus and related nuclei, to the paravertebral and prevertebral ganglia) Dahlström and Fuxe (1965a) observed in the rat a number of catecholamine-containing fibres leaving the spinal cord through the ventral roots. These fibres must originate from supraspinal centres, since catecholamine-containing cell bodies are not present in the spinal cord, but their origin and termination are unknown.

148

9.2   Sacral parasympathetic preganglionic neurons

The sacral parasympathetic preganglionic neurons are located in a cellular column in the intermediate region between ventral and dorsal horns. Its extent is more variable or more ill-defined than that of the sympathetic preganglionic neurons, but it usually occupies 2—3 spinal segments in the sacral region. The nucleus has a similar position as the intermediolateral nucleus of the thoraco-lumbar segments, and some authors describe a thin cellular column connecting the two (Massazza, 1923; Bok, 1928). Another nucleus possibly related to the parasympathetic pathway is the *nucleus medialis myoleioticus*, which extends through the sacral part of the cord (Massazza, 1923; Bok, 1928). In man the sacral parasympathetic outflow is restricted to the 3rd and 4th and to a small extent to the 5th sacral segment (Sheehan, 1941; Pick, 1970). In the cat the outflow is mainly through the 2nd and 3rd sacral nerves (Langley & Anderson, 1895, 1896; Elliott, 1907; De Groat & Ryall, 1968). When studied by intracellular recording the preganglionic parasympathetic neurons of the cat are in many respects similar to the preganglionic sympathetic neurons. The conduction velocities range between $2 \cdot 1 - 15 \text{ ms}^{-1}$, with most of the fibres conducting at $6 - 10 \text{ ms}^{-1}$ (thinly myelinated axons) (De Groat & Ryall, 1968). These neurons are richly supplied with terminals containing 5-hydroxy-tryptamine, which are situated mainly around the cell bodies (Dahlström & Fuxe, 1965b). In the rat the neurons display an intense acetylcholinesterase activity (Navaratnam & Lewis, 1970) (Note 9.1).

Note 9.1
Navaratnam and Lewis (1970) observed that unilateral section of the pelvic nerves of the rat was followed by a reduction of the acetylcholinesterase activity (as usually found in chromatolytic neurons) in about a third of the neurons of the sacral parasympathetic nucleus on both sides of the spinal cord.

Note 9.2
Data on the preganglionic neurons of the cranial parasympathetic system have been briefly reported in Chapters 6 and 8.

10   INNERVATION OF ORGANS

In this last chapter the autonomic innervation of the organs is examined, and for reasons of space only a rather cursory account can be made. When studying the innervation of an organ from an anatomical point of view the information that is usually wanted refers to:

(a) the origin of the nerve fibres innervating the effectors (muscular, glandular) of the organ; site of the cell of origin of the fibres, the path of the fibres themselves.

(b) distribution of the fibres within the organ, density of innervation and pattern of distribution.

(c) characteristics of the neuro-effector junction, frequency of the junctions and distance between the apposed membranes.

(d) types of fibres, for example whether afferent or efferent, their neurotransmitters, their sizes.

The availability of this information is a necessary prerequisite (but not a sufficient one) for any description of the nerve control of the activity of that organ.

10.1   Eye

10.1.1   *Iris*
The iris is supplied by adrenergic fibres originating in the superior cervical ganglion and by post-ganglionic parasympathetic fibres from the ciliary ganglion.

In small-sized, albino mammals the adrenergic innervation of the iris can be easily visualized by fluorescence microscopy on whole-mount preparations of the organ (Falck, 1962; Malmfors, 1965). It consists of a finely-meshed, two-dimensional network of varicose fibres, which is spread over the whole iris (Malmfors, 1965), lying underneath, or on the corneal surface of the muscle cells (myo-epithelial cells) of the dilator pupillae (Nilsson, 1964). The distance between muscle cells and nerve endings is over 70 nm (Nilsson, 1964).

In the region of the sphincter pupillae, a narrow muscular band close to the pupillary endge of the iris, the adrenergic fibres run mostly parallel to the muscle cells (that is, circularly) and are situated within the muscle (Malmfors, 1965). The occurrence of adrenergic fibres, as seen in fluorescence microscopy, in the sphincter pupillae has been confirmed for the rat (Ehinger, 1966), for the monkey and the cat (Laties & Jacobowitz, 1966) and for the rabbit (Laties & Jacobowitz, 1966; Ochi, Konishi, Yoshikawa & Sano, 1968). In electron microscopy adrenergic endings (i.e. endings containing small granular vesicles) were seen after permanganate fixation in the rat (Hökfelt, 1966; Tranzer & Thoenen, 1967), rabbit (Ochi, *et al.*, 1968) and guinea-pig (Nishida & Sears, 1969). According to Nishida and Sears (1969) about 15 per cent of the nerve endings in the sphincter pupillae are adrenergic, the remainder being cholinergic. Ivens, Mottram, Lever, Pesley and Howells (1973) have reported that the rat sphincter pupillae receives no adrenergic fibres.

By partial (sub-total) destruction of the rat superior cervical ganglion Malmfors and Sachs (1965b) could follow the branching of the few adrenergic fibres left in the iris prepared as a whole-mount for fluorescence microscopy. Branches from the same axon are found in different parts of the dilator muscle, in the sphincter and around blood vessels; the same fibre is therefore inhibitory (to the sphincter) and excitatory (to the dilator) (Malmfors & Sachs, 1965b). Whether this arrangement is typical of a partially denervated iris, or if it also occurs in normal conditions, has not yet been ascertained. In the intact iris the network is so thick that individual fibres cannot be followed. It has been calculated that the entire arborization from each ganglion neuron in the rat iris has about 26 000 varicosities (Dahlström, 1967).

The sphincter pupillae is mainly innervated by cholinergic fibres. They are varicose and run parallel to the muscle cells. The fibres are grouped in small bundles but in their final length they can be single and no longer sheathed by Schwann cells. The varicosities, up to $2 \mu m$ in length, are present in the isolated fibres as well as those in bundles. Most of the varicosities lie close to muscle cells, and in about half of them the neuro-muscular gap is only 20 nm (Gabella, 1974). Close neuro-muscular contacts were also seen in the rabbit and cat (Evans & Evans, 1964). At these close neuro-muscular contacts Uehara and Burnstock (1972) observed, sub-surface cisternae of sarcoplasmic reticulum in the muscle cells and a continuous electron-dense layer between the muscle cell membrane and the outer membrane of the cisterna. Another characteristic of some neuro-muscular contacts of the guinea-pig sphincter pupillae are dense projections and membrane thickenings on both sides of the junction (Gabella, 1974). In the rat iris adrenergic and cholinergic axons are in close apposition (20–25 nm) with melanophores (Ehinger & Falck, 1970a).

10.1.2 *Nictitating membrane*

The muscles of the nictitating membrane of the cat are supplied by post-ganglionic myelinated fibres issuing from the superior cervical ganglion, which run in the internal carotid nerve, join the ophthalmic division of the trigeminal nerve and then accompany the nasociliar and infratochlear nerves (Thompson, 1961) (see also p.41). In fluorescence microscopy a thick network of adrenergic fibres is visible in the muscle and around the vessels (Weiner, Langer & Trendelenburg, 1967); it disappears within few days of the exicision of the superior cervical ganglion. The innervation is provided mainly by single axons, without investing Schwann cell processes, which can be as close as 20 nm to a muscle cell (Evans & Evans, 1964; Taxi, 1965).

10.2 Salivary glands

Submandibular and parotid glands receive a dual innervation by adrenergic and cholinergic fibres. In man fluorescent fibres and acetylcholinesterase-positive fibres form a network between and around the acini (Norberg, Hökfelt & Eneroth, 1969). Similar observations were made in numerous mammalian species (Note 10.2) (Norberg & Olson, 1965; Fujiwara, Tanaka, Hikosaka & Okegawa, 1965; Freitag & Engel, 1970; Alm, Bloom & Carlsöö, 1973 and others).

With the electron microscope two types of nerve ending, characterizeed by electron-lucent vesicles and by small granular vesicles respectively (with permanganate fixation), are seen in the rat parotid (Hand, 1972). The axons penetrate the basal lamina and come into close contact (about 10 nm) with one or more acinar cells. Most acinar cells are in contact with a number of nerve terminals (mostly varicosities along the length of the axon) of either or of both types. Close nerve-acinar cells contacts were not observed in the cat parotid (Garrett, 1966) the innervation of which seems to be exclusively cholinergic (Fritz & Botelho, 1969). In the submandibular gland close contacts were observed only in the mucous component of the gland in the cat (Shackleford & Wilborn, 1970) and monkey (Cowley & Shackleford, 1970). Fibres which pierce the basal lamina and make a close (gap of about 20 nm) contact with myo-epithelial or secretory cells were observed in the human submandibular (Tandler, 1965) and labial glands (Tandler & Ross, 1969).

The submandibular gland of the guinea-pig, mouse and rat receives no adrenergic fibres (apart from those related to its blood vessels) and its innervation is entirely cholinergic (Note 10.1) (Norberg & Olson, 1965; Alm *et al.*, 1973). In the hamster, however, the sublingual gland has an adrenergic innervation as rich as the other salivary glands (Alm *et al.*, 1973).

10.3 Skin and appendages

The motor innervation for the muscles of the hairs (arrectores pilorum) is provided by adrenergic fibres from the paravertebral ganglia. Numerous adrenergic fibres are seen by fluorescence microscopy in the arrectores pilorum muscles of man, the rabbit and the cat (Falck & Rorsman, 1963) and of the ox (Thompson, Robertshaw & Findlay, 1969), running parallel to the muscle cells. Adrenergic fibres are not seen in the vicinity of or within hair follicles, eccrine and apocrine sweat glands, or sebaceous glands (Falck & Rorsman, 1963). Whereas apocrine sweat glands are not known to receive any secretory innervation (Lovatt-Evans, 1957), eccrine sweat glands are innervated by sympathetic cholinergic fibres (p.42), which originate from the paravertebral ganglia.

The mammary gland receives a sparse autonomic innervation (Hebb & Linzell, 1970). Adrenergic fibres are abundant in the adventitia of all arteries and among the smooth muscle cells of the teat. Cholinergic fibres are not found in any part of the gland. There is no evidence of a nerve supply to the secretory cells or the myoepithelial cells of the mammary gland (Hebb & Linzell, 1970). The lack of autonomic innervation of the gland proper is in agreement with the observation that unilateral extirpation of the entire sympathetic chain caused no difference in lactation between the mammary glands of the two sides (Bacq, 1932).

10.4 Adipose tissue

In mammals two types of adipose tissue are described, white and brown. The brown fat, which is found only in specific anatomical locations (Cameron & Smith, 1964), is characterized (among other features) by a rich sympathetic innervation (Hausberger, 1934; Bargmann, Hehn & Lindner, 1968); the fibres are adrenergic (readily visible in fluorescence microscopy), and form nest-like networks around every fat cell (Wirsén & Hamberger, 1967; Derry *et al.*, 1969) (Note 10.2). Thin, naked axons are found closely attached to the fat cells, often embedded in invaginations of their surface (Bargmann *et al.*, 1968). In the mouse and rat the noradrenaline content of the brown fat is as high as that of heart or spleen (Sideman *et al.*, 1962), and there is evidence of a direct nervous influence on the metabolism of the brown fat (Sidman & Fawcett, 1954). On the other hand, the white adipose tissue contains no adrenergic fibres, except those related to the blood vessels (Daniel & Derry, 1969), and its noradrenaline content is only about 3 per cent that of brown adipose tissue (Stock & Westerman, 1963).

10.5 Alimentary tract

The main nerve component for the innervation of the alimentary tract are the intramural plexuses (Chapter 7). Extrinsic fibres reach the intramural ganglia within the vagus nerves and as small nerves satellite of blood vessels. The few data available on the endings of the vagal fibres are reported in Chapter 8.

The endings of adrenergic fibres, either synapsing on intramural neurons or as intramuscular or perivascular or mucosal endings, are discussed in Chapter 3 and Section 7.5. Isolated nerve fibres are very rarely observed; up to their end the adrenergic fibres run in small nerve bundles, where they are usually associated with fibres of different types. Biochemical studies have shown that only about 10 per cent of the total content of intraneuronally-stored noradrenaline is presnet in the myenteric plexus, the rest being found in the other

154

layers of the wall (Juorio & Gabella, 1974). Adrenergic fibres are by no means absent from the circular muscle layer (Gabella & Costa, 1969; Read & Burnstock, 1969; Silva *et al.*, 1971), as had previously been claimed. Adrenergic fibres are rare in the longitudinal muscle layer of the guinea-pig ileum, but they are present in the taeniae coli (Åberg & Eränkö, 1967) and in the longitudinal musculature of the large intestine. Intramuscular adrenergic fibres are particularly abundant in some of the sphincters of the alimentary tract, e.g. the cardiac sphincter and the anal sphincter in the guinea-pig (Costa & Gabella, 1968, 1971; Furness & Costa, 1973), the pylorus of the rat (Gillespie & Maxwell, 1971). In Hirschprung's disease the portion of the large intestine affected by congenital lack of intramural neurons shows an extremely rich adrenergic innervation (Gannon, Noblet & Burnstock, 1969). Blood vessels of the intestinal wall have an adventitial adrenergic innervation, very rich in arteries and sparse in veins (Silva *et al.*, 1971; Furness, 1971). It has been suggested that also nerve fibres of intrinsic origin innervate the blood vessels of the small intestine of cat (Biber *et al.*, 1973).

Intramuscular nerve endings are rarely closely associated with smooth muscle cells, a gap of 100 nm or more usually occurring between the two elements (Taxi, 1965). Some neuromuscular contacts with a gap of only 20 nm can be observed on special, small and electron-dense muscle cells lying at the innermost border of the circular layer. It is in this part of the wall that the nerve endings are most numerous. Most or all the intramuscular fibres are varicose in shape; on the basis of their vesicle content they can be classified in the same classes as the nerve endings described in Section 7.5.

10.6 Heart

The innervation of the heart is provided by fibres which originate from or pass through the cardiac plexus (see Chapter 5). Both cholinergic and adrenergic fibres reach the heart, the former (parasympathetic post-ganglionic fibres) originating from ganglion cells of the cardiac plexus, the latter (sympathetic post-ganglionic fibres) originating from ganglion cells of the paravertebral chain. In most species small ganglia, mainly constituted of cholinergic neurons (Jacobowitz, Cooper & Barner, 1967) are consistently found very close to or within the atrial walls, particularly near the sino-atrial and atrio-ventricular nodes. Adrenergic neurons are not found within the atrial

155

walls, but chromaffin, intensely-fluorescent are usually present (Nielsen & Owman, 1968). Adrenergic fibres are abundant in the atria, particularly at the sino-atrial and atrio-ventricular nodes (Angelakos, Fuxe & Torchiana, 1963; Dahlström, Fuxe, Maya-Tu & Zetterström, 1965; Nielsen & Owman, 1968); the nerve fibres are related both to the blood vessels and to the myocardium proper. In a number of mammalian species adrenergic fibres are less conspicuous in the ventricles, with the exception of the cat where adrenergic fibres appear to be more numerous in the ventricles than in the atria (Nielsen & Owman, 1968). Cholinergic fibres are also more numerous in the atrial walls, particularly in the proximity of the sino-atrial and atrio-ventricular nodes, than in other parts of the heart.

Nerve endings form neuro-muscular junctions with a gap of 78–100 nm, with muscle cells of the atria, the interventricular septum and the outer ventricular walls; in the mouse, neuro-muscular junctions seem to be absent from the apex of the heart (Thaemert, 1969). In man, nerve endings containing small granular vesicles (adrenergic) predominate by 2 to 1 in the ventricular myocardium, whereas in the atrial myocardium agranular vesicle containing endings (cholinergic) predominate (Chiba & Yamauchi, 1970). (For the innervation of the heart see a review by Yamauchi, 1973).

10.7 Blood vessels

There is great variability between the various blood vessels as regards their innervation (Burnstock, 1970). Some vessels lack all nerve supply (the umbilical vessels [Lachenmeyer, 1971]), others have an exceedingly rich innervation (e.g. those of the nasal erectile tissue [Dahlström & Fuxe, 1965c]). Arterioles with very rich innervation (e.g. those in the submucosa of the rat stomach) are interpreted as having a sphincteric function (Norberg, 1967).

In most blood vessels the innervation is confined to the adventitia and therefore the majority of muscle cells are not innervated. The nerve bundles form a meshwork mainly developed along the length of the vessel (Grigor'eva, 1962; Falck, 1962). Differences in the density of innervation occur along the vascular arterial tree. For example, in the cat the nerve supply to the arteries greatly increases after they have entered a skeletal muscle (Fuxe & Sedvall, 1965). The innervation is abundant in the muscular arteries and in arterioles (Norberg & Hamberger, 1964). These observations do not clarify to what extent blood vessels are under nervous control, and there is physiological evidence (e.g. Wiedeman, 1968) suggesting that arterioles contract independently of nerve influences. Capillaries are not innervated and only sparse fibres are found around veins. The fibres are varicose, with the vesicles and the neurotransmitter present in the varicosities. It is not clear how long is the varicose portion of a vascular nerve fibres and how many of the fibres, particularly around large vessels, are in transit to more peripheral vessels.

Most of the vascular nerve fibres are adrenergic and are readily visualized in fluorescence microscopy (Falck, 1962). Cholinergic fibres are also present in some blood vessels and the two types of fibre can be situated in the same bundle. In the pial vessels of several mammals about 50 per cent of the fibres are cholinergic (Edvinsson, Nielsen, Owman & Sporrong, 1972).

Even for the muscle cells which are in direct contact with the nerve endings, i.e. those of the outer part of the media, the neuro-muscular distance is considerable. In the pulmonary artery of the cat and rabbit the minimum distance is $0.4\,\mu$m and many nerve endings lie more than $1\,\mu$m from the nearest muscle cell (Verity & Bevan, 1968). In the mammalian pial vessels the smallest neuromuscular distance is $80-110$ nm (Edvinsson *et al.*, 1972). In general the neuro-muscular distance is rarely less than 100 nm. The distance is smaller in arterioles than in small arteries (Devine & Simpson, 1967), and, at least in the rabbit ear artery, the neuro-muscular distance varies with distension and contraction of the vessel (Govyrin, 1975).

Vessels where nerve fibres are found within the media include sheep carotid artery (Keatinge, 1966), the rabbit saphenous artery (Beran & Purdy, 1973), and cutaneous veins (Ehinger, Falck & Sporrong, 1966). Among the veins with a rich adrenergic innervation are those of the cat spleen (Gillespie & Kirpekar, 1965), and the mesenteric vein (Holman & McLean, 1967).

Most of the vascular adrenergic nerve fibres originate from the ganglia of the sympathetic chain. In monkeys, the sympathetic fibres to the cerebral vessels originate from small intracranial ganglia, and therefore do not degenerate after excision of the superior cervical ganglion (Chorobski & Penfield, 1932). There is some evidence that brain vessels may receive adrenergic fibres from neurons of the central nervous system (Hartman, 1973; Edvinsson *et al.*, 1972).

Cholinergic fibres in the vessels of skeletal muscles originate from ganglia of the sympathetic chain (sympathetic cholinergic fibres) and are vasodilator (Bülbring & Burn, 1935). Those of the uterine artery originate from the paracervical ganglion (Bell, 1974) and those of the cerebral vessels from parasympathetic ganglia of the head (Chorobski & Penfield, 1932; Edvinsson et al., 1972). It has been suggested that vasodilator fibres for the vessles of the cat small intestine may originate from the intramural ganglia (Biber et al., 1973).

10.8 Spleen

Numerous post-ganglionic sympathetic fibres innervate the spleen. All the nerve fibres to the spleen of the cat are adrenergic (Thoenen, Tranzer, Hürlimann & Haefely, 1966; Fillenz, 1970). The adrenergic fibres, as shown by fluorescence microscopy, are confined to the smooth muscle in the capsule and trabeculae and in the blood vessels; no fibres are found in the white or red pulp (Gillespie & Kirpekar, 1965). As in most arteries, adrenergic fibres do not penetrate into the media. The veins of the spleen, on the contrary, are more richly innervated than most other veins, and the nerve fibres are found throughout the whole thickness of the wall. In electron microscopy, the adrenergic endings in the spleen capsule of the cat appear to lie at a distance over 100 nm from the smooth muscle cells (Tranzer & Thoenen, 1967).

10.9 Respiratory tract

The autonomic innervation to the lungs is mainly confined to the bronchi and the pulmonary vessels (Larsell, 1921; Honjin, 1956; El-Bermani, 1973), although nerve fibres have been described in the pleura (Larsell, 1921) and in the wall of the alveoli (Hirsch, et al., 1968). The bronchial innervation extends to the level of the respiratory bronchioles (Honjin, 1956; El-Bermani, 1973). The efferent innervation is provided by motor fibres to the bronchial and vascular musculature and secretory fibres to the mucous glands. These fibres are cholinergic and probably parasympathetic in origin. Small ganglia or individual ganglion neurons, intensely acetylcholinesterase positive, are associated with the larger nerves, especially near the hilum. At the level of the hilum some vagal fibres cross over to the lung of the other side (Honjin, 1956).

158

10.10 Female genital tract

The number of nerve fibres in the uterine wall is rather small and relatively few bulbar expansions, close enough to muscle cells to be considered nerve endings, are seen by methylene blue staining (Pallie, Corner & Weddell, 1954; Clegg, 1963). Nerve fibres are also seen in the wall of blood vessels and in the endometrium (Krantz, 1959). Adrenergic fibres are seen by fluorescence microscopy in the myometrium. There are large species variations: the adrenergic innervation is richer in the uterus of the cat (Rosengren & Sjöberg, 1967) than in the rabbit (Owman & Sjöberg, 1966) and guinea-pig (Sjöberg, 1968), and it is apparently limited to the blood vessels in the rat (Norberg & Fredricsson, 1966). In the human uterus the adrenergic innervation is richer in the cervix than in the corpus or fundus (Owman, Rosengren & Sjöberg, 1967). The fibres originate from ganglia of the pelvic plexus situated a short distance from the uterus (Langley & Anderson, 1895; Sjöberg, 1968). In the rat some ganglion cells may be found within the myometrium adjacent to the mesometrium (Clegg, 1962).

In the rabbit, fluorescent fibres increase in number in the first part of pregnancy and are reduced towards the end of gestation (Sjöberg, 1967). A marked reduction during pregnancy is observed also in guinea-pigs (in both the horn which contains the embyos and the contralateral, 'empty' horn) and the total content of noradrenaline falls by more than 80 per cent (Sjöberg, 1968). On the other hand, the ovary, where nerve fibres are found along blood vessels and in the stroma (Rosengren & Sjöberg, 1967; Jacobowitz & Wallach, 1967; Fink & Schofield, 1971), the adrenergic fibres originate from para- and prevertebral ganglia and do not appear altered during preganancy (Sjöberg, 1967).

10.11 Male genital tract

Male internal genital genital organs are richly supplied with adrenergic fibres which originate from ganglia of the pelvic plexus (Langley & Anderson, 1895; Sjöstrand, 1965). The adrenergic innervation is particularly rich in the musculature of the vas deferens and the seminal vesicle. In the vas deferens of the rat and mouse all muscle cells are contacted by one or more nerve endings (Taxi, 1965). In the guinea-pig vas deferens about half the muscle cells have neuro-muscular contacts of 20 nm or less (Merrillees, 1968); many adrenergic endings lie in deep invaginations of the muscle cell surface (Furness & Iwayama, 1972). Cholinergic nerve endings are also present in the vas deferens of the guinea-pig (Furness & Iwayama, 1972); many of the adrenergic fibres penetrate deep into the muscle cell (occasionally tunnelling through it (Furness & Iwayama, 1971)) and are separated by a neuro-muscular gap of only 10–20 nm.

An interesting observation made by Wakade and Kipekar (1973) in the rat is that the reduction in weight of the vas deferens following castration is accompanied by a proportional decrease in total noradrenaline content, so that the concentration of amine per unit weight remains constant. On the other hand, in this organ the concentration of noradrenaline increases during adult life (Sjöstrand & Swedin, 1967), and in the mouse vas deferens the number of axons (per 100 muscle cells) and the number of close (20 nm) neuro-muscular junctions continue to increase up to 6 months of age (Yamauchi & Burnstock, 1969b).

In the electron microscope adrenergic and cholinergic fibres, recognized by their vesicle content, run together in small bundles in the ratio of about 3 to 1 in the rabbit myometrium (Hervonen & Kanerva, 1973). Both types of fibres have vesicle-loaded varicosities which are never less than 20 nm from the nearest muscle cell. In the rat uterus, however, neuro-muscular gaps of only 20–30 nm have been observed (Silva, 1967).

For further details on the innervation of the ovary, oviduct, uterus and vagina, see the reviews of Sjöberg (1967) and Marshall (1970).

Note 10.1
Alm *et al.* (1973) noted that there is not a good correlation between fluorescence microscopy evidence and biochemical estimation of catecholamines in the salivary glands. There are marked differences in noradrenaline content in the salivary glands of various species, in spite of a similar pattern of adrenergic innervation. Moreover, the sublingual gland of the guinea-pig, which is almost devoid of adrenergic fibres, contains about the same amounts of noradrenaline as the cow submandibular gland, which has a rich adrenergic innervation.

Note 10.2
It has been reported that in the rat interscapular (brown) fat the adrenergic fibres for the blood vessels originate from the paravertebral

ganglia, and those for the fat cells from local neurons (Derry *et al.*, 1969). The presence of neurons in the brown fat of rat has not yet been documented, and the fluorescent cells described as neurons have the characteristics of chromaffin cells. Moreover, after section of the nerve to the interscapular brown fat body the noradrenaline content falls virtually to zero (Sidman *et al.*, 1962).

REFERENCES

Aars, H. (1971), Diameter and elasticity of the ascending aorta during infusion of noradrenaline. *Acta physiol. scand.* **83**, 133—138.

Åberg, G. and **Eränkö, O.** (1967), Localization of noradrenaline and acetylcholinesterase in the taenia of the guinea-pig cecum. *Acta physiol. scand.* **69**, 383—384.

Abraham, A. (1952), The comparative histology of the stellate ganglion. *Acta biol. hung.* **2**, 311—354.

Achari, N.K., Dowman, C.B. and **Webster, M.V.** (1968), A cardioinhibitory pathway in the brain stem of the cat. *J. Physiol., Lond.* **197**, 35P.

Acheson, G.H. and **Remolina, J.** (1955), The temporal course of the effects of post-ganglionic axotomy of the inferior mesenteric ganglion of the cat. *J. Physiol., Lond.* **127**, 603—616.

Acheson, G.H. and **Schwarzacher, H.G.** (1956), Correlations between the physiological changes and the morphological changes resulting from axotomy in the inferior mesenteric ganglion of the cat. *J. comp. Neurol.* **106**, 247—267.

Ackerknecht, E.H. (1974), The history of the discovery of the vegetative (autonomic) nervous system. *Med. Hist.* **18**, 1—8.

Adams, W.E. (1942), Observations on the lacertilian sympathetic system. *J. Anat.* **77**, 6—11.

Agostoni, E., Chinnock, J.E., Daly, M.D.B. and **Murray, J.G.** (1957), Functional and histological studies of the vagus nerve and its branches to the heart, lungs and abdominal viscera in the cat. *J. Physiol., Lond.* **135**, 182—205.

Aguayo, A.J., Martin, J.B., and **Bray, G.M.** (1972), Effects of nerve growth factor antiserum on peripheral unmyelinated nerve fibres. *Acta neuropath.* **20**, 288—298.

Aguayo, A.J., Terry, L.C. and **Bray, G.M.** (1973), Spontaneous loss of axons in sympathetic unmyelinated nerve fibers of the rat during development. *Brain Res.* **54**, 360—364.

Ahlman, H. and **Enerbäck, L.** (1974), A cytofluorimetric study of the myenteric plexus in the guinea-pig. *Cell Tiss. Res.* **153**, 419—434.

Aiken, J.W. and **Reit, E.** (1968), Stimulation of the cat stellate ganglion by Angiotensin. *J. Pharmac. exp. Ther.* **159**, 107—114.

Alexander, W.F., Kuntz, A., Henderson, W.P. and **Ehrlich, E.** (1949), Sympathetic ganglion cells in ventral roots. Their relation to sympathectomy. *Science* **109**, 484.

Alm, P., Bloom, G.D. and Carlsöö (1973), Adrenergic and cholinergic nerves of bovine, guinea-pig and hamster salivary glands. *Z.Zellforsch.* **138**, 407–420.

Amprino, R. (1938), Modifications de la structure des neurones sympathiques pendant l'accroissement et la sénéscence. Recherches sur le ganglion cervical supérieur. *C. r. Ass. Anat.* **33**, 3–18.

Anderson, H.K. (1902). The nature of the lesions which hinder the development of nerve-cells and their processes. *J. Physiol., Lond.* **28**, 499–513.

Andres, K.H. and Kautzky, R. (1955), Die Frühentwicklung der vegetativen Hals- und Kopf-ganglien des Menschen. *Z. Anat. Entw. Gesch.* **119**, 55–84.

Andrew, A. (1964), The origin of intramural ganglia. I. The early arrival of precursor cells in the presumptive gut of chick embryo. *J. Anat.* **98**, 421–428.

Andrew, A. (1969), The origin of intramural ganglia. II. The trunk neural crest as a source of enteric ganglion cells. *J. Anat.* **105**, 89–101.

Andrew, A. (1970), The origin of intramural ganglia. III. The 'vagal' source of enteric ganglion cells. *J. Anat.* **107**, 327–336.

Andrew, A. (1971), The origin of intramural ganglia. IV. The origin of enteric ganglia: a critical review and discussion of the present state of the problem. *J. Anat.* **108**, 169–184.

Andrew, B.L. (1956), A functional analysis of the myelinated fibres of the superior laryngeal nerve of the rat. *J. Physiol., Lond.* **133**, 420–432.

Angelakos, E.T., Fuxe, K. and Torchiana, M.L. (1963), Chemical and histochemical evaluation of the distribution of catecholamines in the rabbit and guinea-pig hearts. *Acta physiol. scand.* **59**, 184–192.

Angelakos, E.T., Glassman, P.M., Millard, R.W. and King, M. (1965), Regional distribution and subcellular localization of catecholamines in the frog heart. *Comp. Biochem. Physiol.,* **15**, 313–324.

Angelakos, E.T., King, M.P. and Millard, R.W. (1969), Regional distribution of catecholamines in the hearts of various species. *Ann. N.Y. Acad. Sci.* **156**, 219–240.

Angeletti, P.U. (1972), Chemical sympathectomy in the newborn. In: *Immunosympathectomy,* edited by Steiner, G. and Schönbaum, E., pp. 237–250. Amsterdam: Elsevier.

Angeletti, P.U. and Levi-Montalcini, R. (1970), Sympathetic nerve cell destruction in newborn mammals by 6-hydroxydopamine. *Proc. natn Acad. Sci. U.S.A.* **65**, 114–121.

Angeletti, P.U., Levi-Montalcini, R. and Caramia, F. (1971a), Analysis of the effects of the antiserum to the nerve growth factor in adult mice. *Brain Res.* **27**, 343–355.

Angeletti, P.U., Levi-Montalcini, R. and Caramia, F. (1971b), Ultrastructural changes in sympathetic neurons of newborn and adult mice treated with nerve growth factor. *J. Ultrastruct. Res.* **36**, 24–36.

Angeletti, P.U., Levi-Montalcini, R. and **Caramia, F.** (1972), Structural and ultrastructural changes in developing sympathetic ganglia produced by guanethidine. *Brain Res.* **43**, 515–525.

Anton, A.H. and **Sayre, D.F.** (1964), The distribution of dopamine and dopa in various animals and a method for their determination in diverse biological material, *J. Pharmac. exp. Ther.* **145**, 326–336.

Ariëns Kappers, J. (1960), The development, topographical relations and innervations of the epiphysis cerebri in the albino rat. *Z. Zellforsch.* **52**, 163–215.

Ariëns Kappers, C.U., Huber, G.C. and **Crosby, E.C.** (1936), *The Comparative Anatomy of the Nervous System of Vertebrates, including Man,* Vol. I, New York: Hafner.

Axelrod, J. (1971), Noradrenaline: fate and control of its biosynthesis. *Science* **173**, 598–606.

Axelsson, S., Björklund, A., Falck, B., Lindvall, O. and **Svensson, L.-A.** (1973), Glycoxylic acid condensation: a new fluorescence method for the histochemical demonstration of biogenic amines. *Acta physiol. scand.* **87**, 57–62.

Azuma, T., Binia, A. and **Visscher, M.B.** (1965), Adrenergic mechanisms in the bullfrog and turtle. *Am. J. Physiol.* **209**, 1287–1294.

Babmindra, V.P. and **Diatchkova, L.P.** (1970), Dynamics of processes of degeneration of interneuronal synapses. *Arkh. Anat. Gistol Embryol.* **58**, 82–90. quoted in: Taxi, J. & Babmindra, V.P. (1972).

Bacq, Z.M. (1932), The effect of sympathectomy on sexual functions, lactation, and the maternal behaviour of the albino rat. *Am. J. Physiol.* **99**, 444–453.

Banks, B.E.C., Charlwood, K.A., Edwards, D.C., Vernon, C.A. and **Walter, S.J.** (1975), Effects of nerve growth factors from mouse salivary glands and snake venom on the sympathetic ganglia of neonatal and developing mice. *J. Physiol., Lond.* **247**, 289–298.

Banks, P. and **Mayor, D.** (1973), Intra-axonal transport in noradrenergic neurons in the sympathetic nervous system, *Biochem. Soc. Symp.* **36**, 133–149.

Bannister, J. and **Scrase, J.** (1950), Acetylcholine synthesis in normal and denervated sympathetic ganglia of the cat. *J. Physiol., Lond.* **111**, 437–444.

Bargmann, W., Hehn, G.von and **Lindner, E.** (1968), Über die Zellen des braunen Fettgewebes und ihre Innervation. *Z. Zellforsch.* **85**, 601–613.

Baumgarten, H.G. (1967), Uber die Verteilung von Catecholaminen in Darm des Mesnchen. *Z. Zellforsch.* **83**, 133–146.

Baumgarten, H.G. and **Holstein, A.F.** (1968), Adrenergic Innervation in Hoden und Nebehoden vom Schwan (*Cygnus olor*). *Z. Zellforsch.* **91**, 402–410.

Baumgarten, H.G., Holstein, A.F. and **Owman, Ch.** (1970), Auberbach's plexus of mammals and man: electron microscopic identification of three different types of neuronal processes in myenteric ganglia of the large intestine from rhesus monkey, guinea-pigs and man. *Z. Zellforsch.* **106**, 376–397.

Baumgarten, H.G., Björklund, A., Lachenmayer, L. Nobin, A. and Rosengren, E. (1973), Evidence for the existence of seroronin-, dopamine-, and noradrenaline-containing neurons in the gut of *Lampreta fluviatilis. Z. Zellforsch.* **141**, 33–35.

Becker, K. (1968), Über die vakuolenhaltigen Nervenzellen im Ganglion cervicale uteri der Ratte. *Z. Zellforsch.* **88**, 318–339.

Becker, R.F. and Grunt, J.A. (1957), The cervical sympathetic ganglia. *Anat. Rec.* **127**, 1–14.

Bell, C. (1974), Selective cholinergic denervation of the uterine artery in the guinea-pig. *Experientia* **30**, 257–258.

Bell, C. and McLean, J.R. (1967), Localization of norepinephrine and acetylcholinesterase in separate neurons supplying the guinea-pig vas deferens. *J. Pharmac. exp. Ther.* **157**, 69–73.

Belmonte, C., Simon, J., Gallego, R. and Baron, M. (1972), Sympathetic fibres in the aortic nerve of the cat. *Brain Res.* **43**, 25–25.

Benmiloud, M. and Euler, U.S.von. (1963), Effects of bretylium, reserpine, guanethidine and sympathetic denervation of the noradrenaline content of the rat submaxillary gland. *Acta physiol. scand.* **59**, 34–42.

Bennett, M.R. (1972), *Autonomic Neuromuscular Transmission,* Cambridge: University Press.

Bennett, T. (1969), Studies on the avian gizzard: histochemical analysis of the extrinsic and intrinsic innervation. *Z. Zellforsch.* **98**, 188–201.

Bennett, T. (1970), Interaction of nerve-mediated excitation and inhibition of singel smooth muscle cells of the avian gizzard. *Comp. Biochem. Physiol.* **32**, 669–680.

Bennett, T. (1971), The adrenergic innervation of the pulmonary vasculature, the lung and the thoracic aorta, and on the presence of aortic bodies in the domestic fowl (*Gallus domesticus* L.). *Z. Zellforsch.* **114**, 117–134.

Bennett, T. and Malmfors, T. (1970), The adrenergic nervous system of the domestic fowl (*Gallus domesticus* L.). *Z. Zellforsch.* **106**, 22–50.

Bennett, T., Malmfors, T. and Cobb, J.L.S. (1973), Fluorescence histochemical observations on catecholamine-containing cell bodies in Auerbach's plexus. *Z. Zellforsch.* **139**, 69–81.

Benninghoff, von A. (1951), Vermehrung und Vergrösserung von Nervenzellen bei Hypertrophie des Innervationsgebietes. *Z. Naturf.* **6**b, 38–41.

Bernard, C. (1851), Influence du grand sympathique sur la sensibilité et sur la calorification. *C.r. hebd. Séanc. Soc. Biol.,* Paris **3**, 163–164.

Bernard, C. (1858), *Oevres.* vol. V, p.185. Paris: Baillière.

Berselli, L. and Mattioli, G. (1955), *La* dégénérescence des expansions sympat-

165

iques intraganglionnaires régénérées: *Acta anat.* 25, 53—64.

Berselli, L. and Rossi, G. (1953), Recherches sur la régénération des fibres préganglionnaires du sympathique. *Acta anat.* 19, 132—148.

Bevan, J.A. and Purdy, R.E. (1973), Variations in the adrenergic innervation and contractile responses of the rabbit saphenous artery. *Circulation Res.* 32, 746—751.

Biber, B., Fara, J. and Lundgren, O. (1973), Intestinal vasodilatation in response to transmural electrical field stimulation. *Acta physiol. scand.* 87, 277—282.

Bichat, M.-F.-X. (1800), *Recherches Physiologiques sur la Vie et la Mort.* Paris: Brosson, Gabon & Cie.

Billingsley, P.R. and Ranson, S.W. (1918), On the number of nerve cells in the ganglion cervicale superius and of nerve fibers in the cephalic end of the truncus sympathicus in the cat and on the numerical relations of preganglionic and postganglionic neurons. *J. comp. Neurol.* 29, 359—366.

Birks, R.I. (1974), The relationship of transmitter release and storage to fine structure in a sympathetic ganglion. *J. Neurocytol.* 3, 133—160.

Bisby, M.A. and Fillenz, M. (1971), The storage of endogenous noradrenaline in sympathetic nerve terminals. *J. Physiol., Lond.* 215, 163—180.

Bisby, M.A., Fillenz, M. and Smith, A.D. (1973), Evidence for the presence of dopamine-β-hydroxylase in both preparations of noradrenaline storage vesicles in sympathetic nerve terminals of the rat vas deferens. *J. Neurochem.* 20, 245—248.

Bishop, G.H. and Heinbecker, P. (1930), Differentiation of axon types in visceral nerves by means of the potential record. *Am. J. Physiol.* 94, 170—200.

Bishop, G.H. and Heinbecker, P. (1932), A functional analysis of the cervical sympathetic nerve supply to the eye. *Am. J. Physiol.* 100, 519—532.

Bishop, G.H. and O'Leary, J. (1938), Pathways through the sympathetic nervous system in the bullfrog. *J. Neurophysiol.* 1, 442—454.

Bjerre, Bo, Björklund, A. and Mobley, W. (1973), A stimulatory effect by nerve growth factor on the regrowth of adrenergic nerve fibres in the mouse peripheral tissues after chemical sympathectomy with 6-hydroxydopamine. *Z. Zellforsch.* 146, 15—43.

Björklund, A., Cegrell, L., Falck, B., Ritzén, M. and Rosengren, E. (1970), Dopamine-containing cells in sympathetic ganglia. *Acta physiol. scand.* 78, 334—338.

Björklund, A., Falck, B., Lindvall, O. and Svensson, L.Å. (1973), New aspects on reaction mechanisms in the formaldehyde histofluorescence method for monoamines. *J. Histochem. Cytochem.* 21, 17—25.

Björklund, A. and Stenevi, U. (1972), Nerve growth factor; stimulation of regenerative growth of central noradrenergic neurons. *Science*, 175, 1251—1253.

Black, I.B. and Green, S.C. (1973), Trans-synaptic regulation of adrenergic neuron development: inhibition by ganglionic blockade. *Brain Res.* **63**, 291–302.

Black, I.B., Hendry, I.A. and Iversen, L.L. (1971), Trans-synaptic regulation of growth and development of adrenergic neurons in a mouse sympathetic ganglion. *Brain Res.* **34**, 229–240.

Black, I.B., Hendry, I.A. and Iversen, L.L. (1972), The role of post-synaptic neurons in the biochemical maturation of presynaptic cholinergic nerve terminals in a mouse sympathetic ganglion. *J. Physiol., Lond.* **221**, 149–159.

Blackman, J.G., Crowcroft, P.J., Devine, C.E., Holman, M.E. and Yonemura, K. (1969), Transmission from preganglionic fibres in the hypogastric nerve to peripheral ganglia of male guinea-pig. *J. Physiol., Lond.* **201**, 723–743.

Blackman, J.G., Ginsborg, B.L. and Ray, C. (1963), Synaptic transmission in the sympathetic ganglion of the frog. *J. Physiol., Lond.* **167**, 355–373.

Blackman, J.G. and Purves, R.D. (1969), Intracellular recordings from ganglia of the thoracic sympathetic chain of the guine-pig. *J. Physiol., Lond.* **203**, 173–198.

Blaschko, H.K.F. and Smith, A.D. (1971), A discussion on subcellular and macromolecular aspects of synaptic transmission. *Phil. Trans. R. Soc. Ser. B* **261**, 273–437.

Blaschko, H. and Welch, A.D. (1953), Localization of adrenaline in cytoplasmic particles of the bovine adrenal medulla. *Arch. exp. Path. Pharmak.* **219**, 17–22.

Blinzinger, K. and Kreutzberg, G. (1968), Displacement of synaptic terminals from regenerating motoneurons by microglial cells. *Z. Zellforsch.* **85**, 145–157.

Blotevogel, W. (1927), Sympathikus und Sexualzyklus. I. Das Ganglion cervicale uteri des normalen Tieres. *Z. mikrosk.-anat. Forsch.* **10**, 140–168.

Blotevogel, W. (1968), Sympathikus und Sexualzyklus. II. Das Ganglion cervicale uteri des kastrierten Tieres. *Z. mikrosk.-anat. Forsch.* **13**, 625–668.

Boeke, J. (1917), Studien zur Nervenregeneration. II. *Verhandl. kon. Akad. Wetensch., Amst.* **19**, 1–69.

Bok, S.T. (1928), Das Rückenmark, In: *Hanbuch der mikroskopischen Anatomie des Menschen.* edited by Möllendorf, W. von., Part IV, vol. I, pp.479–578, Berlin: Springer.

Bok, S.T. (1936), An quantitative analysis of the structure of cerebral cortex. *Proc. Acad. Sci., Amst.* **35**, 1–55.

Borison, H.L. and Domjan, D. (1970), Persistence of the cardioinhibitory response to brain stem ischaemia after destruction of the area postrema and the dorsal vagal nuclei. *J. Physiol., Lond.* **211**, 263–277.

Bornstein, J.C. (1974), The effects of physostigmine on synaptic transmission in the inferior mesenteric ganglion of guinea-pigs. *J. Physiol., Lond.* **309–325.**

167

Botar, J., Afra, D., Moritz, P., Schiffman, H. and Scholz, M. (1950), Die nerven-zellen und Ganglien des N. vagus. *Acta anat.* **10**, 284−314.

Boyd, J.D. (1957), Intermediate sympathetic ganglia. *Br. Med. Bull.* **13**, 207−212.

Bray, G.M. and Aguayo, A.J. (1974), Regeneration of periphral unmyelinated nerves. Fate of the axonal sprouts which develop after injury. *J. Anat.* **117**, 517−529.

Bray, G.M., Aguayo, A.J. and Martin, J.B. (1973), Immunosympathectomy: late effects on the composition of rat cervical sympathetic trunk and influence on axonal regeneration after crush. *Acta neuropath.* **26**, 345−352.

Brimble, M.J., Wallis, D.I. and Woodward, B. (1972), Facilitation and inhibition of ganglion cell groups within the superior cervical ganglion of the rabbit. *J. Physiol., Lond.* **226**, 629−652.

Brown, G.L. and Pascoe, J.E. (1954), The effect of degenerative section of ganglion axons on transmission through the ganglion. *J. Physiol., Lond.* **123**, 565−573.

Brown, M.E. (1936), The occurrence of sensory neurons below the ganglion nodosum of the vagus. *J. comp. Neurol.* **63**, 421−429.

Bruce, A. (1908), Distribution of the cells in the intermedio-lateral tract of the spinal cord. *Trans. R. Soc. Edinb.* **45**, 105−131.

Brzin, M., Tennyson, V.M. and Duffy, P.E. (1966), Acetylcholinesterase in frog sympathetic and dorsal root ganglia. A study by electron microscope cytochemistry and microgasometric analysis with the magnetic diver. *J. Cell Biol.* **31**, 215−242.

Buckley, G., Consolo, S., Giacobini, E. and Sjöqvist, F. (1967), Cholinacetylase in innervated and denervated sympathetic ganglia and ganglion cell of the cat. *Acta physiol. scand.* **71**, 348−356.

Bülbring, E. (1944), The action of adrenaline on transmission in ·the superior cervical ganglion. *J. Physiol., Lond.* **103**, 55−67.

Bülbring, E. and Burn, J.H. (1935), The sympathetic dilator fibres in the muscles of the cat and dog. *J. Physiol., Lond.* **83**, 483−501.

Burdman, J.A. (1968), Uptake of (^{3}H)catecholamines by chick embryo sympathetic ganglia in tissue culture. *J. Neurochem.* **15**, 1321−1323.

Burn, J.H. and Rand, M.J. (1959), Sympathetic postganglionic mechanisms. *Nature* **184**, 163−165.

Burnstock, G. (1959), The innervation of the gut of the brown trout (*Salmo trutta*). *Q. Jl. microsc. Sci.* **100**, 199−220.

Burnstock, G. (1970), Structure of smooth muscle and its innervation, In: *Smooth Muscle*, edited by Bülbring, E., Brading, A.F., Jones, A.W. and Tomita, T. pp.1−99, London: Arnold.

Burnstock, G. (1972), Purinergic nerves. *Pharmac. Rev.* **24**, 509−581.

168

Burnstock, G., Campbell, G., Bennett, H. and Holman, M.E. (1964), Innervation of the guinea-pig taenia coli: are there intrinsic inhibitory nerves which are distinct from sympathetic nerves? *Int. J. Neuropharmacol.* **3**, 163–166.

Burnstock, G., Campbell, G., Satchell, D. and Smythe, A. (1970), Evidence that adenosine triphosphate or a related nucleotide is the transmitter released by non-adrenergic inhibitory nerves in the gut. *Br. J. Pharmac. Chemother.* **40**, 668–688.

Burnstock, G. and Costa, M. (1975), *Adrenergic Neurons: their organization, function and control in the peripheral nervous system,* London: Chapman & Hall.

Burnstock, G., Evans, B., Gannon, B.J., Heath, J.W. and James, V. (1971), A new method of destroying adrenergic nerves in adult animals using guanethidine. *Br. J. Pharmac.* **43**, 295–301.

Butson, A.R.C. (1950), Regeneration of the cervical sympathetic. *Br. J. Surg.* **38**, 223–239.

Cajal, S.R. (1909), *Histologie du Système nerveux de l'Homme et des Vertébrés,* vol. I, Paris: Maloine.

Cajal, S. Ramon y. (1911), *Histologie du Systeme nerveux de l'Homme et des Vertébrés,* vol. II, Paris: Maloine.

Calaresu, F.R. and Pearce, J.W. (1965), Effects on heart rate of electrical stimulation of medullary vagal structures in the cat. *J. Physiol., Lond.* **176**, 241–251.

Cameron, I. and Smith, R.E. (1964), Cytological responses of brown fat in cold exposed rats. *J. Cell Biol.* **23**, 89–100.

Cameron, M.L. (1933), Regeneration of the peripheral vagus. *Q. Jl. exp. Physiol.* **23**, 229–262.

Cannon, W.B., Newton, H.F., Bright, E.M. Menkin, V. and Moore, R.M. (1929), Some aspects of animals surviving complete exclusion of sympathetic nerve impulses. *Am. J. Physiol.* **89**, 84–107.

Cannon, W.B. and Rosenblueth, A. (1937), *Autonomic neuroeffector systems.* New York: Macmillan.

Cantino, D. and Mugnaini, E. (1974), Adrenergic innervation of the parasympathetic ciliary ganglion in the chick. *Science* **185**, 279–281.

Cantino, D. and Mugnaini, E. (1975), The structural basis for electrotonic coupling in the avian ciliary ganglion. *J. Neurocytol.* **5**, 505–536.

Carpenter, F.W. (1911), The ciliary ganglion of birds. *Folia neurobiologica* **5**, 738–754.

Carpenter, F.W. (1912), On the histology of the cranial autonomic ganglia of the sheep. *J. comp. Neurol.* **22**, 447–459.

Carpenter, F.W. and Conel, J.L. (1914), A study of ganglion cells in the sympathetic nervous system with special reference to intrinsic sensory neurons.

J. comp. Neurol. **24**, 269–281.

Catania, V. (1924), Il plesso del ganglio sottomascellare ed il suo ramo faringeo nell'uomo ed in alcuni mammiferi. *Archo. ital. Anat. Embriol.* **21**, 487–532.

Cauna, N., Naik, N.T., Leaming, D.B. and Alberti, P. (1961), The distribution of cholinesterase in the autonomic ganglia of man and some mammals. *Biblphie anat.* **2**, 90–96.

Cavazzana P. and Borsetto, P.L. (1948), Recherches sur l'aspect microscopique des plexus nerveux intramuraux et sur les modifications morphologiques de leurs neurones dans les divers traits de l'intestin humain pendant la vie. *Acta anat.* **5**, 17–41.

Ceccarelli, B., Clementi, F. and Mantegazza, P. (1971), Synaptic transmission in the superior cervical ganglion of the cat after reinnervation by vagus fibres. *J. Physiol., Lond.* **216**, 87–98.

Ceccarelli, B., Clementi, F. and Mantegazza P. (1972), Adrenergic reinnervation of smooth muscle of nictitating membrane by preganglionic sympathetic fibres. *J. Physiol., Lond.* **220**, 211–227.

Chamley, J.H., Campbell, G.R. and Burnstock, G. (1973), An analysis of the interactions between sympathetic nerve fibers and smooth muscle cells in tissue culture. *Devl. Biol.* **33**, 344–361.

Chamley, J.H., Mark, G.E., Campbell, G.R. and Burnstock, G. (1972a), Sympathetic ganglia in culture. I. Neurons. *Z. Zellforsch.* **135**, 287–314.

Chamley, J.H., Mark, G.E. and Burnstock, G. (1972b), Sympathetic ganglia in culture. II. Accessory cells. *Z. Zellforsch.* **135**, 315–327.

Champlain, J. De, Malmfors, T., Olson, L. and Sachs, Ch. (1970), Ontogenesis of peripheral adrenergic neurons in the rat: pre- and postnatal observations. *Acta physiol. scand.* **80**, 276–288.

Chang, P.Y., and Hsu, F.Y. (1942a), The chemical excitability of the isolated rabbit small intestine. *Q. Jl. exp. Physiol.* **31**, 299–310.

Chang, P.Y., and Hus, F.Y. (1942b), The localization of the intestinal inhibitory reflex arc. *Q. Jl. exp. Physiol.* **31**, 311–318.

Chen, I-li and Yates, R.D. (1970), Ultrastructural studies of vagal paraganglia in syrian hamsters. *Z. Zellforsch.* **108**, 309–323.

Chiba, T. and Yamauchi, A. (1970), On the fine structure of the nerve terminals in the human myocardium. *Z. Zellforsch.* **108**, 324–338.

Chorobski, J. and Penfield, W. (1932), Cerebral vasodilatator nerves and their pathway from the medulla oblongata. *Archs. Neurol. Psychiat.* **28**, 1257–1289.

Christ, D.D. and Nishi, S. (1971), Effects of adrenaline on nerve terminals in the superior cervical ganglion of the rabbit. *Br. J. Pharmac.* **41**, 331–338.

Chu, C.H.U. (1968), Solitary neurons of the human tongue. *Anat. Rec.* **162**, 505–510.

Clark, S.L. (1933), A histological study of the tissues of animals surviving complete exclusion of thoracico-lumbar autonomic impulses. *J. comp. Neurol.* **58**, 553–591.

Clegg, P.C. (1962), The effect of adrenergic blocking agents on the guinea-pig uterus *in vitro* and a study of the histology of the intrinsic myometrial nerves. *J. Physiol., Lond.* **169**, 73–90.

Cohen, A.M. (1972), Factor affecting the expression of sympathetic nerve traits in cells of neural crest origin. *J. exp. Zool.* **179**, 167–182.

Colborn, G.L. and Adamo, N.J. (1969), The ultrastructure of sympathetic ganglia of the lizard Cnemidophorus neomexicanus. *Anat. Rec.* **164**, 185–203.

Collier, B. and MacIntosh, F.C. (1969), The source of choline for acetylcholine synthesis in a sympathetic ganglion. *Can. J. Pharmacol.* **47**, 127–135.

Consolo, S., Giacobini, E. and Karjalainen (1968), Monoamine oxidase in sympathetic ganglia of the cat. *Acta physiol. scand.* **74**, 513–520.

Coppée, G. and Bacq, Z.M. (1938), Dégénérescence, conduction et transmission synaptique dans le sympatique cervical. *Arch. int. Physiol. Biochem.* **47** 313–320.

Corrodi, H. and Jonsson, G. (1967), The formaldehyde fluorescence method for the histochemical demonstration of biogenic monamines. A review on the methodology. *J. Histochem. Cytochem.* **15**, 65–78.

Costa, M. and Furness, J.B. (1971), Storage, uptake and synthesis of catecholamines in the intrinsic adrenergic neurons in the proximal colon of the guinea-pig. *Z. Zellforsch.* **120**, 364–385.

Costa, M. and Furness, J.B. (1973), Observations on the anatomy and amine histochemistry of the nerves and ganglia which supply the pelvic viscera and on the associated chromaffin tissue in the guinea-pig. *Z. Anat. EntwGesch* **140**, 85–108.

Costa, M., Furness, J.B. and Gabella, G. (1971), Catecholamine-containing nerve cells in the mammalian myenteric plexus. *Histochemie* **25**, 103–106.

Costa, M. and Gabella, G. (1968), L'innervation adrenergique des sphincters digestifs. *C.r. Ass. Anat.* **53**, 884–888.

Costa, M. and Gabella, G. (1971), Adrenergic innervation of the alimentary canal. *Z. Zellforsch.* **122**, 357–377.

Cottle, M.K.W. and Mitchell, R. (1966), Degeneration time for optimal staining by Nauta technique. A study on transected vagal fibers of the cat. *J. comp. Neurol.* **128**, 209–222.

Coupland, R.E. (1965), Electron microscopic observations on the structure of the rat adrenal medulla. The ultrastructure and organization of chromaffin cells in the normal adrenal medulla. *J. Anat.* **99**, 231–254.

Cowley, L.H. and Shackleford, J.M. (1970), An ultrastructural study of the submandibular glands of the squirrel monkey, *Saimiri sciureus. J. Morph.* **132**, 117–136.

Cragg, B.G. (1965), Failure of conduction and of synaptic transmission in degenerating mammalian C fibres. *J. Physiol., Lond.* **179**, 95–112.

Cragg, B.G. (1970), What is the signal for chromatolysis? *Brain Res.* **23**, 1–22.

Crain, S.M., Benitez, H.H. and Vatter, A.E. (1964), Some cytological effects of salivary nerve growth factor on tissue cultures of peripheral ganglia. *Ann. N.Y. Acad. Sci.* **118**, 206–231.

Cravioto, H. and Merker, H. (1963), Elektronenmikroskopische Untersuchungen an Satellitenzellen der sympatischen Ganglien des Menschen. *Arch. Psychiat. NervKrankh.* **204**, 1–10.

Crouch, R.L. (1936), The efferent fibers of the Edinger-Westphal nucleus. *J. comp. Neurol.* **64**, 365–373.

Crouse, G.S. and Cucinotta, A.J. (1965), Progressive neuronal differentiation in the submandibular ganglia of a series of human fetuses. *J. comp. Neurol.* **125**, 259–272.

Crowcroft, P.J., Holman, M.E. and Szurszewski, J.H. (1971), Excitatory input from the distal colon to the inferior mesenteric ganglion in the guinea-pig. *J. Physiol., Lond.* **219**, 443–461.

Crowcroft, P.J. and Szurszewski, J.H. (1971), A study of the inferior mesenteric and pelvic ganglia of guinea-pig with intracellular electrodes. *J. Physiol., Lond.* **219**, 421–441.

Csillik, B., Kâlmàn, G. and Knyihar, E. (1967), Adrenergic nerve endings in the feline cervicale superius ganglion. *Experientia,* **23**, 477–478.

Dahlström, A. (1967), The intraneuronal distribution of noradrenaline and the transport and life span of amine storage granules in the sympathetic adrenergic neuron. *Arch. exp. Path. Pharmac.* **257**, 93–115.

Dahlström, A. and Fuxe, K. (1964), A method for the demonstration of adrenergic nerve fibres in peripheral nerves. *Z. Zellforsch.* **62**, 602–607.

Dahlström, A., and Fuxe, K., (1965a), Evidence for the existence of an outflow of noradrenaline nerve fibres in the ventral roots of the rat spinal cord. *Experientia* **21**, 409–410.

Dahlström, A. and Fuxe, K. (1965b), Evidence for the existence of monoamine neurons in the central nervous system. II. Experimentally-induced changes in the interneuronal amine levels of bulbospinal neuron systems. *Acta physiol. scand.* **64**, suppl. 247, 7–34.

Dahlström, A. and Fuxe, K. (1965c), The adrenergic innervation of the nasal mucosa of certain mammals. *Acta oto-laryng.* **59**, 65–72.

Dahlström, A., Fuxe, K., Hillarp, N.-Å. and Malmfors, T. (1964), Adrenergic mechanisms in the pupillary light-reflex path. *Acta physiol. scand.* **62**, 119–124.

Dahlström, A., Fuxe, K., Maya-Tu, M. and Zetterström, B.E.M. (1965), Observation on the adrenergic innervation of dog heart. *Am. J. Physiol.* **209**, 289–692.

Dahlström, A. and Häggendal, J. (1966a), Some quantitative studies on the noradrenaline content in the cell bodies and terminals of a sympathetic adrenergic neuron system. *Acta physiol. scand.* **67**, 271–277.

Dahlström, A., and Häggendal, J. (1966b), Studies on the transport and life span of amine storage granules in a peripheral adrenergic neuron system. *Acta physiol. scand.* **67**, 278–288.

Dahlström, A., Häggendal, J. and Hökfelt, T. (1966), The noradrenaline content of the varicosities of sympathetic adrenergic nerve terminals in the rat. *Acta physiol. scand.* **67**, 289–294.

Dale, H.H. and Feldberg, W. (1934), The chemical transmission of secretory impulses to the sweat glands of the cat. *J. Physiol., Lond.* **82**, 121–127.

Daniel, H. and Derry, D.M., (1969), Criteria for differentiation of brown and white fat in the rat. *Can. J. Physiol. Pharmacol.* **47**, 941–945.

Dargent, J. (1963), Attenuation précoce de l'activité de la cholinesterase neuroplasmique non specifique après axotomie. *C.r. Séanc. Soc. Biol.* **157**, 2334–2337.

Davidovich, A. and Luco, J.V., (1956), The synaptic transmission of sympathetic ganglia during wallerian degeneration. Effect of length of degenerating nerve fibers. *Acta physiologica latino-americana*, **6**, 49–59.

Davies, F.E., Francis, T.B. and King, T.S. (1952), Neurological studies of the cardiac ventricles of mammals. *J. Anat.* **86**, 130–143.

Dawson, I.M., Hossack, J. and Wyburn, G.M. (1956), Observations on the Nissl's substance, cytoplasmic filaments and the nuclear membrane of spinal ganglion cells. *Proc. R. Soc. B.*, **144**, 132–142.

Deane, B.M., Howe, A. and Morgan, M. (1974), Abdominal vagal paraganglia of the rat: distribution and structure. *J. Physiol., Lond.* **241**, 81–82.

De Castro, F. (1923), Evoluciòn de los ganglios simpàticos vertebrales y prevertebrales. Conexiones y citoarquitectonia de algunos grupos de ganglios, en el nino y hombre adulto *Trab. Lab. Invest. biol. Univ. Madr.* **20**, 113–208.

De Castro, F. (1932), Sympathetic ganglia: normal and pathological, In: *Cytology and cellular pathology of the nervous system*, edited by Penfield, W., vol. I, pp.319–379. New York: Hoeber.

De Castro, F. (1934), Note sur la régénération fonctionelle hétérogénétique dans les anastomoses des nerfs pneumogastrique et hypoglosse avec le sympatique cervical. *Trab. Lab. Invest. biol. Univ. Madr.*, **29**, 397–416.

De Castro, F. (1937), Sur la régénération fonctionelle dans le sympatique (anastomoses croisées avec des nerfs de type iso- et hétéromorphes). Une référence spéciale sur la constitution des synapses. *Trab. Lab. Rech. Biol. Madr.* **31**, 271–345.

De Castro, F. (1942), Modelacion de un arco reflejo en el simpatico, uniendolo con la raiz aferente central del vago. Nuevas ideas sobre la sinapsis. *Trab. Inst. Cajal Invest. Biol.* **34**, 217–301.

De Castro, F. (1951), Aspects anatomiques de la transmission synaptique ganglionnaire chez les mammifères. *Arch. int. Physiol. Biochim.* **59**, 479—511.

De Castro, F. and Herreros, M.L. (1945), Actividad funcional del ganglio cervical superior, en relacion al numero y modalidad de sus fibras preganglionicas. Modelo de la sinapsis. *Trab. Inst. Cajal Invest. Biol.* **37**, 287—342.

De Groat, W.C. and Ryall, R.W. (1968), The identification and characteristics of sacral parasympathetic preganglionic neurons. *J. Physiol., Lond.* **196**, 563—577.

De Groat, W.C. and Saum, W.R. (1971), Adrenergic inhibition in mammalian parasympathetic ganglia. *Nature New Biology* **231**, 188—189.

De Groat, W.C. and Saum, W.R. (1972), Sympathetic inhibition of the urinary bladder and of pelvic ganglionic transmission in the cat. *J. Physiol., Lond.,* **220**, 297—314.

De Iraldi, A. and Zieher, L.M. (1966), Noradrenaline and dopamine of normal, decentralized and denervated pineal gland of the rat. *Life Sci.* **5**, 149—154.

De Lemos, C. and Pick, J. (1966), The fine structure of thoracic sympathetic neurons in the adult rat. *Z. Zellforsch.* **71**, 189—206.

Delorenzi, E. (1931), Modificazioni dei neuroni simpatici dei Mammiferi domestici in relazione all'accrescimento somatico e alla senescenze. *Archo. Ital. Anat. Embriol.* **28**, 528—552.

De Lorenzo, A.J. (1960), The fine structure of synapses in ciliary ganglion of the chick. *J. biophys. biochem. Cytol.* **7**, 31—36.

De Lorenzo, A.J. (1966), Electron microscopy: tight junctions in synapses of the chick ciliary ganglion. *Science,* **152**, 76—78.

De Robertis, E.D.P. and Bennett, H.S. (1954), Submicroscopic vesicular component in the synapse. *Fedn. Am. Socs. exp. Biol.* **13**, 35.

De Robertis, E.D.P. and Bennett, H.S. (1955), Some features of the submicroscopic morphology of synapses in frog and earthworm. *J. biophys. biochem. Cytol.* **1**, 47—58.

De Robertis, E.D.P. and De Iraldi, A. (1961), Plurivesicular secretory processes and nerve endings in the pineal gland of the rat. *J. biophys. biochem. Cytol.* **10**, 361—372.

Derry, D.M., Schönbaum, E. and Steiner, G. (1969), Two sympathetic nerve supplies to brown adipose tissue of the rat. *Can. J. Physiol. Pharmacol.* **47**, 57—63.

Devine, C.E. and Simpson, F.O. (1967), The fine structure of vascular sympathetic neuromuscular contacts in the rat. *Am. J. Anat.* **121**, 153—174.

Diner, O.C.R. (1967), L'expulsion des granules de la médullo-surrénale chez le hamster. *C.r. hebd. Séanc. Acad. Sci., Paris,* **265**, 616—619.

Dixon, J.S. (1966), The fine structure of parasympathetic nerve cells in the otic ganglia of the rabbit. *Anat. Rec.* **156**, 239—252.

Dogiel, A.S. (1896), Zwei Arten sympathischer Nervenzellen. *Anat. Anz.* **11**, 679–687.

Dogiel, A.S. (1899), Ueber den Bau der Ganglien in den Geflechten des Darmes und der Gallenblase des Menschen und der Säugetieren. *Arch. Anat. Phys. Anat. Abt.* 130–158.

Dolgo-Saburoff, B. (1935), Zur Lehere vom Aufbau des Vagussystems. I Mitt.: Ueber die Nervenzellen in des Stämmen des N. vagus. *Z. Anat. EntwGesch.* **105**, 79–93.

Douglas, W.W. (1966), The mechanism of release of catecholamines from the adrenal medulla. *Pharmac. Rev.* **18**, 471–480.

DuBois, F.S. and Foley, J.O. (1935), Experimental studies on the vagus and spinal accessory nerves in the cat. *J. comp. Neurol.* **64**, 285–307.

Dubois, F.S. and Foley, J.O. (1937), Quantitative studies of the vagus nerve in the cat. II. The ratio of jugular to nodose fibres. *J. comp. Neurol.* **67**, 69–87.

Duel, A.B. and Ballance, C. (1932), A note on the result which follows the grafting of the raw peripheral end of the divided cervical sympathetic nerve to another nerve in the vicinity. *Brain* **55**, 226–231.

Dun, N. and Nishi, S. (1974), Effects of dopamine on the superior cervical ganglion of the rabbit. *J. Physiol., Lond.* **239**, 155–164.

Dunant, Y. (1967), Organization topographique et fonctionelle du ganglion cervical superieur chez le rat. *J. Physiol., Paris* **59**, 3–24.

Duncan, D. and Keyser, L.L. (1936), Some determinations of the ratio of nerve cells to nerve fibers in the thoracic dorsal roots and ganglia of the cat. *J. comp. Neurol.* **64**, 303–312.

Duncan, D. and Yates, R. (1967), Ultrastructure of the carotid body of the cat as revealed by various fixatives and the use of reserpine. *Anat. Rec.* **157**, 667–682.

Dupont, J.-R., Jervis, H.R. and Sprinz, H. (1965), Auerbach's plexus of the rat cecum in relation to the germfree state. *J. comp. Neurol.* **125**, 11–18.

Ebbeson, S.O.E. (1963), A quantitative study of human superior cervical sympathetic ganglia. *Anat. Rec.* **146**, 353–356.

Ebbeson, S.O.E. (1968a), Quantitative studies of superior cervical sympathetic ganglia in a variety of primates including man. I. The ratio of preganglionic fibres to ganglionic neurons. *J. Morph.* **124**, 117–132.

Ebbeson, S.O.E. (1968b), Quantitative studies of superior cervical sympathetic ganglia in a variety of primates including man. II. Neuronal packing density. *J. Morph.* **124**, 181–186.

Eccles, J.C. (1935), The action potential of the superior cervical ganglion. *J. Physiol., Lond.* **85**, 179–206.

Eccles, R.M. (1955), Intracellular potentials recorded from a mammalian sympathetic ganglion. *J. Physiol., Lond.* **130**, 572–584.

Edds, M.V. (1953), Collateral nerve regeneration. *Rev. Biol.* **28**, 260–276.

Edvinsson, L., Nielsen, K.C., Owman, Ch. and Sporrong, B. (1972), Cholinergic mechanisms in pial vessels. *Z. Zellforsch.* **134**, 311–325.

Edwards, L.F. and Baker, R.C. (1940), Variations in the formation of the splanchnic nerves in man. *Anat. Rec.* **77**, 335–342.

Ehinger, B. (1966), Connections between adrenergic nerves and other tissue components in the eye. *Acta physiol. scand.* **67**, 57–64.

Ehinger, B. (1967), Adrenergic nerves in the avian and ciliary ganglion. *Z. Zellforsch.* **82**, 577–588.

Ehinger, B., and Falck, B. (1970a), Innervation of iridic melanophores. *Z. Zellforsch.* **105**, 538–542.

Ehinger, B. and Falck, B. (1970b), Uptake of some catecholamines and their precursors into neurons of the rat ciliary ganglion. *Acta physiol. scand.* **78**, 132–141.

Ehinger, B., Falck, B., Persson, H. and Sporrong, B. (1968), Adrenergic and cholinesterase-containing neurons in the heart. *Histochemie* **16**, 197–205.

Ehinger, B., Falck, B. and Sporrong, B. (1966), Adrenergic fibres to the heart and to peripheral vessles. *Biblphie anat.* **8**, 35–45.

Ehinger, B., Falck, B. and Sporrong, B. (1970), Possible axo-axonal, synapses between adrenergic and cholinergic nerve terminals. *Z. Zellforsch.* **107**, 508–521.

Ekholm, J. and Skoglund, S. (1966), Autonomic contributions to myelinated fibres in peripheral nerves. *Acta morph. neerl.-scand.* **6**, 55–63.

El-Badawi, A. and Schenk, E.A. (1968), The peripheral adrenergic innervation apparatus. I. Intraganglionic and extra-ganglionic adrenergic ganglion cells. *Z. Zellforsch.* **87**, 218–225.

El-Bermani, A.W.L. (1973), Innervation of the rat lung. Acetylcholinesterase-containing nerves of the bronchial tree. *Am. J. Anat.* **137**, 19–30.

Elfvin, L.-G. (1963a), The ultrastructure of the superior cervical sympathetic ganglion of the cat. I. The structure of the ganglion cell processes as studied by serial sections. *J. Ultrastruct. Res.* **8**, 403–440.

Elfvin, L.-G. (1963b), The ultrastructure of the superior cervical sympathetic ganglion of the cat. II. The structure of the preganglionic end fibers and the synapses as studied by serial sections. *J. Ultrastruct. Res.* **8**, 441–476.

Elfvin, L.-G. (1965), The fine structure of the cell surface of chromaffin cells in the rat adrenal medulla. *J. Ultrastruct. Res.* **12**, 263–286.

Elfvin, L.-G. (1968), A new granule-containing cell in the inferior mesenteric ganglion of the rabbit. *J. Ultrastruct. Res.* **22**, 37–44.

Elfvin, L.-G. (1971a), Ultrastructural studies on the synaptology of the inferior mesenteric ganglion of the cat. I. Observations on the cell surface of the post-ganglionic perikarya. *J. Ultrastruct. Res.* **37**, 411–425.

Elfvin, L.-G. (1971b), Ultrastructural studies on the synaptology of the inferior mesenteric ganglion of the cat. II. Specialized serial neuronal contacts between preganglionic end fibres. *J. Ultrastruct. Res.* **37**, 426—431.

Elfvin, L.-G. (1971c), Ultrastructural studies on the synaptology of the inferior mesenteric ganglion of the cat. III. The structure and distribution of the axo-dendritic and dendrodentritic contacts. *J. Ultrastruct. Res.* **37**, 432—448.

Elliott, T.R. (1907), The innervation of the bladder and urethra. *J. Physiol., Lond.* **35**, 367—445.

Enemar, A., Falck, B. and Häkanson, R. (1965), Observations on the appearance of norepinephrine in the sympathetic nervous system of the chick embryo. *Devl. Biol.* **11**, 268—283.

Enerbäck, L., Olsson, Y. and Sourander, P. (1965), Mast cells in normal and sectioned peripheral nerve. *Z. Zellforsch.* **66**, 596—608.

England, J.M. and Goldstein, M.N. (1969), The uptake the localization of catecholamines in chick embryo sympathetic neurons in tissue culture. *J. Cell Sci.* **4**, 677—691.

Eränkö, L. (1972), Ultrastructure of the developing sympathetic nerve cell and the storage of catecholamines. *Brain Res.* **46**, 159—175.

Eränkö, O. (1966), Demonstration of catecholamines and cholinesterases in the same section. *Pharmac. Rev.* **18**, 353—358.

Eränkö, O. (1972), Light and electron microscopic histochemical evidence of granular and non-granular storage of catecholamines in the sympathetic ganglion of the rat. *Histochem. J.* **4**, 213—224.

Eränkö, O. and Eränkö, L. (1971), Small, intensely fluorescent granule-containing cells in the sympathetic ganglion of the rat. *Prog. Brain Res.* **31**, 39—51.

Eränkö, O. and Eränkö, L. (1974), Small intensely fluorescent (SIF) cells *in vivo* and *in vitro*, In: *Frontiers in Catecholamine Research,* edited by Usdin S., and Snyder, S.H., pp.431—437. Oxford: Pergamon Press.

Eränkö, O., Eränkö, L., Hill, C. and Burnstock, G. (1972a), Hydrocortisone-induced increase in the number of small intensely fluorescent cells and their histochemically demonstrable catecholamine content in cultures of sympathetic ganglia of the newborn rat. *Histochem. J.* **4**, 49—58.

Eränkö, O. and Härkönen, M. (1965), Monoamine-containing cells in the superior cervical ganglion of the rat and an organ composed of them. *Acta physiol. scand.* **63**, 511—512.

Eränkö, O., Heath, J. and Eränkö, L. (1972b), Effects of hydrocortisone on the ultrastructure of the small, intensely fluorescent, granule-containing cells in cultures of sympathetic ganglia of newborn rats. *Z. Zellforsch.* **134**, 297—310.

Erici, I., Folkow, B. and Uvnäs, B. (1952), Sympathetic vasodilator nerves to the tongue of the cat. *Acta physiol. scand.* **25**, 1—9.

Erulkar, S.D. and Woodward, J.K. (1968), Intracellular recording from mammalian superior cervical ganglion *in situ*. *J. Physiol., Lond.* **199**, 189—203.

Etemadi, A.A. (1961), The dorsal nucleus of the vagus. *Acta anat.* **47**, 328—332.

Euler, U.S.von (1946), A specific sympathomimetic ergone in adrenergic nerve fibres (sympathin) and its relation to adrenaline and noradrenaline. *Acta physiol. scand.* **12**, 73—97.

Euler, U.S.von (1971), Adrenergic neurotransmitter function. *Science* **173**, 202—206.

Evans, D.H.L. and Evans, E.M. (1964), The membrane relationships of smooth muscles: an electromicroscope study. *J. Anat.* **98**, 37—46.

Evans, D.H.L. and Murray, J.G. (1954), Histological and functional studies on the fibre composition of the vagus nerve of the rabbit. *J. Anat.* **88**, 320—337.

Eve, F.C. (1896), Sympathetic nerve cells and their basophilic constituents in prolonged activity and repose. *J. Physiol., Lond.* **20**, 334—353.

Falck, B., (1962), Observations on the possibilities of the cellular localization of monoamines by a fluorescence method. *Acta physiol. scand.* **56**, suppl. 197.

Falck, B. and Owman, B. (1965), A detailed methodological description of the fluorescence method for cellular localization of biogenic amines. *Acta Univ. lund* Section II, N.7

Falck, B. and Rorsman, H. (1963), Observation on the adrenergic innervation of the skin. *Experientia* **19**, 205—206.

Farrell, K.E. (1968), Fine structure of nerve fibres in smooth muscle of the vas deferens in normal and reserpinized rats. *Nature* **217**, 279—281.

Fatt, P. and Katz, B. (1952), Spontaneous subthreshold activity at motor nerve endings. *J. Physiol., Lond.* **117**, 109—128.

Feldberg, W. (1943), Synthesis of acetylcholine in sympathetic ganglia and cholinergic nerves. *J. Physiol., Lond.* **101**, 432—445.

Feldberg, W. and Gaddum, J.H. (1934), The chemical transmitter at synapses in a sympathetic ganglion. *J. Physiol., Lond.* **81**, 305—319.

Feldberg, W. and Lin, R.C.Y. (1950), Synthesis of acetylcholine in the wall of the digestive tract. *J. Physiol., Lond.* **163**, 475—487.

Fernholm, M. (1971), On the development of the sympathetic chain and the adrenal medulla in the mouse. *Z. Anat. EntwGesch.* **133**, 305—317.

Fillenz, M. (1970), The innervation of the cat spleen. *Proc. R. Soc. B.* **174**, 459—468.

Filogamo, G. and Vigliani, F. (1954), Ricerche sperimentali sulla correlazione tra estensione del territorio di innervazione e grandezza e numero delle cellule gangliari del plesso mienterico (di Auerbach), nel cane. *Riv. Patol. nerv. ment.* **75**, 441—462.

Finch, L., Haësler, G. and Thoenen, H. (1973), A comparison of the effects of chemical sympathectomy by 6-hydroxydopamine in newborn and adult rats. *Br. J. Pharmac. Chemother.* **47**, 249—260.

Fink, G. and Schofield, G.C. (1971), Experimental studies on the innervation of the ovary in cats. *J. Anat.* **109**, 115–126.

Fischer, J.E. and Snyder, S. (1965), Disposition of norepinephrine-H^3 in sympathetic ganglia. *J. Pharmacol. exp. Therap.* **150**, 190–195.

Foley, J.O. (1943), Composition of the cervical sympathetic trunk. *Proc. Soc. exp. Biol., N.Y.* **52**, 212–214.

Foley, J.O. (1945), The components of the cervical sympathetic trunk with special reference to its accessory cells and ganglia. *J. comp. Neurol.* **82**, 77–92.

Foley, J.O. (1948), The functional types of nerve fibres and their numbers in the great splanchnic nerve. *Anat. Rec.* **100**, 766–767.

Foley, J.O. and DuBois, F.S. (1937), Quantitative studies of the vagus nerve in the cat. I. The ratio of sensory to motor fibers. *J. comp. Neurol.* **67**, 49–67.

Foley, J.O. and DuBois, F.S. (1940), A quantitative and experimental study of the cervical sympathetic trunk. *J. comp. Neurol.* **72**, 587–603.

Foley, J.C. and Schnitzlein, H.N. (1957), The contribution of individual thoracic spinal nerves to the upper cervical sympathetic trunk. *J. comp. Neurol.* **108**, 109–120.

Folkow, B., Johansson, B. and Oberg, B. (1958), A stimulation threshold of different sympathetic fibres groups as correlated to their functional differentiation. *Acta physiol. scand.* **44** 146–156.

Forssman, W.G. (1964), Studien über den Feinbau des Ganglion cervicale superius der Ratte. I. Normale Struktur. *Acta anat.* **59**, 420–433.

Francillon, M.R. (1928), Zur Topographie der Ganglien des menschlichen Herzens. *Z. Anat. EntwGesch.* **85**, 131–165.

Fredricsson, B. and Sjöqvist, F. (1962), A cytomorphological study of cholinesterase in sympathetic ganglia of the cat. *Acta morph. neerl.-scand.* **5**, 140–166.

Freitag, P. and Engel, M.B. (1970), Autonomic innervation in rabbit salivary glands. *Anat. Rec.* **167**, 87–106.

Friedman, W.F., Pool, P.E., Jacobowitz, D., Seagren, S.C. and Braunwald, E. (1968), Sympathetic innervation of the developing rabbit heart. *Circulation Res.* **23**, 25–32.

Fritz, M.E. and Botelho, S.Y. (1969), Role of autonomic nerve impulses in secretion by the parotid gland of the cat. *Am. J. Physiol.* **216**, 1392–1398.

Fujimoto, S. (1967), Some observations on the fine structure of the sympathetic ganglion of the toad, *Bufo vulgaris japonicum. Arch. hist. jap.* **28**, 313–335.

Fujiwara, M., Tanaka, C., Hikosaka, H., and Okegawa, H. (1966), Cytological localization of noradrenaline, monoaminoxidase and acetylcholinesterase in salivary glands of dog. *J. Histochem. Cytochem.* **14**, 483–490.

Furness, J.B. (1969), The presence of inhibitory nerves in the colon after sympathetic denervation. *Eur. J. Pharmacol.* **6**, 349–352.

179

Furness, J.B. (1970), The origin and distribution of adrenergic fibres in the guinea-pig colon. *Histochemie* **21**, 295–306.

Furness, J.B. (1971), The adrenergic innervation of the vessels supplying and draining the gastrointestinal tract. *Z. Zellforsch.* **113**, 67–82.

Furness, J.B. and **Costa, M.** (1971), Morphology and distribution of intrinsic adrenergic neurons in the proximal colon of the guinea-pig. *Z. Zellforsch.* **120**, 346–363.

Furness, J.B. and **Costa, M.** (1973), The ramifications of adrenergic nerve terminals in the rectum, anal sphincter and anal accessory muscles of the guinea-pig. *Z. Anat. EntwGesch.* **140**, 109–128.

Furness, J.B. and **Costa, M.** (1974), The adrenergic innervation of the gastrointestinal tract. *Ergebn. Physiol.* **69**, 1–51.

Furness, J.B. and **Iwayama, T.** (1971), Terminal axons ensheathed in smooth muscle cells in the vas deferens. *Z. Zellforsch.* **113**, 259–270.

Furness, J.B. and **Iwayama, T.** (1972), The arrangement and identification of axons innervating the vas deferens of the guinea-pig. *J. Anat.* **113**, 179–196.

Furness, J.B. and **Malmfors, T.** (1971), Aspects of the arrangement of the adrenergic innervation in guinea-pigs as revealed by the fluorescence histochemical method applied to stretched, airdried preparations. *Histochemie* **25**, 297–309.

Furness, J.B., McLean, J.R. and **Burnstock, G.** (1970), Distribution of adrenergic nerves and changes in neuromuscular transmission in the mouse vas deferens during post-natal development. *Devl. Biol.* **21**, 490–505.

Fuxe, K. (1965), Evidence for the existence of monoamine neurons in the central nervous system. IV. Distribution of monoamine nerve terminals in the central nervous system. *Acta physiol. scand.* **64**, suppl. 247, 39–85.

Fuxe, K., Goldstein, T., Hökfelt, T. and **Joh, T.H.** (1971), Cellular localization of dopamine-hydroxylase and phenylethanolamine-*N*-methyl transferase as revealed by immunohistochemistry. *Prog. Brain Res.* **34**, 127–138.

Fuxe, K. and **Nilsson, B.Y.** (1965), Mechanoreceptors and adrenergic nerve terminals. *Experientia,* **21**, 641–642.

Fuxe, K. and **Sedvall, G.** (1965), The distribution of adrenergic nerve fibres to the blood vessels of skeletal muscle. *Acta physiol. scand.* **64**, 75–86.

Gabella, G. (1969), Detection of nerve cells by a histochemical technique. *Experientia* **25**, 218–219.

Gabella, G. (1971), Neuron size and number in the myenteric plexus of the newborn and adult rat. *J. Anat.* **109**, 81–95.

Gabella, G. (1972), Fine structure of the myeneteric plexus in the guinea-pig ileum. *J. Anat.* **111**, 69–97.

Gabella, G. (1974), The sphincter pupillae of the guinea-pig: structure of muscle cells, intercellular relations and density of innervation, *Proc. R. Soc. B.* **186**, 369–386.

Gabella, G. and Costa, M. (1967), Le fibre adrenergiche nel canale alimentare. *Giorn. Accad. Med. Torino* **130**, 199−221.

Gabella, G. and Costa, M. (1968), Sulla presenza di particolari cellule a catecolamine (S.I.F. cells) lungo il nervo vago. *Boll. Soc. ital. Biol. sper.* **441**, 1656−1657.

Gabella, G. and Costa, M. (1969), Adrenergic innervation of the intestinal smooth musculature. *Experientia* **25**, 395−396.

Gabella, G. and Juorio, A.V. (1975), Effect of extrinsic denervation on endogenous noradrenaline and (^{3}H)noradrenaline uptake in the guinea-pig colon. *J. Neurochem.* **25**, 631−634.

Gabella, G. and Miller, J. (1975), In preparation.

Gabella, G. and Pease, H.L. (1973), Number of axons in the abdominal vagus of the rat. *Brain Res.* **58**, 465−469.

Gagel, O. (1928), Zur Histologie und Topographie der vegetativen Zentren im Rückenmark. *Z. Anat. EntwGesch.* **85**, 213−250.

Gairns, F.W. and Garven, H.S.D. (1953), Ganglion cells and their relationship with one another in the human lumbar sympathetic ganglia. *J. Physiol, Lond.* **122**, 16−17.

Gamble, H.J. and Goldby, S. (1961), Mast cells in peripheral nerve trunks. *Nature* **189**, 766−767.

Gannon, B.J., Noblet, H.R. and Burnstock, G. (1969), Adrenergic innervation of bowel in Hirschprung's disease. *Br. med. J.* **3**, 338−340.

Garrett, J.R. (1966), The innervation of salivary glands. II. The ultrastructure of nerves in normal glands of the cat. *J. R. microsc. Soc.* **85**, 149−162.

Gaskell, W.H. (1886), On the structure, distribution and function of the nerves which innervate the visceral and vascular systems. *J. Physiol., Lond.* **7**, 1−81.

Geffen, L.B. and Livett, B.G. (1971), Synaptic vesicles in sympathetic neurons. *Physiol. Rev.* **51**, 98−157.

Geffen, L.B. and Ostberg, A. (1969), Distribution of granular vesicles in normal and constricted sympathetic neurons. *J. Physiol., Lond.* **204**, 583−592.

Geffen, L.B. and Rush, R.A. (1968), Transport of noradrenaline in sympathetic nerves and the effect of nerve impulses on its contribution to transmitter stores. *J. Neurochem.* **15**, 925−930.

Geohegan, W.A. and Aidar, O.J. (1942), Functional reorganization following preganglionectomy. *Proc. Soc. exp. Biol., N.Y.* **50**, 365−369.

Gershon, M.D. and Thompson, E. (1973), The maturation of neuromuscular function in a multiply innervated structure: development of the longitudinal smooth muscle of the foetal mammalian gut and its cholinergic excitatory, adrenergic inhibitory, and non-adrenergic inhibitory innervation. *J. Physiol., Lond.* **234**, 257−277.

Getz, B. and Sirnes, T. (1949), The localization within the dorsal motor vagal nucleus. An experimental investigation. *J. comp. Neurol.* **90**, 95−110.

Giacobini, E. (1956), Demonstration of AChE activity in isolated nerve cells. *Acta physiol. scand.* **36**, 276–290.

Giacobini, E. (1959), The distribution and localization of cholinesterases in nerve cells. *Acta physiol. scand.* **45**, suppl. 156.

Giacobini, E., Karjalainen, K., Kerpel-Fronius, S. and Ritzén, M. (1970), Monoamines and monoamine oxidase in denervated sympathetic ganglia of the cat. *Neuropharmacol.* **9**, 59–66.

Gibson, W.C. (1940), Degeneration and regeneration of sympathetic synapses. *J. Neurophysiol.* **3**, 237–247.

Gillespie, J.S. and Kirpekar, S.M. (1965), The localization of endogenous and infused noradrenaline in the spleen. *J. Physiol., Lond.* **179**, 46–47.

Gillespie, J.S. and Maxwell, J.D. (1971), Adrenergic innervation of the sphincteric and nonsphincteric smooth muscle in the rat intestine. *J. Histochem. Cytochem.* **19**, 676–681.

Goldstein, M.N. (1967), Incorporation and release of H^3-catecholamines by cultured fetal human sympathetic nerve cells and neuroblastoma cells. *Proc. Soc. exp. Biol. Med. N.Y.* **125**, 993–996.

Goormaghtigh, N. (1936), On the existence of abdominal vagal paraganglia in the adult mouse. *J. Anat.* **71**, 77–90.

Govyrin, V.A. (1975), Spatial neuromuscular relations in rabbit ear arteries. In: *Physiology of Smooth Muscle*, edited by Bülbring, E. and Shuba, M.F., New York: Raven Press.

Gray, E.G. (1963), Electron microscopy of presynaptic organelles of the spinal cord. *J. Anat.* **97**, 101–106.

Grigor'eva, T.A. (1962), *The Innervation of Blood Vessels.* New York: Pergamon Press.

Grillo, M.A. (1966), Electron microscopy of sympathetic tissues. *Pharmac. Rev.* **18**, 387–399.

Grillo, M.A., Jacobs, L. and Comroe, J.H.Jr. (1974), A combined fluorescence histochemical and electron microscopic method for studying special monoamine-containing cells (S.I.F. cells). *J. comp. Neurol.* **153**, 1–14.

Gunn, M. (1951), A study of the enteric plexuses in some amphibians. *Q. Jl. microsc. Sci.* **92**, 55–77.

Gunn, M. (1959), Cell types in the myenteric plexus of the cat. *J. comp. Neurol.* **111**, 83–100.

Gunn, M. (1968), Histological and histochemical observations on the myenteric and sub-mucous plexuses of mammals. *J. Anat.* **102**, 223–239.

Gunn, C.G., Sevelius, M.J., Puiggari, M.J. and Myers, K. (1968), Vagal cardiomotor mechanisms in the hindbrain of the dog and cat. *Am. J. Physiol.* **214**, 258–262.

Guth, L. (1956), Regeneration in the mammalian peripheral nervous system. *Physiol. Rev.* **36**, 441–478.

Guth, L. and Jacobson, S. (1966), The rate of regeneration of the vagus nerve of the cat. *Exptl. Neurol.* **14**, 430—447.

Guth, L., Stoutter, L., Frank, K., Campbell, J.B. and Lloyd, J.B. (1960), Diaphragmatic function following the anastomosis of recurrent laryngeal and phrenic nerves. *Exptl. Neurol.* **2**, 251—260.

Hamberger, B., Levi-Montalcini, R., Norberg, K.A. and Sjöqvist, F. (1965), Monoamines in immunosympathectomized rats. *Int. J. Neuropharmacol.* **4**, 91—96.

Hamberger, B. and Norberg, K.A. (1963), Monoamines in sympathetic ganglia studied with fluorescence microscopy. *Experientia*, **19**, 580—581.

Hamberger, B. and Norberg, K.A. (1965), Adrenergic synaptic terminals and nerve cells in bladder ganglia of the cat. *Int. J. Neuropharmacol.* **4**, 41—45.

Hamberger, B., Norberg, K.A., and Sjöqvist, F. (1965), Correlated studies of monoamines and AChE in sympathetic ganglia, illustrating distribution of adrenergic and cholinergic neurons. pp.41—54. In: *Pharmacology of Cholinergic and Adrenergic Transmission.* edited by Koelle, J.B., Douglas, W.W. and Carlsson, A., Pergamon: Oxford.

Hamberger, B., Norberg. K.A. and Ungerstedt, U. (1965), Adrenergic synaptic terminals in autonomic ganglia. *Acta physiol. scand.* **64**, 285—286.

Hamlyn, L.H. (1954), The affect of preganglionic section in the neurons of the superior cervical ganglion in rabbits. *J. Anat.* **88**, 184—191.

Hammond, W.S. and Yntema, C.L. (1947), Depletions in the thoraco-lumbar sympathetic system following removal of neural crest in the chick. *J. comp. Neurol.* **86**, 237—265.

Hammond, W.S. and Yntema, C.L. (1958), Origin of the ciliary ganglia in the chick. *J. comp. Neurol.* **110**, 367—389.

Hamori, J., Lang, E. and Simon, L. (1968), Experimental degeneration of the preganglionic fibers in the superior cervical ganglion of the cat. *Z. Zellforsch.* **90**, 37—52.

Hand, A.R. (1972), Adrenergic and cholinergic nerve terminals in the rat parotid gland. Electron microscopic observations on permanganate-fixed glands. *Anat Rec.* **173**, 31—140.

Härkönen, M. (1964), Carboxylic esterase, oxidative enzymes and catecholamines in the superior cervical ganglion of the rat and the effect of pre- and post-ganglionic nerve division. *Acta physiol. scand.* **63**, suppl. 237, 1—94.

Härkönen, M. and Penttilä, A. (1971), Catecholamines, monoamine oxidase and cholinesterase in the human sympathetic ganglion. *Acta physiol. scand.* **82**, 310—321.

Harper, A.A., McSwiney, B.A. and Suffolk, S.F. (1935), Afferent fibres from the abdomen in the vagus nerves. *J. Physiol., Lond.* **85**, 267—276.

Harris, A.J. (1943), An experimental analysis of the inferior mesenteric plexus. *J. comp. Neurol.* **79**, 1—17.

Hartman, B.K. (1973), The innervation of cerebral blood vessels by central noradrenergic neurons, In: *Frontiers in Catecholamine Research*, edited by Usdin, E. and Snyder, S.H. pp.91–96, New York: Pergamon Press.

Hausberger, F.X. (1934), Uber die Innervation der Fettorgane. *Z. Zellforsch.* 36, 231–266.

Hebb, C., and Linzell, J.L. (1970), Innervation of the mammary gland. A histochemical study in the rabbit. *Histochem. J.* 2, 491–505.

Henry, J.L., and Calaresu, F.R. (1972), Topography and numerical distribution of neurons of the thoraco-lumbar intermedio-lateral nucleus in the cat. *J. comp. Neurol.* 144, 205–214.

Hervonèn, A. and Kanerva, L. (1973), Fine structure of the autonomic nerves of the rabbit myometrium. *Z. Zellforsch.* 139, 19–30.

Hervonen, A., Kanerva, L. and Teräväinen, H. (1972), The fine structure of the paracervical (Frankenhäuser) ganglion of the rat after permanganate fixation. *Acta physiol. scand.* 85, 506–510.

Hess, A. (1965), Developmental changes in the structure of the synapse on the myelinated cell bodies of the chicken ciliary ganglion. *J. Cell Biol.* 25, 1–19.

Hess. A. (1966), The fine structure of the striated muscle fibers and their nerve terminals in the avian iris: morphological 'twitch-slow' fibers. *Anat. Rec.* 154, 357.

Hess, A., Pilar, G. and Weakley, J.N. (1969), Correlation between transmission and structure in avian ciliary ganglion synapses. *J. Physiol., Lond.* 202, 339–354.

Hill, C.J. (1927), A contribution to our knowledge of the enteric plexuses. *Phil. Trans. R. Soc. Ser. B* 215, 355–387.

Hillarp, N.A. (1946), Structure of the synapse and the peripheral innervation apparatus of the autonomic nervous system. *Acta Anat.* suppl. IV, 1–153.

Hines, M. and Tower, S.S. (1928), Studies on the innervation of skeletal muscle. *Bull. Johns Hopkins Hosp.* 5, 264–307.

Hirsch, E.F., Kaiser, G., Barner, H.B., Nigro, S.L., Hamouda, F., Cooper, T. and Adams, W.E. (1968), The innervation of the mammalian lung. III *Arch Surgery* 96, 149–155.

Hirst, G.D.S., Holman, M.E. and Spence, I. (1974), Two types of neurons in the myenteric plexus of the duodenum in the guinea-pig. *J. Physiol., Lond.* 236, 303–326.

Hirst, G.D.S. and McKirdy, H.C. (1974), A nervous mechanism for descending inhibition in guinea-pig small intestine. *J. Physiol., Lond.* 238, 129–143.

Hirt, A. (1921), Der Grenzstrang des Sympathicus bei einigen Sauriern. *Z. Anat. EntwGesch.* 62, 536–551.

His, W. Jr. (1897), Ueber die Entwicklung des Bauchsympathicus beim Huhnchen und Menschen. *Arch. Anat. Physiol. (Lpz.)* Suppl. 137–170.

Hogg, I.D. (1964), Observations on the development of the peripheral portion of the oculomotor nerve in man and the albino rat. *J. comp. Neurol.* **122**, 91−111.

Hökfelt, T. (1966), Electron microscopic observations on nerve terminals in the intrinsic muscle of the albino rat iris. *Acta physiol. scand.* **67**, 255−256.

Hökfelt, T. (1968), *In vitro* studies on central and peripheral monoamine neurons at the ultrastructural level. *Z. Zellforsch.* **91**, 1−74.

Hökfelt, T. (1969), Distribution of noradrenaline storing particles in peripheral adrenergic neurons as revealed by electron microscopy. *Acta. physiol. scand.* **76**, 427−440.

Hökfelt, T., Fuxe, K., Goldstein, M. and Joh, T.H. (1973), Immunohistochemical localization of three catecholamine synthesizing enzymes: aspects on methodology. *Histochemie* **33**, 231−254.

Hollinshead, W.H. (1941), Chemoreceptors in the abdomen. *J. comp. Neurol.* **74**, 269−285.

Hollinshead, W.H. (1946), The function of the abdominal chemoreceptors of the rat and mouse. *Am. J. Physiol.* **147**, 654−660.

Hollinshead, M.B. and Gertner, S.B. (1969), Mast cell changes in denervated sympathetic ganglia. *Exptl. Neurol.* **24**, 487−496.

Holman, M.E., Hirst, G.D.S., Spence, I. (1972), Preliminary studies of the neurons of Auerbach's plexus using intracellular microelectrodes. *Aust. J. exp. Biol. med. Sci.* **50**, 795−801.

Holman, M.E. and McLean, A. (1967), The innervation of sheep mesenteric veins. *J. Physiol., Lond.* **190**, 55−69.

Holmstedt, B. and Sjöqvist, F. (1957), Distribution of acetylcholinesterase in various sympathetic ganglia. *Acta. physiol. scand.* **suppl. 145**, 72−73.

Holmstedt, B. and Sjöqvist, F. (1959), Distribution of acetylcholinesterase in the ganglion cells of various sympathetic ganglia. *Acta. physiol. scand.* **47**, 284−296.

Holzbauer, M. and Sharman, D.F. (1972), The distribution of catecholamines in vertebrates. *Handbook exp. Pharmacol.* **33**, 110−185.

Honjin, R. (1956), Experimental degeneration of the vagus, and its relation to the nerve supply of the lung of the mouse, with special reference to the crossing innervation of the lung by the vagi. *J. comp. Neurol.* **106**, 1−17.

Honma, S. (1970a), Histochemical demonstration of catecholamines in the toad sympathetic ganglia. *Jap. J. Physiol.* **20**, 186−197.

Honma, S. (1970b), Functional differentiation in sB and sC neurons in toad sympathetic ganglia. *Jap. J. Physiol.* **20**, 281−295.

Hörtangle, M., Hörtangle, H. and Winkler, H. (1969), Bovine splenic nerve characterization of noradrenaline-containing vesicles and other cell organelles by density gradient centrifugation. *J. Physiol., Lond.* **205**, 103114.

Huber, G.C. (1899), A contribution on the minute anatomy of the sympathetic ganglion of the different classes of vertebrates. *J. Morph.* **16**, 27–86.

Hudovernig, C. (1908), Beiträge zur mikroskopischen Anatomie und zur Lokalisationslehre einiger Gehirnnervenkern (Nervus Hypoglossus, Vagus und Facialis) *J. Psychol. Neurol., Lpz.* **10**, 247–273.

Hunt, C.C. and Nelson, P.G. (1965), Structural and functional changes in the frog sympathetic ganglion following cutting of the presynaptic nerve fibres. *J. Physiol., Lond.* **177**, 1–20.

Hunt, C.C. and Riker, W.K. (1966), Properties of frog sympathetic neurons in normal ganglia and after axon section. *J. Neurophysiol.* **29**, 1096–1114.

Hutter, O.F. and Loewenstein, W.R. (1955), Nature of neuromuscular facilitation by sympathetic stimulation in the frog. *J. Physiol., Lond.* **130**, 559–571.

Hutter, O.F. and Trauttwein, W. (1956), Neuromuscular facilitation by stretch of motor nerve endings. *J. Physiol., Lond.* **133**, 610–625.

Iggo, A. (1956), Central nervous control of gastric movements in sheep and goats. *J. Physiol., Lond.* **131**, 248–256.

Ignarro, L.J. and Shideman, F.E. (1968), Appearance and concentrations of catecholamines in the embryonic and developing chick. *J. Pharmac. exp. Ther.* **159**, 38–48.

Irving, J.T., McSwiney, B.A. and Suffolk, S.F. (1937), Afferent fibres from the stomach and small intestine. *J. Physiol., Lond.* **89**, 407–420.

Irwin, D.A. (1931), The anatomy of Auerbach's plexus. *Am. J. Anat.* **49**, 141–166.

Isomura, G. (1974), Nerve centers for sphincter muscles of the iris in the fowl. *Anat. Anz.* **135**, 178–190.

Ivens, C., Mottram, D.R., Lever, J.D., Presley, R. and Howells, G. (1973), Studies on the acetylcholinesterase (AChE)-positive and -negative autonomic axons supplying smooth muscle in the normal and 6-hydroxydopamine (6-OHDA) treated rat iris. *Z. Zellforsch.* **138**, 211–222.

Iversen, L.L. (1967), *The Uptake and Storage of Noradrenaline in Sympathetic Nerves.* Cambridge: University Press.

Iversen, L.L., De Champlain, J., Glowinski, J. and Axelrod, J. (1967), Uptake, storage and metabolism of norepinephrine in tissues of the developing rat. *J. Pharmac. exp. Ther.* **157**, 509–516.

Iwayama, T. (1970), Ultrastructural changes in the nerves innervating the cerebral artery after sympathectomy. *Z. Zellforsch.* **109**, 465–480.

Jabonero, V. (1953), Der anatomische Aufbau des peripherischen neurovegetativen Systems. *Acta neuroveg.* **suppl. 4**, 1–159.

Jacobowitz, D. (1965), Histochemical studies of the autonomic innervation of the gut. *J. Pharmac. exp. Ther.* **149**, 358–364.

186

Jacobowitz, D. (1967), Histochemical studies of the relationship of chromaffin cells and adrenergic nerve fibres to the cardiac ganglia of several species. *J. Pharmac. exp. Ther.* **158**, 227–240.

Jacobowitz, D. (1970), Catecholamine fluorescence studies of adrenergic neurons and chromaffin cells in sympathetic ganglia. *Fedn. Proc. Fedn. Am. Socs. exp. Biol.* **29**, 1929–1944.

Jacobowitz, D., Cooper, Th. and Barner, H.B. (1967), Histochemical and chemical studies of the localization of adrenergic and cholinergic nerves in normal and denervated cat hearts. *Circulation Res.* **20**, 289–298.

Jacobowitz, D. and Greene, L.A. (1974), Histofluorescence study of chromaffin cells in dissociated cell cultures of chick embryo sympathetic ganglia. *J. Neurobiol.* **5**, 65–83.

Jacobowitz, D. and Wallach, E.E. (1967), Histochemical and chemical studies of the autonomic innervation of the ovary. *Endocrinology* **81**, 1132–1139.

Jacobowitz, D. and Woodward, J.K. (1968), Adrenergic neurons in the cat superior cervical ganglion and cervical sympathetic nerve trunk. A histochemical study. *J. Pharmac. exp. Ther.* **162**, 213–226.

Jacobs, L. and Comroe, H.J.Jr. (1971), Reflex apnea, bradycardia, and hypotension produced by serotonin and phenyldiguanide on the nodose ganglia of the cat. *Circulation Res.* **29**, 145–155.

Jansson, G. (1969), Extrinsic nervous control of gastric motility. *Acta physiol. scand.* suppl. **326**.

Johansson, B. and Langston, B. (1964), Reflex influence of mesenteric afferents on renal, intestinal and muscle blood flow and on intestinal motility. *Acta. physiol. scand.* **61**, 400–412.

Johnson, S.E. (1918), On the question of commissural neurons in the sympathetic ganglia. *J. comp. Neurol.* **29**, 385–404.

Johnson, S.E. (1925), Experimental degeneration of the extrinsic nerves of the small intestine in relation to the structure of the myenteric plexus. *J. comp. Neurol.* **38**, 299–314.

Johnstone, J. (1764), Essay on the use of the ganglions of the nerves. *Phil. Trans. R. Soc. Ser. B* **54**, 177.

Jones, R.L. (1937), Cell fibre ratios in the vagus nerve. *J. comp. Neurol.* **67**, 469–482.

Juorio, A.V. and Gabella, G. (1974), Noradrenaline in the guinea pig alimentary canal: regional distribution and sensitivity to denervation and reserpine. *J. Neurochem.* **22**, 851–858.

Kanerva, L. Lietzén, R. and Teräväinen, H. (1972), Catecholamines and cholinesterase in the paracervical (Frankenhäuser) ganglion of normal and pregnant rats. *Acta physiol. scand.* In press.

Kanerva, L. and Teräväinen, H. (1972), Electron microscopy of the paracervical (Frankenhäuser) ganglion of the adult rat. *Z. Zellforsch.* **129**, 161–177.

187

Kapeller, K. and Mayor, D. (1969), An electron microscopic study of the early changes proximal to a constriction in sympathetic nerves. *Proc. R. Soc. B* **172**, 39–51.

Kasa, P. and Csernovszki, E. (1967), Electron microscopic localization of acetylcholinesterase in the superior cervical ganglion of the rat. *Acta histochem.* **28**, 274–285.

Keatinge, W.R. (1966), Electrical and mechanical responses of arteries to stimulation of sympathetic nerves. *J. Physiol., Lond.* **185**, 701–715.

Kemp, D.R. (1973), A histological and functional study of the gastric mucosal innervation of the dog. I. The quantification of the fibre content of the normal supradiaphragmatic vagal trunks and their abdominal branches. *Aust. N.Z. J. Surg.* **43**, 289–294.

Kerr, F.W.L. (1969), Preserved vagal visceromotor function following destruction of the dorsal motor nucleus. *J. Physiol., Lond.* **202**, 755–769.

Kerr, F.W.L., Hendler, N. and Bowron, P. (1970), Viscertopic organization of the vagus. *J. comp. Neurol.* **138**, 279–290.

Kim, S.U. and Munkacsi, I. (1972), Cytochemical demonstration of catecholamine and acetylcholinesterase in cultures of chick sympathetic ganglia. *Experientia* **28**, 824–825.

Kirpekar, S.M., Cervoni, P. and Furschgott, R.F. (1962), Catecholamine content of the cat nictitating membrane following procedures sensitizing it to norepinephrine. *J. Pharmac. exp. Ther.* **135**, 180–190.

Kirshner, N., Sage, H.J., Smith, W.J. and Kirschner, A.G. (1966), Release of catecholamines and specific protein from adrenal glands. *Science* **154**, 529–531.

Klingman, G.I. (1970), The distribution of acetylcholinesterase in sympathetic ganglia of immuno-sympathectomized rats. *J. Pharmac. exp. Ther.* **173**, 205–211.

Klingman, G.I. (1972). In: *Immunosympathectomy* edited by Steiner, G. and Schönbaum, E. Amsterdam: Elsevier.

Klingman, G.I. and Klingman, J.D. (1967), Catecholamines in peripheral tissues of mice and cell counts of sympathetic ganglia after the prenatal and postnatal administration of the nerve growth factor antiserum. *Int. J. Neuropharmacol.* **6**, 501–508.

Knoche, H. and Terwort, H. (1973), Elektronenmikroskopischer Beitrag zur Kenntnis von Degenerationsformen der vegetativen Endstrecke nach Durchschneidung postganglionärer Fasern. *Z. Zellforsch.* **141**, 181–202.

Koelle, G.B. (1951), The elimination of enzymatic diffusion artifacts in the histochemical localization of cholinesterases and a survey of their cellular distribution. *J. Pharmac. exp. Ther.* **103**, 153–171.

Koelle, G.B. (1954), The histochemical localization of cholinesterases in the central nervous system of the rat. *J. comp. Neurol.* **100**, 211–228.

Koelle, G.B., Davis, R. and Koelle, W.A. (1974), Effects of aldehyde fixation and of preganglionic denervation on acetylcholinesterase and butyrocholinesterase of cat autonomic ganglia. *J. Histochem. Cytochem.* **22**, 244–251.

Koelle, W.A. and Koelle, G.B. (1959), The localization of external or functional acetylcholinesterase at the synapses of autonomic ganglia. *J. Pharmac. exp. Ther.* **126**, 1–8.

Koenig, H.L. (1965), Relations entre la distribution de l'activité acétylcholinestérasique et celle de l'ergastoplasme dans les neurons du ganglion ciliaire du poulet. *Archs Anat. microsc. Morph. exp.* **54**, 937–964.

Koenig, H.L. (1967), Quelques particularitès ultrastructurales des zones synaptiques dans le ganglion ciliaire du poulet. *C. r. Ass. Anat.* **52**, 711–719.

Kohno, K. and Nakayama, Y. (1973), Fine structure of the axon collaterals of Huber in frog spinal ganglia. *J. Neurocytol.* **2**, 383–391.

Korneliussen, H. (1972), Elongated profiles of synaptic vesicles in motor endplates. Morphological effects of fixative variations. *J. Neurocytol.* **1**, 279–296.

Kosaka, K. (1909), Über die Vaguskerne des Hundes. *Neurol. Zbl.* **28**, 406–410.

Kosterlitz, H.W. and Lees, G.W. (1972), Interrelationship between adrenergic and cholinergic mechanisms. *Handbook Exp. Pharmacol.* **33**, 762–812.

Kosterlitz, H.W., Lydon, R.J. and Watt, A.J. (1970), The effects of adrenaline, noradrenaline and isoprenaline on inhibitory α- and β-adrenoceptors in the longitudinal muscle of the guinea-pig ileum. *Br. J. Pharmac. Chemother.* **39**, 398–413.

Kosterlitz, H.W. and Robinson, J.A. (1957), Inhibition of the peristaltic reflex of the isolated guinea-pig ileum. *J. Physiol., Lond.* **136**, 249–262.

Kosterlitz, H.W., Thompson, J.W. and Wallis, D.I. (1964), The compound action potential in the nerve supplying the medial smooth muscle of the nictitating membrane of the cat. *J. Physiol., Lond.* **171**, 426–433.

Krantz, K.E. (1959), Innervation of the human uterus. *Ann. N.Y. Acad. Sci.* **75**, 770–784.

Krinke, G., Schnider, K. and Hess, R. (1974), Quantitation of noradrenaline fluorescence in the superior cervical ganglion of the rat and the effect of postganglionic axotomy. *Experientia* **30**, 37–38.

Kubozoe, T., Daikoku, S. and Takita, S. (1969), Electromicroscopic observations on Auerbach's plexus in a 12 mm human embryo. *J. Neuro-visc. rel.* **31**, 291–307.

Kudo, S. (1971), Fine structure of autonomic ganglion in the chicken pancreas. *Arch. histol. jap.* **32**, 455–497.

Kuffler, S.W., Dennis, M.J. and Harris, A.J. (1971), The development of chemosensitivity in extrasynaptic areas of the neuronal surface after denervation of parasympathetic ganglion cells of the heart of the frog. *Proc. R. Soc. B.* **177**, 555–563.

189

Kuntz, A., (1910a), The development of the sympathetic nervous system in mammals. *J. comp. Neurol.* **20**, 211–258.

Kuntz, A. (1910b), The development of the sympathetic nervous system in birds. *J. comp. Neurol.* **20**, 283–308.

Kuntz, A. (1914), Further studies on the development of the cranial sympathetic ganglia. *J. comp. Neurol.* **24**, 235–267.

Kuntz, A. (1922), On the occurrence of reflex arcs in the myentric and submucous plexuses. *Anat. Rec.* **24**, 193–210.

Kuntz, A. (1938), The structural organization of the celiac ganglia. *J. comp. Neurol.* **69**, 1–12.

Kuntz, A. (1940), The structural organization of the inferior mesenteric ganglia. *J. comp. Neurol.* **72**, 371–382.

Kuntz, A. (1946), *The Autonomic Nervous System.* London: Baillière, Tindall and Cox.

Kuntz, A. (1956), Components of the splanchnic and intermesenteric nerves. *J. comp. Neurol.* **105**, 251–268.

Kuntz, A., Hoffman, H.H. and Jacobs, M.W. (1956), Nerve fiber components of communicating rami and sympathetic roots in man. *Anat. Rec.* **126**, 29–41.

Kuntz, A., Hoffman, H.H. and Schaeffer, E.M. (1957), Fiber components of the splanchnic nerves. *Anat. Rec.* **128**, 139–146.

Kuntz, A. and Moseley, R.L. (1936), An experimental analysis of the pelvic autonomic ganglia in the cat. *J. comp. Neurol.* **64**, 63–75.

Kuntz, A. and Sulkin, N. (1947), The neuroglia of the autonomic ganglia: cytologic structure and reaction to stimulation. *J. comp. Neurol.* **86**, 466–477.

Kyösola, K. and Rechardt, L. (1973), Adrenergic innervation of the choledocoduodenal junction in the cat and dog. *Histochemie* **34**, 325–332.

Lachenmayer, L. (1971), Adrenergic innervation of the umbilical vessels. *Z. Zellforsch.* **120**, 120–136.

Lakos, I. (1970), Ultrastructure of chronically denervated superior cervical ganglion in the cat and rat. *Acta biol. hung.* **21**, 425–427.

Landmesser, L. (1971), Contractile and electrical responses of vagus-innervated frog sartorius. *J. Physiol., Lond.* **213**, 707–725.

Landmesser, L. (1972), Pharmacological properties, cholinesterase activity and anatomy of nerve-muscle junctions in vagus-innervated from sartorius. *J. Physiol., Lond.* **220**, 243–256.

Landmesser, L. and Pilar, G. (1970), Selective reinnervation of two cell populations in the adult pigeon ciliary ganglion. *J. Physiol., Lond.* **211**, 203–216.

Landmesser, L. and Pilar, G. (1972), The onset and development of transmission in the chick ciliary ganglion. *J. Physiol., Lond.* **222**, 691–713.

Landmesser, L. and Pilar, G. (1974a), Synapse formation during embryogenesis on ganglion cells lacking a periphery. *J. Physiol., Lond.* **241**, 715–736.

Landmesser, L. and Pilar, G. (1974b), Synaptic transmission and cell death during normal ganglionic development. *J. Physiol., Lond.* **241**, 737—749.

Langer, S.Z. (1973), The regulation of transmitter release elicited by nerve stimulation through a presynaptic feed-back mechanism, In: *Frontiers in Catecholamine Research.* pp.543—549, Edited by Usdin, E. and Snyder, S.H. New York: Pergamon Press.

Langley, J.N. (1892), On the origin from the spinal cord of the cervical and upper thoracic sympathetic fibres with some observations on white and gray rami communicantes. *Phil. Trans. R. Soc. Ser. B* **183**, 85—124.

Langley, J.N. (1896), Observations on the medullated fibres of the sympathetic system and chiefly on those of the gray rami communicantes. *J. Physiol., Lond.* **20**, 55—76.

Langley, J.N. (1899), On axon-reflexes in the preganglionic fibres of the sympathetic system. *J. Physiol., Lond.* **25**, 364—398.

Langley, J.N. (1900), Notes on the regeneration of the preganglionic fibres in the sympathetic system. *J. Physiol., Lond.* **25**, 417—426.

Langley, J.N. (1904), On the sympathetic system of birds, and on the muscles which move the feathers. *J. Physiol., Lond.* **30**, 221—252.

Langley, J.N. (1916), Sketch of the progress of discovery in the eighteenth century as regards the autonomic nervous system. *J. Physiol., Lond.* **50**, 225—258.

Langley, J.N. (1921), *The Autonomic Nervous System.* Cambridge: Heffer.

Langley, J.N. and Anderson, H.K. (1894—1895), The constituents of the hypogastric nerves. *J. Physiol., Lond.* **17**, 177—191.

Langley, J.N. and Anderson, H.K. (1895), The innervation of the pelvic and adjoining viscera. I. The lower portion of the intestine. *J. Physiol., Lond.* **18**, 67—105.

Langley, J.N. and Anderson, H.K. (1896), The innervation of the pelvic and adjoining viscera. V. Position of the nerve cells on the course of the efferent nerve fibres. *J. Physiol., Lond.* **19**, 131—139.

Langley, J.N. and Anderson, H.K. (1904), On the union of the fifth cervical nerve with the superior cervical ganglion. *J. Physiol., Lond.* **30**, 439—442.

Langley, J.N. and Orbeli, L.A. (1911), Some observations on the degeneration in the sympathetic and sacral autonomic nervous system of amphibia following nerve section. *J. Physiol., Lond.* **42**, 113—124.

Lapique, L. (1946), Cytoarchitectonique du ganglion sympatique en fonction du poids du corps. *C.r. hebd. Séanc. Acad. Sci., Paris* **222**, 255—258.

Larsell, O. (1921), Nerve terminations in the lung of the rabbit. *J. comp. Neurol.* **33**, 105—132.

Laties, A.M. and Jacobowitz, D. (1966), A comparative study of the autonomic innervation of the eye in monkey, cat and rabbit. *Anat. Rec.* **156**, 383—396.

Lawrentjew, B.I. (1931), Zur Lehre von der Cytoarchitektonik des peripherischen autonomen Nervensystems. I. Die Cytoarchitektonik der Ganglien des Verdauungskanal beim Hunde. *Z. Mikrosk.-anat. Forsch.* **23**, 527–551.

Leaming, D.B. and **Cauna, N.** (1961), A qualitative and quantitative study of the myenteric plexus in the small intestine of the cat. *J. Anat.* **95**, 160–169.

Le Douarin, N.M. and **Teillet, A.-A.** (1973), The migration of neural crest cells to the wall of the digestive tract in avian embryo. *J. Embryol. exp. Morph.* **30**, 31–48.

Lee, F.C. (1930), The regeneration of sympathetic nerve fibers. *Ass. Res. nerv. ment. Dis.* **9**, 417–436.

Lehmann, H.J. and **Stange, H.H.** (1953), Über das Vorkommen vakuolenhaltiger Ganglienzellen im Ganglion cervicale uteri trächtiger und nichtträchtiger Ratten. *Z. Zellforsch.* **38**, 230–236.

Leiberman, A.R. (1971), The axon reaction. A review of the principal features of perykarial responses to axon injury. *Int. Rev. Neurobiol.* **14**, 49–124.

Lenhossek, M.V. (1911), Das Ganglion ciliare der Vogel. *Arch. mikrosk. Anat. EntwMech.* **76**, 745–769.

Lennon, A.M., **Vera, C.L.**, **Rex, A.L.** and **Luco, J.V.** (1967), Cholinesterase activity of the nictitating membrane reinnervated by cholinergic fibers. *J. Neurophysiol.* **30**, 1523–1530.

Lever, J.D. and **Presley, R.** (1971), Studies on the sympathetic neuron *in vitro*. *Prog. Brain Res.* **34**, 499–512.

Levi, G. (1925), Wachstum und Korpergrosse. *Ergbn. Anat. EntwGesch.* **26**, 87–342.

Levi-Montalcini, R. (1966), The nerve growth factor: its mode of action on sensory and sympathetic nerve cells. *Harvey Lectures* **60**, 217–259.

Levi-Montalcini, R. (1972), The morphological effects of immunosympathectomy. In: *Immunosympathectomy*, edited by Steiner, G. and Schönbaum, E. pp.55–78, Amsterdam: Elsevier.

Levi-Montalcini, R. and **Amprino, R.** (1946), Recherches experimentales sur l'origine du ganglion ciliaire dans l'embryon de poulet. *Arch. Biol., Liège.* **62**; 265–288.

Levi-Montalcini, R. and **Angeletti, P.U.** (1966), Immunosympathectomy, *Pharmac. Rev.* **18**, 619–628.

Levi-Montalcini, R. and **Angeletti, P.U.** (1968), Nerve growth factor. *Physiol. Rev.* **48**, 534–569.

Levi-Montalcini, R. and **Booker, B.** (1960a), Excessive growth of the sympathetic ganglia evoked by a protein isolated from mouse salivary glands. *Proc. natn. Acad. Sci. U.S.A.* **46**, 373–384.

Levi-Montalcini, R. and **Booker, B.** (1960b), Destruction of the sympathetic ganglia in mammals by an antiserum to a nerve-growth protein. *Proc. natn. Acad. Sci. U.S.A.* **46**, 384–391.

Levi-Montalcini, R. and Cohen, S. (1960), Effects of the extracts of the mouse submaxillary salivary glands on the sympathetic system of mammals. *Ann. N.Y. Acad. Sci.* **85**, 324—341.

Levi-Montalcini, R. and Levi, G. (1944), Correlazioni nello sviluppo tra varie parti del sistema nervoso. Consequenze della demolizione dell'abbozzo di un arto sui centri nervosi dell'embrione di pollo. *Comment. Pontif. Acad. Sci.* **8**, 527—569.

Levinsohn, G. (1903), Ueber das Verhalten des Ganglion cervical supremum nach Durchschneidung seiner pre-bezw. postcellulären Fasern. *Arch. Physiol., Lpz.* 438—459.

Lewis, P.R., Blundell Jones, P., Breathnach, S.M. and Navaratnam, V. (1972), Regenerative capacity of visceral preganglionic neurones. *Nature New Biology* **236**, 181—182.

Libet, B. and Owman, Ch. (1974), Concomitant changes in formaldehyde-induced fluorescence of dopamine interneurons and in slow inhibitory post-synaptic potentials of the rabbit superior cervical ganglion, induced by stimulation of the preganglionic nerve or by a muscarinic agent. *J. Physiol., Lond.* **237**, 635—662.

Libet, B. and Tosaka, T. (1969), Slow inhibitory and excitatory postsynaptic responses in single cells of mammalian sympathetic ganglia. *J. Neurophysiol.* **32**, 43—50.

Lloyd, D.P.C. (1937), The transmission of impulses through the inferior mesenteric ganglia. *J. Physiol., Lond.* **91**, 296—313.

Loewenstein, W.R. and Altamirano-Ortego, R. (1956), Enhancement of activity in a Pacinian corpuscle by sympathomimetic agents. *Nature* **178**, 1292—1293.

Loewi, O. (1921), Ueber humorale Uebertragbarkeit der Herznervenwirkung. *Arch. ges. Physiol.* **189**, 239—242.

Lorenz, J. (1962), Observations comparatives sur l'innervation intramurale du cardia, du pylore et de la valvule iéo-coecale chez l'homme normal au cours de l'âge. *Z. mikrosk.-anat. Forsch.* **68**, 540—563.

Lovatt-Evans, C. (1957), Sweating in relation to sympathetic innervation. *Br. med. Bull.* **13**, 197—201.

Lucas, A.M. and Miksicek, J.E. (1936), Nerve cells without central processes in the 4th spinal ganglion of the bullfrog. *Science* **84**, 207—208.

Luco, J.V. and Eyzaguirre, C. (1955), Fibrillation and hypersensitivity to ACh in denervated muscle: effect of degenerating nerve fibres. *J. Neurophysiol.* **18**, 65—73.

Lutz, G. (1968), Die Entwicklung des Halssympathicus und des Nervus vertebralis. *Z. Anat. EntwGesch.* **127**, 187—200.

Malmfors, T. (1965), The adrenergic innervation of the eye as demonstrated by fluorescence microscopy. *Acta physiol. scand.* **64**, suppl. 248.

Malmfors, T. and Nilsson, O. (1966), Parasympathetic post-ganglionic denervation of the iris and the parotid gland of the rat. *Acta morph. neer.-scand.* **6**, 81—85.

Malmfors, T. and Sachs, C. (1965a), Direct studies on the disappearance of the transmitter and changes in the uptake-storage mechanisms of degenerating adrenergic nerves. *Acta physiol. scand.* **64**, 211—223.

Malmfors, T. and Sachs, C. (1965b), Direct demonstration of the system of terminals belonging to an individual adrenergic neuron and their distribution in the rat iris. *Acta physiol. scand.* **64**, 377—382.

Manukhin, B.N. (1969), Quoted by Holzbauer and Sharman (1972).

Marinesco, G. (1907), Le méchanisme de la régénérescence nerveuse. II. Les transplantations nerveuses. *Revue gen. Sci.* **18**, 190—198.

Marks, B.H., Samorajski, T. and Webster, E.J. (1962), Radioautographic localization of norepinephrine-H^3 in the tissues of mice. *J. Pharmac. exp. Ther.* **138**, 376—381.

Marrazzi, A.S. (1939), Adrenergic inhibition at sympathetic synapses. *Am. J. Physiol.* **127**, 738—744.

Marshall, J.M. (1970), Adrenergic innervation of the female reproductive tract: anatomy, physiology and pharmacology. *Ergebn. Physiol.* **62**, 6—67.

Martin, A.R. and Pilar, G. (1963), Dual mode of synaptic transmission in the avian ciliary ganglion. *J. Physiol., Lond.* **168**, 443—463.

Marwitt, R., Pilar, G. and Weakly, J.N. (1971), Characterization of two ganglion cell populations in avian ciliary ganglia. *Brain Res.* **25**, 317—354.

Mascorro, J.A. and Yates, R.D. (1974), Innervation of abdominal paraganglia: an ultrastructural study. *J. Morph.* **142**, 153—164.

Maslennikova, L.D. (1962), On the relation between the motor function of the intestine and the gradient of its nervous elements. *Bull. ex. Biol. Med. U.S.S.R.* (English translation) **52**, 972—976.

Massazza, A. (1923), La citoarchitetonica del midollo spinale umano. II *Archs Anat. Histol. Embryol.* **2**, 1—56.

Massazza, A. (1924), La citoarchitetonica del midollo spinale umano. III *Archs Anat. Histol Embryol.* **3**, 115—186.

Masurovsky, E.B. and Benitez, H.H. (1967), Apparent innervation of chick cardiac muscle by sympathetic neurons in organized culture. *Anat. Rec.* **157**, 285.

Matsumura, M. and Koelle, G.B. (1961), The nature of synaptic transmission in the superior cervical ganglion following reinnervation by the afferent vagus *J. Pharmac. exp. Ther.* **134**, 28—46.

Matsuo, H. (1934), A contribution on the anatomy of Auerbach's plexus. *Jap. J. med. Sci. Anat.* **4**, 417—428.

Matthews, M.R. (1971), Evidence from degeneration experiments for the preganglionic origin of afferent fibres to the small granule-containing cells of the rat superior cervical ganglion. *J. Physiol., Lond.* **218**, 95–96 P.

Matthews, M.R. (1973), An ultrastructural study of axonal changes following constriction of post-ganglionic branches of the superior cervical ganglion in the rat. *Phil. Trans. R. Soc. Ser. B* **264**, 479–508.

Matthews, M.R. and Nash, J.R.G. (1970), An afferent synapse from small-granule containing cells to a principal neuron in the superior cervical ganglion. *J. Physiol. Lond.* **210**, 11–13.

Matthews, M.R. and Nelson, V.H. (1975), Detachment of structurally intact nerve endings from chromatolytic neurons of rat superior cervical ganglion during the depression of synaptic transmission induced by post-ganglionic axotomy. *J. Physiol., Lond.* **245**, 91–135.

Matthews, M.R. and Ostberg, A. (1973), Effects of preganglionic nerve section upon the afferent innervation of the small granule-containing cells in the rat superior cervical ganglion. *Acta physiol. pol.* **24**, 215–223.

Matthews, M.R. and Raisman, G. (1969), The ultrastructure and somatic efferent synapses of small granule-containing cells in the superior cervical ganglion. *J. Anat.* **105**, 255–282.

Matthews, M.R. and Raisman, G. (1972), A light and electron microscopic study of the cellular response to axonal injury in the superior cervical ganglion of the rat. *Proc. R. Soc. B* **181**, 43–79.

Matthieu, J.-M. (1970), Effet des variations de la P_{CO_2}, du pH et de la HCO_3^- sur la production de lactate et la transmission synaptique du ganglion sympatique cervical insolé du rat. *Brain Res.* **18**, 1–14.

McDougal, M.D. and West, G.B. (1954), The inhibition of the peristaltic reflex by sympathomimetic amines. *Br. J. Pharmac. Chemother.* **9**, 131–137.

McIsaac, R.J. and Koelle, G.B. (1959), Comparison of the effects of inhibition of external, internal and total acetyl-cholinesterase upon ganglionic transmission. *J. Pharmac. exp. Ther.* **126**, 9–20.

McLachlan, E.M. (1974), The formation of synapses in mammalian sympathetic ganglia reinnervated with preganglionic or somatic nerves. *J. Physiol., Lond.* **237**, 217–242.

McNutt, N.S. and Weinstein, R.S. (1973), Membrane ultrastructure at mammalian intercellular junctions. *Prog. Biophys. Mol. Biol.* **26**, 45–101.

McSwiney, B.A. and Suffolk, S.F. (1938), Segmental distribution of certain visceral afferent neurons in the pupillo-dilator reflex of the cat. *J. Physiol., Lond.* **93**, 104–116.

Merrillees, N.C. (1968), The nervous environment of individual smooth muscle cells of the guinea-pig vas deferens. *J. Cell Biol.* **37**, 794–817.

Miledi, R. and Slater, C.R. (1970), On the degeneration of rat neuromuscular junctions after nerve section. *J. Physiol., Lond.* **207**, 507–528.

Milhaud, M. and Pappas, G. (1966), The fine structure of neurons and synapses

195

of the habenula of the cat with special reference to subjunctional bodies. *Brain Res.* **3**, 158–173.

Mills, E. (1968), Activity of aortic chemoreceptors during electrical stimulation of the stellate ganglion in the cat. *J. Physiol., Lond.* **199**, 103–114.

Mislavsky, M. (1902), Suture du sympathique cervical et du récurrent et centres corticaux du larynx. *C.r. Soc. Séanc. Biol.* **54**, 841.

Mitchell, G.A.G. (1953), *Anatomy of the Autonomic Nervous System.* Edinburgh-London: E. & S. Livingstone.

Mitchell, G.A.F. and Warwick, R. (1955), The dorsal vagal nucleus. *Acta anat.* **25**, 371–395.

Mizell, S. (1965), Seasonal changes in energy reserves in the common frog, *Rana pipiens. J. cell. comp. Physiol.* **66**, 251–258.

Mizeres, N.J. (1957), The course of the left cardioinhibitory fibers in the dog. *Anat. Rec.* **127**, 109–115.

Mohiuddin, A. (1953), Vagal preganglionic fibres to the alimentary canal. *J. comp. Neurol.* **99**, 289–318.

Monro, P.A.G. (1954), Anterior rhizotomy of preganglionic fibres in man. *J. Anat.* **88**, 567 P.

Morest, D.K. (1967), Experimental study of the projections of the nucleus of the tractus solitarius and the area postrema in the cat. *J. comp. Neurol.* **130**, 277–300.

Müller, E. (1921), Über das Darmnervensystes. *Upsala Lakareforenings Forsch.* N.F. **26**, 1–22.

Müller, L.R. and Dahl, W. (1910), Die Beteiligung des sympathischen Nervensystems an der Kopfinnervation. *Dt. Arch. klin. Med.* **99**, 48–107.

Müller, E. and Ingvar, S. (1923), Ueber den Ursprung des Sympathicus beim Hunchen. *Arch. mikrosk. Anat. EntwMech.* **99**, 650–671.

Muratori, G. (1932), Contributo all'innervazione del tessuto paragangliare annesso al sistema del vago (glomo carotico, paragangli estravagali ed intravagali) e all'innervazione del seno carotideo. *Anat. Anz.* **75**, 115–123.

Murobayashi, T., Mori, J., Fujiwara, M. and Shimamoto, K. (1968), Fluorescence histochemical demonstration of adrenergic nerve fibers in the vagus nerve of cats and dogs. *Jap. J. Pharmacol.* **18**, 285–293.

Murray, J.G. (1957), Innervation of the intrinsic muscles of the cat's larynx by the recurrent laryngeal nerve: a unimodal nerve. *J. Physiol., Lond.* **135**, 206–212.

Murray, J.G. and Thompson, J.W. (1957), The occurrence and function of collateral sprouting in the sympathetic nervous system of the cat. *J. Physiol., Lond.* **135**, 133–162.

Muscholl, E. and Vogt, M. (1958), The action of reserpine on the peripheral sympathetic system. *J. Physiol., Lond.* **141**, 132–155.

Muscholl, E. and Vogt, M. (1964), Perfusion of extramedullary chromaffine tissue. *J. Physiol., Lond.* **169**, 93—94 P.

Mustonen, H. and Terävainen, H. (1971), Synaptic connections of the para-cervical (Franfenhäuser) ganglion of the rat uterus examined with the electron microscope after division of the sympathetic and sacral para-sympathetic nerves. *Acta physiol. scand.* **82**, 264—267.

Nakamura, M. and Koketsu, K. (1972), The effect of adrenaline on sympathetic ganglion cells of bullfrogs. *Life Sci.* **11**, 1165—1174.

Navaratnam, V. and Lewis, P.R. (1970), Cholinesterase-containing neurons in the spinal cord of the rat. *Brain Res.* **18**, 411—425.

Nelson, P.G. (1975), Nerve and muscle cells in culture. *Physiol. Rev.* **55**, 1—61.

Nielsen, K.C. and Owman, Ch. (1968), Difference in cardiac adrenergic innerv-ation between hibernators and non-hibernating mammals. *Acta physiol. scand.* suppl. **316**, 1—30.

Nielsen, K.O., Owman, Ch. and Santini, M. (1969), Anastomising adrenergic nerves from the sympathetic trunk to the vagus at the cervical level in the cat. *Brain Res.* **12**, 1—9.

Niijima, A. (1975), Observation on the localization of mechano-receptors in the kidney and afferent nerve fibres in the renal nerves in the rabbit. *J. Physiol., Lond.* **81**—90.

Nilsson, B.Y. (1972), Effects of sympathetic stimulation on mechanoreceptors of cat vibrissae. *Acta physiol. scand.* **85**, 390—397.

Nilsson, O. (1964), The relationship between nerves and smooth muscle cells in the rat iris. I. The dilatator muscle. *Z. Zellforsch.* **64**, 166—171.

Nishi, S. and Christ, D. (1971), Electrophysiological properties and activities of mammalian parasympathetic ganglion cells. *Fedn. Proc. Fedn. Am. Socs exp. Biol.* **30**, 489.

Nishi, S. and North, R.A. (1973), Intracellular recording from the myenteric plexus of the guinea-pig ileum. *J. Physiol., Lond.* **231**, 471—491.

Nishi, S., Soeda, H. and Koketsu, K. (1965), Studies on sympathetic B and C neurons and patterns of preganglionic innervation. *J. cell. comp. Physiol.* **66**, 19—32.

Nishi, S., Soeda, H. and Koketsu, K. (1967), Release of acetylcholine from sympathetic nerve terminals. *J. Neurophysiol.* **30**, 114—134.

Nishida, S. and Sears, M. (1969), Dual innervation of the iris sphincter muscle of the albino guinea pig. *Exp. Eye Res.* **8**, 467—469.

Nolf, P. (1934), Les nerfs extrinsèques de l'intestin chez l'oiseau. I. Les nerfs vagues. II. Les nerfs coeliaques et mesenteriques. III. Le nerf de Remak. *Arch. int. Physiol. Biochim.* **39**, 113—256.

Norberg, K.-A. (1964), Adrenergic innervation of the intestinal wall by fluor-escence microscopy. *Int. J. Neuropharmacol.* **3**, 379—382.

Norberg, K.-A. (1967), Transmitter histochemistry of the sympathetic adrenergic nervous system. *Brain Res.* **5**, 125—170.

Norberg, K.-A. and Fredricsson, B. (1966), Cellular distribution of monoamines in the uterine and tubal walls of the rat. *Acta physiol. scand.* suppl. **277**, 1—149.

Norberg, K.-A. and Hamberger, B. (1964), The sympathetic adrenergic neuron. Some characteristics revealed by histochemical studies on the intraneuronal distribution of the transmitter. *Acta physiol. scand.* suppl. **238**, 1—42.

Norberg, K.-A., Hökfelt, T. and Eneroth, C.M. (1969), The autonomic innervation of human submandibular and parotid glands *J. Neuro-visc. rel.* **31**, 280—290.

Norberg, K.-A. and McIsaac, R.J. (1967), Cellular localization of adrenergic amines in frog sympathetic ganglia. *Experientia* **23**, 1052.

Norberg, K.-A. and Olson, L. (1965), Adrenergic innervation of the salivary glands in the rat. *Z. Zellforsch.* **68**, 183—189.

Norberg, K.-A., Ritzén, M. and Ungerstedt, U. (1966), Histochemical studies on a special catecholamine-containing cell type in sympathetic ganglia. *Acta physiol scand.* **67**, 260—270.

Obrador, S. and Odoriz, J.B. (1936), Transmission through a lumbar sympathetic ganglion. *J. Physiol., Lond.* **86**, 269—276.

Ochi, J., Konishi, M., Yoshikawa, H. and Sano, Y. (1968), Fluorescence and electron microscopic evidence for the dual innervation of the iris sphincter muscle of the rabbit. *Z. Zellforsch.* **91**, 90—95.

Ogura, J.H. and Lam, R.L. (1953), Anatomical and physiological correlations on stimulating the human superior laryngeal nerve. *Laryngoscope* **63**, 947—959.

Ohkubo, K. (1936a), Studien über das intramurale Nervensystem des Verdauugskanals. II. Die plexus myentericus und Plexus subserosus des Meerschweinchens. *Jap. J. med. Sci. Anat.* **6**, 21—37.

Ohkubo, K. (1936b), Studien über das intramurale Nervensystem des Verdauungskanals. III. Affe und Mensch. *Jap. J. med. Sci. Anat.* **6**, 219—247.

O'Lague, P.H., Obata, K., Claude, P., Furshpan, E.J. and Potter, D.D. (1974), Evidence for cholinergic synapses between dissociated rat sympathetic neurons in cell culture. *Proc. natn. Acad. Sci U.S.A.* **71**, 3602—3606.

Olivieri-Sangiacomo, C. (1969), Sumicroscopic organization of the otic ganglion of the adult rabbit. *Z. Zellforsch.* **95**, 290—309.

Olson, L. (1969), Intact and regenerating sympathetic noradrenaline axons in the rat sciatic nerve. *Histochemie* **17**, 349—367.

Olson, M.I. and Bunge, R.P. (1973), Anatomical observations on the specificity of synapse formation in tissue culture. *Brain Res.* **59**, 19—33.

Olson, L. and Malmfors, T. (1970), Growth characteristics of adrenergic nerves in the adult rat. *Acta physiol. scand.* suppl. **348**, 1—112.

Oosaki, T. and Sugai, N. (1974), Morphology of extraganglionic fluorescent neurons in the myenteric plexus of the small intestine of the rat. *J. comp. Neurol.* **158**, 109–120.

Osborne, L.W. and Silva, D.G. (1970), Histological, acetylcholinesterase, and fluorescence histochemical studies on the atrial ganglia of the monkey heart. *Expl. Neurol.* **27**, 497–511.

Owman, Ch., Rosengren, E. and Sjöberg, N.-O. (1967), Adrenergic innervation of the human female reproductive organs. *Obstet. Gynecol.* **30**, 763–773.

Owman, Ch. and Santini, M. (1966), Adrenergic nerves in spinal ganglia of the cat. *Acta physiol. scand.* **68**, 127–128.

Owman, Ch. and Sjöberg, N.O. (1966), Adrenergic nerves in the female genital tract of the rabbit. *Z. Zellforsch.* **74**, 182–197.

Owman, Ch., Sjöberg, N.-O. and Swedin, G. (1971), Histochemical and chemical studies on pre- and postnatal development of the different systems of 'short' and 'long' adrenergic neurons in peripheral organs of the rat. *Z. Zellforsch.* **116**, 319–341.

Owman, Ch. and Sjöstrand, N.O. (1965), Short adrenergic neurons and catecholamine containing cells in vas deferens and accessory male genital glands of different mammals. *Z. Zellforsch.* **66**, 300–320.

Paintal, A.S. (1973), Vagal sensory receptors and their reflex effects. *Physiol. Rev.* **53**, 159–227.

Palay, S., Sotelo, C., Peters, A. and Orkand, P.M. (1968), The axon hioock and the initial segment. *J. Cell. Biol.* **38**, 193–201.

Pallie, W., Corner, G.W. and Weddell, G. (1954), Nerve terminations in the myometrium of the rabbit. *Anat. Rec.* **118**, 789–811.

Papez, W.P. (1929), *Comparative Neurology* New York: Thomas Y. Crowell.

Papka, R.E. (1972), Ultrastructural and fluorescence histochemical studies of developing sympathetic ganglia in the rabbit. *Am. J. Anat.* **134**, 337–364.

Pappas, G.D. and Waxman, S.G. (1972), In: *Structure and Function of Synapses.* edited by Pappas, G.D. and Purpura, D.P. pp.1–43, New York: Raven Press.

Paton, V.D.M. and Vizi, E.S. (1969), The inhibitory action of noradrenaline and adrenaline on acetylcholine output by guinea-pig ileum longitudinal muscle strip. *Br. J. Pharmac. Chemother.* **35**, 10–28.

Paton, W.D.M. and Zar, M.A. (1968), The origin of acetylcholine released from guinea-pig intestine and longitudinal muscle strips. *J. Physiol., Lond.* **194**, 13–33.

Pera, L. (1971), Sui rapporti tra nervo vago e gangli prevertebrali nel gatto. *Archo. ital. Anat. Embriol.* **76**, 7–17.

Perman, E. (1924), Anatomische Untersuchungen über die Herznerven bei den höneren Säugetieren und beim Menschen. *Z. Anat. EntwGesch.* **71**, 382–457.

Perri, V., Sacchi, O. and Casella, C. (1970), Electrical properties and synaptic connections of the sympathetic neurons in the rat and guinea-pig superior cervical ganglion. *Pflügers Arrh. ges. Physiol.* **314**, 40–54.

Perry, W.L.M. (1953), Acetylcholine release in the cat's superior cervical ganglion. *J. Physiol., Lond.* **119**, 439–454.

Perry, W.L.M. and Talesnik, J. (1953), The role of acetylcholine in synaptic transmission at parasympathetic ganglia. *J. Physiol., Lond.* **119**, 455–469.

Petras, J.M. and Cummings, J.F. (1972), Autonomic neurons in the spinal cord of the rhesus monkey: a correlation of the findings of cytoarchitectonics and sympathectomy with fiber degeneration following dorsal rhizotomy. *J. comp. Neurol.* **146**, 189–218.

Pick, J. (1957), Sympathectomy in amphibians (anatomical considerations). *J. comp. Neurol.* **107**, 169–207.

Pick, J. (1963), On the submicroscopic organization of the sympathetic ganglion in the frog (*Rana pipiens*). *J. comp. Neurol.* **120**, 409–462.

Pick, J. (1970), *The Autonomic Nervous System*. Philadelphia and Toronto: Lippincott.

Pick, J., De Lemos, C. and Gerdin, C. (1964), The fine structure of sympathetic neurons in the man. *J. comp. Neurol.* **122**, 19–68.

Pilar, G., Jeden, D.J. and Campbell, B. (1973), Distribution of acetylcholine in the normal and denervated pigeon ciliary ganglion. *Brain Res.* **49**, 245–256.

Pines, J.L. (1927), Die Morphologie des Ganglion ciliare beim Menschen. *Z. mikrosk.-anat. Forsch.* **10**, 313–380.

Puriton, T., Fletcher, T. and Bradley, W. (1971), Sensory perikarya in autonomic ganglia. *Nature* **231**, 63–64.

Quilliam, J.P. and Tamarind, D.L. (1967), Ultrastructural changes in the superior cervical ganglion of the rat following preganglionic denervation. *J. Physiol., Lond.* **189**, 13–15.

Quilliam, J.P. and Tamarind, D.L. (1972), Electron microscopy of degenerative changes in decentralized rat superior cervical ganglia. *Micron.* **3**, 454–472.

Raisman, G., Field, P.M., Ostberg, A.J.C., Iversen, L.L. and Zigmond, R.E. (1974), A quantitative ultrastructural and biochemical analysis of the process of reinnervation of the superior cervical ganglion in the adult rat. *Brain Res.* **71**, 1–16.

Ranson, S.W. (1915), The vagus nerve of the snapping turtle (*Chelydra serpentina*). *J. comp. Neurol.* **25**, 301–316.

Ranson, S.W. and Billingsley, P.R. (1918), The superior cervical ganglion and the cervical portion of the sympathetic trunk. *J. comp. Neurol.* **29**, 313–358.

Ranson, S.W. and Davenport, H.K. (1931), Unmyelinated sensory fibers in the spinal nerves. *Anat. Rec.* **48**, 61.

Ranson, S.W., Foley, J.O. and Alpert, C.D. (1933), Observations on the structure of the vagus nerve. *Am. J. Anat.* **53**, 289–315.

Read, J.B. and Burnstock, G. (1968), Comparative histochemical studies of adrenergic nerves in the enteric plexuses of vertebrate large intestine. *Comp. Biochem. Physiol.* **27**, 505–517.

Read, J.B. and Burnstock, G. (1969), Adrenergic innervation of the gut musculature in Vertebrates. *Histochemie* **17**, 263–272.

Rees, R. and Bunge, R. (1974), Morphological and cytochemical studies of synapses formed in culture between isolated rat superior cervical ganglion neurons. *J. comp. Neurol.* **157**, 1–12.

Reinert, H. (1963), Role and origin of noradrenaline in the superior cervical ganglion. *J. Physiol., Lond.* **167**, 18–29.

Réthelyi, M. (1972), Cell and neuropil architecture of the intermedio-lateral (sympathetic) nucleus of cat spinal cord. *Brain Res.* **46**, 203–213.

Rexed, B. (1954), A cytoarchitectonic atlas of the spinal cord in the cat, *J. comp. Neurol.* **100**, 297–379.

Richardson, K.C. (1966), Electron microscopic identification of autonomic nerve endings. *Nature* **210**, 756.

Robinson, R.G. and Gershon, M.D. (1971), Synthesis and uptake of 5-hydroxytryptamine by the myenteric plexus of the guinea-pig ileum. A histochemical study. *J. Pharmac. exp. Ther.* **178**, 311–324.

Rodriguez-Echandia, E.L., Donoso, A.O. and Pedroza, E. (1972), A further contribution to the study of catecholamine flow in amphibian nerves. *Acta physiologica latino-americana* **22**, 161–165.

Romanoff, A.L. (1960), *The Avian Embryo.* New York: Macmillan.

Rosenbluth, J. (1962), Subsurface cisterns and their relationship to the neuronal plasma membrane. *J. Cell Biol.* **13**, 405–422.

Rosengren, E. and Sjöberg, N.O. (1967), The adrenergic nerve supply to the female reproductive tract of the cat. *Am. J. Anat.* **12L**, 271–284.

Ross, J.G. (1958), On the presence of centripetal fibres in the superior mesenteric nerves of the rabbit. *J. Anat.* **92**, 189–197.

Ross, L.L. and Gershon, M.D. (1970), Adrenergic innervation of the myenteric plexus of the guinea-pig. Ultrastructural, biochemical and histofluorimetric studies using 6-hydroxydopamine. *J. Cell Biol.* **47**, 175a.

Roth, C.D. and Richardson, K.C. (1969), Electron microscopical studies on axonal degeneration in the rat iris following ganglionectomy. *Am. J. Anat.* **124**, 341–360.

Sabatini, M.T., Pellegrino, De Iraldi, A. and De Robertis, E. (1965), Early effects of antiserum against nerve growth factor on fine structure of sympathetic neurons. *Expl. Neurol.* **12**, 370–383.

Saccomanno, G. (1943), The components of the upper thoracic sympathetic nerves. *J. comp. Neurol.* **79**, 355–378.

Sampson, S.R. (1972), Mechanism of efferent inhibition of carotid body chemoreceptors in the cat, *Brain Res.* **45**, 266–270.

Sano, J., Odake, G. and Yonezawa, T. (1967), Fluorescence microscopic observations of catecholamines in cultures of the sympathetic chain. *Z. Zellforsch.* **80**, 345–352.

Santini, M. (1969), New fibres of sympathetic nature in the inner core region of Pacinian corpuscles. *Brain Res.* **16**, 535–538.

Sauer, M.E. and Rumble, C.T. (1946), The number of nerve cells in the myenteric and submucous plexuses of the small intestine of the cat. *Anat. Rec.* **96**, 373–381.

Sawyer, C.H. and Hollinshead, W.H. (1945), Cholinesterase in sympathetic fibers and ganglia. *J. Neurophysiol.* **8**, 137–153.

Schabadasch, A. (1930), Intramurale Nervengeflechte des Darmrohrs. *Z. Zellforsch.* **10**, 320–385.

Schaumann, W. (1958), Zusammenhänge zwischen der Wirkung der Analgetica und Sympathomimetica auf den Meerschweinen-Dünndarm. *Arch. exp. Path. Parmak.* **233**, 112–124.

Schmitt, F.O., Hall, C.E. and Jakus, M.A. (1942), Electron microscope investigations of the structure of collagen. *J. cell comp. Physiol.* **20**, 11–33.

Schneider, F.H., Smith, A.D. and Winkler, H. (1967), Secretion from the adrenal medulla: biochemical evidence for exocytosis. *Br. J. Pharmac. Chemother.* **31**, 94–104.

Schnitzlein, H.N., Rowe, L.C. and Hoffman, H.H. (1958), The myelinated component of the vagus nerves in man. *Anat. Rec.* **131**, 649–667.

Schofield, G.C. (1968), Anatomy of muscular and neural tissues in the alimentary canal, In: *Handbook of Physiology*, Section 6, vol. IV. edited by Code, C.F., pp.1579–1627, Washington: American Physiological Society.

Schucker, F. (1972), Effects of NGF-antiserum in sympathetic neurons during early postnatal development. *Expl. Neurol.* **36**, 59–78.

Schulman, C.C., Duarte-Escalante, O. and Boyarsky, S. (1972), The ureterovesical innervation. *Br. J. Urol.* **44**, 698–712.

Schwieler, G.H., Douglas, J.S. and Bouhuys, A. (1970), Postnatal development of autonomic efferent innervation in the rabbit. *Am. J. Physiol.* **219**, 391–397.

Schwyn, R. and Hall, J. (1965), Studies of neurological activity in autonomic ganglia during electrical stimulation and drug administration. *Anat. Rec.* **151**, 414.

Seite, R. (1970), Inclusions paracristallines dans les neurones sympathique chez le chien. *C.r. Acad. Sci. Paris*, **271**, 1011–1014.

Seite, R., Escaig, J. and Couineau, S. (1971), Microfilaments et microtubules nucléaires et organisation ultrastructurale des batonnets intranucléaires des neurones sympathiques. *J. Ultrastruct. Res.* **37**, 449–478.

Shackleford, J.M. and Wilborn, W.H. (1970), Ultrastructural aspects of cat submandibular glands. *J. Morph.* **131**, 253–276.

Sheehan, D. (1933), On the unmyelinated fibers in the spinal nerves. *Anat. Rec.* **55**, 111—116.

Sheehan, D. (1936), Discovery of the autonomic nervous system. *Archs. Neurol. Psychiat., Chicago* **35**, 1081—1115.

Sheehan, D. (1941), Spinal autonomic outflows in man and monkey. *J. comp. Neurol.* **75**, 341—370.

Sidman, R. and Fawcett, D.W. (1954), The effect of peripheral nerve section on some metabolic responses of brown adipose tissue in mice. *Anat. Rec.* **118**, 497—507.

Sidman, R.L., Perkins, M., Weiner, N. (1962), Noradrenaline and adrenaline content of adipose tissues. *Nature* **193**, 36—37.

Siegrist, G., De Ribaupierre, F., Dolivo, M. and Rouiller, C. (1966), Les cellules chromaffines des ganglions cervicaux supérieurs du rat. *J. Microscopie* **5**, 791—794.

Siegrist, G., Dolivo, M., Dunant, Y., Forogloukerameus, C., De Ribaupierre, Fr. and Rouiller, Ch. (1968), Ultrastructure and function of the chromaffin cells in the superior cervical ganglion of the rat. *J. Ultrastruct. Res.* **25**, 381—407.

Silberstein, S.D., Berv, K.R. and Jacobowitz, D.M. (1972b), Heterologous re-innervation of the iris from sympathetic ganglia in organ culture. *Nature* **239**, 466—468.

Silberstein, S.D., Johnson, D.G., Jacobowitz, D.M. and Kopin, I.J. (1971), Sympathetic reinnervation of the rat iris in organ culture. *Proc. Nat. Acad. Sci. U.S.A.* **68**, 1121—1124.

Silberstein, S.D., Johnson, D.G., Hanbauer, I., Bloom, F.E. and Kopin, I.J. (1972), Axonal sprouts and ^{3}H norepinephrine uptake by superior cervical ganglia in organ culture. *Proc. natn. Acad. Sci. U.S.A.* **69**, 1450—1454.

Silva, D.G. (1967), The ultrastructure of the myometrium of the rat with special reference to the innervation. *Anat. Rec.* **158**, 21—34.

Silva, D.G., Ross, G. and Osborne, L.W. (1971), Adrenergic innervation of the ileum of the cat. *Am. J. Physiol.* **220**, 347—352.

Simmler, G.M. (1949), The effects of wing bud extirpation on the brachial sympathetic ganglia of the chick embryo. *J. exp. Zool.* **110**, 247—257.

Simmons, H.T. and Sheehan, D. (1939), The causes of relapse following sympathectomy of the arm. *Br. J. Surg.* **27**, 234—255.

Simpson, F.O. and Devine, C.E. (1966), The fine structure of autonomic neuro-muscular contacts in arterioles of sheep renal cortex. *J. Anat.* **100**, 127—137.

Simpson, S.A. and Young, J.Z. (1945), Regeneration of fibre diameter after cross-union of visceral and somatic nerves. *J. Anat.* **79**, 48—65.

Sjöberg, N.-O. (1967), The adrenergic transmitter of the female reproductive tract: distribution and functional changes. *Acta physiol. scand.* **suppl. 305**, 1—32.

Sjöberg, N.-O. (1968), Considerations on the cause of disappearance of the adrenergic transmitter in uterine nerves during pregnancy. *Acta physiol. scand.* **72**, 510–517.

Sjoqvist, F., Taylor, P.W. and Titus, E. (1967), The effect of immunosympathectomy on the retention and metabolism of noradrenaline *Acta physiol. scand.* **69**, 13–22.

Sjöstrand, N.O. (1965), The adrenergic innervation of the vas deferens and the accessory male genital organs. *Acta physiol. scand.* suppl. **257**, 1–82.

Sjöstrand, N.O. and Swedin, G. (1967), Effect of chronic denervation on the noradrenaline content of the vas deferens and the accessory male reproductive glands of the rat. *Experientia* **23**, 817–818.

Skok, V.I. (1973), *Physiology of Autonomic Ganglia.* Tokyo: Igaku Shoin.

Skoog, T. (1947), Ganglia in the communicating rami of the cervical sympathetic trunk. *Lancet* **2**, 457–460.

Slavich, E. (1932), Confronti fra la morfologia di gangli del parasimpatico encefalico e del simpatico cervicale con speciale riguardo alla struttura del ganglio ciliare. *Z. Zellforsch.* **15**, 688–730.

Smirnow, A. (1890), Die Struktur der Nervenzellen im Sympathicus der Amphibien. *Arch. mikrosk. Anat. Entwmech.* **35**, 407–424.

Smith, S.W. (1959), 'Reticular' and 'areticular' Nissl bodies in sympathetic neurons of a lizard. *J. Biophys. Biochem. Cytol.* **6**, 77–84.

Smith, A.D. (1971), Secretions of proteins (chromogranin A and dopamine-β-hydroxylase) from a sympathetic neuron. *Phil. Trans. R. Soc. Ser. B* **261**, 363–370.

Smith, A.D. (1972), Subcellular localization of noradrenaline in sympathetic neurons. *Pharmac. Rev.* **24**, 435–457.

Smith, C.B., Trendelenburg, U., Langer, S.Z. and Tsai, T.H. 1966), The relation of norepinephrine-H^3 content of the nictitating membrane of the spinal cat during development of denervation supersensitivity. *J. Pharmac. exp. Ther.* **151**, 87–94.

Smith, R.D. (1971), The occurrence and location of intrinsic cardiac ganglia and nerve plexuses in the human neonate. *Anat. Rec.* **169**, 33–40.

Sokolowa, M.L. (1931), Zur Lehre von der Cytoarchitektonik des peripherischen autonomen Nervesystems. II. Die Architektur der intramuralen Ganglien des Verdauungstrakts des Rindes. *Z. mikrosk. anat. Forsch.* **23**, 552–570.

Sotelo, C. (1968), Permanence of postsynaptic specializations in the frog sympathetic cells after denervation. *Expl. Brain Res.* **6**, 294–305.

Sotelo, C. and Taxi, J. (1973), On the axonal migration of catecholamines in constricted sciatic nerve of the rat. A radioautographic study. *Z. Zellforsch.* **138**, 345–370.

Spoendlin, H. and Lichtensteiger, W. (1966), The adrenergic innervation of the labyrinth. *Acta oto-laryng., Stockholm* **61**, 423–434.

Starke, K. (1971), Influence of α-receptors stimulants on noradrenaline release. *Naturwissenschaften* **58**, 420.

Stock, K. and Westermann, E.D. (1963), Concentration of norepinephrine, serotonin and histamine and of amine-metabolizing enzymes in mammalian adipose tissue. *J. Lipid Res.* **4**, 297–304.

Stöhr, P. Jr. (1932), Mikroskopische Studien zur Innervation des Magen-Darm-Kanals. I, II. *Z. Zellforsch.* **16**, 123–197.

Stöhr, P. (1939), Über 'Nebenzellen' und deren Innervation in Ganglien des vegetativen Nervensystem, zugleich ein Beitrag zur Synapsenfrage. *Z. Zellforsch.* **29**, 569–612.

Suden, C.T., Hart, E.R., Lindenberg, R. and Marrazzi, A.S. (1951), Pharmacological and anatomical indications of adrenergic neurons participating in synapses at parasympathetic ganglia (ciliary) *J. Pharmac. exp. Ther.* **103**, 354–365.

Sumner, B.E.H. and Sutherland, F.I. (1973), Quantitative electron microscopy of the injured hypoglossal nucleus in the rat. *J. Neurocytol.* **2**, 315–328.

Swedin, G. (1971), Biphasic mechanical response of the isolated vas deferens to nerve stimulation. *Acta physiol. scand.* **81**, 574–576.

Swedin, G. (1972), Postnatal development of the mechanical response of the isolated rat vas deferens to nerve stimulation. *Acta physiol. scand.* **84**, 217–223.

Szabo, T. and Dussardier, M. (1964), Les noyaux d'origine du nerf vague chez le mouton. *Z. Zellforsch.* **63**, 247–276.

Szentàgothai, J. (1964), The structure of the autonomic interneuronal synapse. *Acta neuroveg.* **26**, 338–359.

Szentàgothai, J., Donhoffer, A. and Rajkovits, K. (1954), Die Lokalisation der Cholinesterase in der interneuronalen Synapse. *Acta histochem.* **1**, 272–281.

Tafuri, W.L. (1957), Auerbach's plexus in the guinea-pig. I. A quantitative study of the ganglia and nerve cells in the ileum, caecum and colon. *Acta anat.* **31**, 522–530.

Tafuri, W.L. and De Almeida Campos, F. (1958), Der Auerbasche Plexus bei der Maus. *Z. Naturf.* **13**B, 816–819.

Takahashi, O. (1960), On the formation of vacuoles in the nerve cells of the ganglion cervicalis uteri on the rat and mouse. *Okajimas Folia anat. jap.* **34**, 189–200.

Takahashi, K. and Hama, K. (1965a), Some observations on the fine structure of the synaptic area in the ciliary ganglion of the chick. *Z. Zellforsch.* **67**, 174–184.

Takahashi, K. and Hama, K. (1965b), Some observations on the fine structure of nerve cell bodies and their satellite cells in the ciliary ganglion of the chick. *Z. Zellforsch.* **67**, 835–843.

Tamarind, D.L. and Quilliam, J.P. (1971), Synaptic organisation and other ultra-

205

structural features of the superior cervical ganglion of the rat, kitten and rabbit. *Micron.* **2**, 204–234.

Tandler, B. (1965), Ultrastructure of the human submaxillary gland. III. Myoepithelium. *Z. Zellforsch.* **68**, 852–863.

Tandler, B. and Ross, L.L. (1969), Observations of nerve terminals in human labial salivary glands. *J. Cell Biol.* **42**, 339–343.

Taxi, J. (1958), Sur la structure du plexus d'Auerbach de la souris, étudié au microscope électronique. *hebd. Séanc Acad. Sci., Paris* **246**, 1922–1925.

Taxi, J. (1961), Etude de l'ultrastructure des zones synaptiques dans les ganglions sympathiques de la grenouille. *C.r. hebd. Séanc Acad. Sci., Paris* **252**, 174–176.

Taxi, J. (1965), Contribution a l'étude des connexions des neurones moteurs du système nerveux autonomie. *Annls. Sci. nat. (Zool.)* **7**, 413–674.

Taxi, J. (1967), Observations on the ultrastructure of the ganglionic neurons and synapses of the frog *Rana esculenta L.*, In: *The Neuron,* edited by Hydén, H. pp.221–254, Amsterdam: Elsevier.

Taxi, J. (1974), Dynamics of transmissional ultrastructures in sympathetic neurons of the rat. *J. Neural. Trans.* suppl. XI. 103–124.

Taxi, J. and Babmindra, V.P. (1972), Light and electron microscopic studies of normal and heterogeneously regenerated ganglionic synapses in dog. *J. Neural Trans.* **33**, 257–274.

Taxi, J. and Droz, B. (1966a), Etude de l'incorporation de noradrénaline-^{3}H (NA-^{3}H) et de 5-hydroxytryptophane-^{3}H (5-HTP-^{3}H) dans l'épiphyse et le ganglion cervical superieur. *C.r. hebd. Séanc. Acad. Sci., Paris* **263**, 1326–1329.

Taxi, J. and Droz, B. (1966b), Etude de l'incorporation de noradrenaline-H^3 (NA-^{3}H) et de 5-hydroxy-tryptophane-H^3 (5-HTP-^{3}H) dans les fibres nerveuses du canal deferent et de l'intestin. *C.r. hebd. Séanc. Acad. Sci., Paris* **263**, 1237–1240.

Taxi, J. and Droz, B. (1969), Radioautographic study of the accumulation of some biogenic amines in the autonomic nervous system, In: *Cellular Dynamics of the Neuron,* edited by Barondes, S.H. *Symposia Int. Soc. Cell Biol.* **8**, 175–190.

Taxi, J., Gautron, J. and L'Hermite, P. (1969) Données ultrastructurales sur une éventuelle modulation adrénergique de l'activité du ganglion cervical supérieur due rat. *C.r. hebd. Séanc. Acad. Sci., Paris* **269**, 1281–1284.

Terni, T. (1922), Ricerche sulla struttura e sull'evoluzione del simpatico dell'uomo. *Monitore zoologico italiano* **33**, 63–72.

Terni, T. (1924), Il ganglio toracico e la porzione cervicale del vago negli uccelli. *Archo. ital. Anat. Embriol.* **21**, 404–434.

Terni, T. (1925), Osservazioni sulla presenza di cellule del ganglio nodoso nel ganglio cervicale superiore dell'uomo e considerazioni sul loro significato. *Monit. zool. ital.* **36**, 207–218.

Terni, T. (1931), Il simpatico cervicale degli amnioti. *Z. Anat. EntwGesch.* **96**, 289–426.

Terzuolo, C. (1951), Ricerche sul ganglio ciliare degli uccelli. Connessioni, mutamenti in relazioneall'età a dopo recisione delle fibre pregangliari. *Z. Zellforsch.* **36**, 255–267.

Thaemert, J.C. (1969), Fine structure of neuromuscular relationships in mouse heart. *Anat. Rec.* **163**, 575–586.

Thoenen, H. (1972), Surgical, immunological and chemical sympathectomy. Their application in the investigation of the physiology and pharmacology of the sympathetic nervous system. *Handbook Exp. Pharmacology,* **33**, 813–844.

Thoenen, H., Saner, A., Angeletti, P.U. and Levi-Montalcini, R. (1972), Increased activity of choline acetyltransferase in sympathetic ganglia after prolonged administration of nerve growth factor. *Nature New Biology* **236**, 26–28.

Thoenen, H. and Tranzer, J.P. (1971), Functional importance of subcellular distribution of false adrenergic transmitters. *Prog. Brain Res.* **34**, 223–236.

Thoenen, H. Tranzer, J.P., Hürlimann, A. and Haefely, W. (1966), Untersuchungen zue Frage eines cholinergischen Glides in der postganglionären sympathischen Transmission. *Helv. physiol. pharmac. Acta.* **24**, 229–246.

Thomas, P.K. (1963), The connective tissue of peripheral nerve: an electron microscope study. *J. Anat.* **97**, 35–44.

Thomas, M.R. and Calaresu, F.R. (1974), Localization and function of medullary sites mediating vagal bradycardia in the cat. *Am. J. Physiol.* **226**, 1344–1349.

Thompson, G.E., Robertshaw, D. and Findlay, J.D. (1969), Noradrenergic innervation of the arrectores pilorum muscles of the ox (*Bos taurus*). *Can. J. Physiol. Pharmacol.* **47**, 310–311.

Thompson, J.W. (1961), The nerve supply to the nictitating membrane. *J. Anat.* **95**, 371–385.

Thurn, C. (1972), Über die postnatale Entwicklung des Ganglion stellatum der Katze (*Felis domestica*). *Z. Anat. EntwGesch.* **136**, 59–72.

Tomasch, J. and Ebnessajjade D. (1961), The human nucleus ambiguus. A quantitative study. *Anat. Rec.* **141**, 247–252.

Tower, S.S. (1932), The effects of sympathetic denervation of mammalian tissues during the period of post-natal growth. *Am. J. Physiol.* **100**, 295–300.

Tranzer, J.P. (1972), A new storing compartment in adrenergic axons. *Nature New Biology* **237**, 57–58.

Tranzer, J.P. (1973), New aspects of the localisation of catecholamines in adrenergic neurons, In: *Frontiers in Catecholamine Research*, pp.453–458. Edited by Usdin, E. and Snyder, S.H. New York: Pergamon Press.

Tranzer, J.P. and Thoenen, H. (1967), Significance of 'empty vesicles' in post-ganglionic sympathetic nerve terminals *Experientia* **23**, 123–124.

Tranzer, J.P. and Thoenen, H. (1968), Various types of amine-storing vesicles in peripheral adrenergic nerve terminals. *Experientia* **24**, 484–486.

Trumble, H.C. (1934), The plan of the visceral nerves in the lumbar and sacral outflows of the autonomic nervous system. *Br. J. Surg.* **21**, 664–676.

Turkanis, S.A. (1973), Effects of muscle stretch on transmitter release at end-plates of rat diaphragm and frog sartorius muscle. *J. Physiol., Lond.* **230**, 391–403.

Uchizono, K. (1964), On different types of synaptic vesicles in the sympathetic ganglia of amphibia. *Jap. J. Physiol.* **14**, 210–219.

Uehara, Y. and Burnstock, G. (1972), Postsynaptic specialization of smooth muscle at close neuromuscular junctions in the guinea pig sphincter pupillae. *J. Cell Biol.* **53**, 849–853.

Ungváry, Gy. and Léránth, Cs. (1970), Termination in the prevertebral abdominal sympathetic ganglia of axons arising from the local (terminal) vegetative plexus of visceral organs. *Z. Zellforsch.* **110**, 185–191.

Uvnäs, B. (1954), Sympathetic vasodilator outflow. *Physiol. Rev.* **34**, 608–618.

Vandervael, F. (1943), Recherches sur l'évolution des neurones sympathiques du ganglion cervical supérier chez l'homme. *Arch. Biol.* **54**, 53–74.

Van Orden, L.S., III, Bensch, K.G., Langer, S.Z. and Trendelenburg, U. (1967), Histochemical and fine structural aspects of the onset of denervation super-sensitivity in the nictitating membrane of the spinal cat. *J. Pharmac. exp. Ther.* **157**, 274–283.

Van Orden, L.S. III, Burke, J.P., Geyer, M. and Lodoen, F.V. (1970a), Localization of depletion-sensitive and depletion-resistant norepinephrine storage sites in autonomic ganglia. *J. Pharmac. exp. Ther.* **174**, 56–71.

Van Orden, L.S. III, Schaefer, J.-M., Burke, J.P. and Lodoen, F.V. (1970b), Differentiation of norepinephrine storage compartments in peripheral adrenergic nerves. *J. Pharmac. exp. Ther.* **174**, 357–368.

Vanov, S. and Vogt, M. (1963), Catecholamine-containing structures in the hypogastric nerves of the dog. *J. Physiol., Lond.* **168**, 939–944.

Vera, C.L., Vial, J.D. and Luco, J.V. (1957), Reinnervation of nictitating membrane of cat by cholinergic fibres. *J. Neurophysiol.* **20**, 365–373.

Verity, M.A. and Bevan, J.A. (1968), Fine structural study of the terminal effector plexus, neuromuscular and intermuscular relationships in the pulmonary artery. *J. Anat.* **103**, 49–63.

Verney, E.B. and Vogt. M. (1938), An experimental investigation into hypertension of renal origin, with some observations on convulsive 'uraemia'. *Q. Jl. exp. Physiol.* **28**, 253–303.

Vogt, M. (1964), Sources of noradrenaline in the 'immunosympathectomized' rat. *Nature* **204**, 1315–1316.

Volle, R.L. (1966), Modification by drugs of synaptic mechanisms in autonomic ganglia. *Pharmac. Rev.* **18**, 199—200.

Wacksman, J., Farr, W.C. and Grupp, G. (1969), Localization of the cardiac sympathetic synapses in the dog. *Proc. Soc. exp. Biol. Med.* **131**, 336—339.

Wakade, A.R. and Kirpekar, S.M. (1973), 'Trophic' influence on the sympathetic nerves of the vas deferens and seminal vesicle of the guinea pig. *J. Pharmac. exp. Ther.* **186**, 528—536.

Ward, J.W. (1936), A histological study of transplanted sympathetic ganglia. *Am. J. Anat.* **58**, 147—170.

Warwick, R. (1954), The ocular parasympathetic nerve supply and its mesencephalic sources. *J. Anat.* **88**, 71—93.

Watanabe, H. (1971), Adrenergic nerve elements in the hypogastric ganglion of the guinea-pig. *Am. J. Anat.* **130**, 305—330.

Watanabe, H. (1972), The fine structure of the ciliary ganglion of the guinea-pig. *Arch. histol. jap.* **34**, 261—276.

Watari, N. (1968), Fine structure of nervous elements in the pancreas of some vertebrates. *Z. Zellforsch.* **85**, 291—314.

Webb, J.G., Moss, J., Kopin, I.J. and Jacobowitz, D.M. (1974), Biochemical and histofluorescence studies of catecholamines (CA) in superior cervical ganglia (G) in organ culture. *Fedn. Proc. Fedn. Am. Socs. Biol.* **33**, 511.

Wechsler, W. and Schmekel, L. (1967), Elektronenmikroskopische Untersuchungen der Entwicklung der vegetativen (Grenzstrang-) und spinalen Ganglien bei *Gallus domesticus. Acta neuroveg.* **30**, 427—444.

Weiner, N., Langer, S.Z. and Trendelenburg, U. (1967), Demonstration by the histochemical fluorescence method of the prolonged disappearance of catecholamines from the denervated nictitating membrane of the cat. *J. Pharmac. exp. Ther.* **157**, 284—289.

Welsh, J.H. and Hyde, J.E. (1944), Acetylcholine content in the myenteric plexus and resistance to anoxia. *Proc. Soc. exp. Biol. Med.* **55**, 256—257.

Weston, J.A. (1963), A radioautographic analysis of the migration and localization of trunk neural crest cells in the chick. *Devl. Biol.* **6**, 279—310.

White, E.G. (1935), Die Struktur des Glomus caroticum, seine Pathologie, und Physiologie, und seine Beziehung zum Nervensystem. *Beitr. path. Anat.* **96**, 177—227.

Whitteridge, D. (1937), The transmission of impulses through the ciliary ganglion. *J. Physiol., Lond.* **89**, 99—111.

Wiedeman, M.P. (1968), Blood flow through terminal arterial vessels after denervation of the bat wing. *Circulation Res.* **22**, 83—89.

Williams, T.H., Black, A.C.Jr., Chiba, T. and Bhalla, R.C. (1975), Morphology and biochemistry of small, intensely fluorescent cells of sympathetic ganglia. *Nature*, **256**, 315—317.

Williams, T.H., Jew, J. and Palay, S.L. (1973), Morphological plasticity in the sympathetic chain. *Expl. Neurol.* **39**, 181–203.

Williams, T.H. and Palay, S.L. (1969), Ultrastructure of the small neurons in the superior cervical ganglion. *Brain Res.* **15**, 17–34.

Windle, W.F. (1933), Neurofibrillar development in the central nervous system of the cat embryo between 8 and 12 mm long. *J. comp. Neurol.* **58**, 643–723.

Winkler, C. and Potter, A. (1914), *Anatomical Guide to Experimental Researches on the Cat Brain.* W. Versluys: Amsterdam.

Winslow, J.B. (1732), *Exposition Anatomique du Corps Humain.* Paris: G. Desprez.

Wirsén, L. and Hamberger, B. (1967), Catecholamines in brown fat. *Nature* **214**, 625.

Wolf, G.A. (1941), The ratio of preganglionic neurons in the visceral nervous system. *J. comp. Neurol.* **75**, 235–243.

Wolff, H.G., Hare, K. and Cattell, M. (1938), Functional connections established by spinal nerves regenerating into preganglionic sympathetic trunks. *Am. J. Physiol.* **123**, 218–219.

Wong, W.C., Helme, R.D. and Smith, G.C. (1974), Degeneration of noradrenergic nerve terminals in submucous ganglia of the rat duodenum following treatment with 6-hydroxydopamine. *Experientia* **30**, 282–284.

Wong, W.C. and Tan, C.K. (1974), Degeneration in the adult rat spinal cord following systemic treatment with 6-hydroxy-dopamine. Electron microscopic study. *Experientia* **30**, 1455–1458.

Woods, R.I. (1970a), The innervation of the frog's heart. I. An examination of the autonomic post-ganglionic nerve fibres and a comparison of autonomic and sensory ganglion cells. *Proc. R. Soc. Ser. B.* **176**, 43–54.

Woods, R.I. (1970b), The innervation of the frog's heart. III. Electronmicroscopy of the autonomic nerve fibres and their vesicles. *Proc. R. Soc. Ser. B.* **176**, 63–68.

Wozniak, W. and Skowronska, U. (1967), Comparative anatomy of pelvic plexus in cat, dog, rabbit, macaque and man. *Anat. Anz.* **120**, 457–473.

Wrete, M. (1941), Die Entwicklung und Topographie der intermediären vegetativen Ganglien bei gewissen Versuchstieren. *Z. mikrosk.-anat. Forsch.* **49**, 503–515.

Wrete, M. (1959), Die Anatomie der sympatischen Granzstränge beim Menschen und bei Saugetieren mit specieller Rücksicht auf die Nomenklatur. *Anat. Anz.* **106**, 304–322.

Wurtman, R.J. and Axelrod, J. (1966), A 24-hour rhythm in the content of norepinephrine in the pineal and salivary glands of the rat. *Life Sci.* **5**, 665–669.

Yamamoto, T. (1963), Some observations on the structure of the sympathetic ganglion of the bullfrog. *J. Cell Biol.* **16**, 159–170.

Yamauchi, A. (1973), Ultrastructure of the innervation of the mammalian heart, In: *Ultrastructure of the Mammalian Heart,* edited by Challice, C.E. and Viragh, S., pp.127–178, New York and London: Academic Press.

Yamauchi, A. and Burnstock, G. (1969a), Post-natal development of smooth muscle cells in the mouse vas deferens. A fine structural study. *J. Anat.* **104,** 1–15.

Yamauchi, A. and Burnstock, G. (1969b), Post-natal development of the innervation of the mouse vas deferens. A fine structural study. *J. Anat.* **104,** 17–32.

Yamauchi, A. and Lever, J.D. (1971), Correlations between formol fluorescence and acetylcholinesterase (AChE) staining in the superior cervical ganglion of normal rat, pig and sheep. *J. Anat.* **110,** 435–443.

Yntema, C.L. (1947), The development of the autonomic nervous system. *Biol. Rev.* **22,** 244–359.

Yntema, C.L. and Hammond, W.S. (1945), Depletions and abnormalities in the cervical sympathetic system of the chick following extirpation of neural crest. *J. exp. Zool.* **100,** 237–259.

Yntema, C.L. and Hammond, W.S. (1955), Experiments on the origin and development of the sacral autonomic nerves in the chick embryo. *J. exp. Zool.* **129,** 375–414.

Yokota, R. (1973), The granule-containing cell somata in the superior cervical ganglion of the rat, as studied by a serial sampling method for electron microscopy. *Z. Zellforsch.* **141,** 331–345.

Zaimis, E., Berk, L. and Callingham, B.A. (1965), Morphological, biochemical and functional changes in the sympathetic nervous system of rats treated with nerve growth factor-antiserum. *Nature* **206,** 1220–1222.

Zalewski, A.A. (1970), Trophic influence of in vivo transplanted sensory neurons on taste buds. *Expl. Neurol.* **29,** 462–467.

Zenker, W. and Krammer, E. (1967), Untersuchungen über Feinstruktur und Innervation der inneren Augenmuskulatur des Hühnes. *Z. Zellforsch.* **83,** 147–168.

211

SUBJECT INDEX